Viruses of Vertebrates

VIRUSES

of

VERTEBRATES

BY

Sir CHRISTOPHER ANDREWES

M.D., F.R.C.P., F.R.S., Wellcome Trust Fellow,
*Late Deputy-Director, National Institute for Medical Research,
Mill Hill, London*

BALTIMORE
THE WILLIAMS AND WILKINS COMPANY
1964

Made at the Pitman Press, Bath
Printed in Great Britain

Preface

There are books on the principles of virology and books on virus
diseases, especially those of man. This volume deals rather with the
viruses themselves, their properties and their relations to one another.
Their pathogenic effects are, in principle, considered only so far as
is necessary to identify a virus and to indicate its importance. In
practice an account of the disease-producing powers of viruses will
be found to occupy considerable space, for it is largely by their deeds
that we know them.

Viruses attacking only insects are not considered nor are plant
viruses. The book does, however, deal not only with viruses of man
but also with those affecting other vertebrates. The wider view is
necessary if one is to consider viruses from the point of view of
taxomony. Moreover, with the widespread use of various laboratory
animals and of tissue cultures derived from various species, workers
are bound to encounter viruses of unknown origin. The importance
of the zoonoses—diseases of other animals transmissible to man—
also is increasingly recognized.

The book will, it is hoped, serve three purposes. By the orderly
arrangement of the known facts about viruses it should help the
enquirer to discover rapidly whether this or that is known about a
particular virus, and guide him to fuller sources of information on
the matter. Secondly it is intended to help him, as Bergey's manual
helps the bacteriologist, to identify an unknown virus which he may
encounter. Thirdly, there is, I hope, a long-term scientific justification for the book. We do not know enough to classify all viruses
in an orderly manner. A partial attempt to do so is made in Parts
I and II by arranging into groups such viruses as seem ripe for such
an attempt. I have tried to avoid what I feel is a pit-fall, the proposal
of a classification in advance of adequate knowledge: so Part III
contains the viruses which we cannot yet classify rationally, arranged
according to the species they attack. It is hoped that as knowledge

grows, one may be able, in possible future editions, to promote more and more viruses from Part III to a more satisfactory status in Parts I and II.

Finally I apologize, particularly to many veterinary friends, for the presumptuous attempt of an individual virologist to deal with all viruses of vertebrates.

January, 1964

C. H. Andrewes

Acknowledgments

I wish to thank the Wellcome Trust for a personal and expenses grant; also the librarians at the National Institute for Medical Research, Mill Hill, the Microbiological Research Establishment, Porton, and the Commonwealth Bureau of Animal Health, Weybridge, for valuable help. A number of friends, authorities in particular fields, have kindly read and criticized certain chapters: I am grateful especially to Dr. A. C. Allison, Sir Samuel Bedson, Prof. A. W. Downie, Dr. K. R. Dumbell, Prof. F. Fenner, Drs. D. A. Haig, R. J. C. Harris, A. Isaacs, H. G. Pereira and J. S. Porterfield, Prof. M. G. P. Stoker and Drs. J. O'H. Tobin and D. A. J. Tyrrell.

C. H. A.

Contents

Part I. RNA viruses

Part II. DNA viruses

Part III. Unclassified viruses

Part IV. Chlamydozoaceae

List of Tables

Introduction

A few words are necessary concerning the plan adopted in writing this book. Facts are as far as possible marshalled under twelve main headings, some of them with subdivisions. There is naturally some overlap as between the section on antigenic properties and that on control, which mainly deals with vaccines. Where information is lacking, that section is omitted.

Synonyms included are those in common use in English. Some are given in French, German or other languages where these are not etymologically related to English names. Synonyms in italics are names of viruses; those in roman letters are names of diseases.

Morphology and developmental cycle. Estimates of size of many viruses vary widely, particularly where workers have used different techniques—filtration, centrifugation or electron microscopy. Many early records based on filtration gave too low an estimate; many based on electron microscopy, unless with special precautions, probably over-estimate diameters. There is still disagreement as to interpretation of negatively stained preparations, especially as regards numbers of capsomeres.

Chemical composition. RNA viruses are included in Part I, DNA viruses in Part II. There is often, as elsewhere in the book, an element of intelligent anticipation. Many viruses are placed in Parts I or II on inferential grounds, because they are clearly related to better studied ones; their own nucleic acid composition may not have been directly determined.

Physico-chemical characters. Many reports on virus inactivation, especially by heat, do not specify suspending medium and other conditions; moreover kinetic studies yield more information than simpler data. Full details of techniques cannot be included in a book of this size. The figures given as to thermostability and other physical properties of viruses are useful, therefore, only for rough comparative purposes. Temperatures are given in Centigrade.

Hæmagglutination and **Antigenic properties.** No special comment is needed.

Interference. A few data are included, but this section is of rather doubtful value, since interference has been demonstrated between so many otherwise unrelated viruses.

Cultivation. Where data are available, this section deals first with cultivation in fertile eggs, then with tissue culture.

Distribution may be assumed to be world-wide if there is no comment.

Pathogenicity. Symptomatology and lesions are dealt with more briefly than in most text-books, since this book is about viruses rather than virus diseases. There is, wherever possible, brief mention of host range, symptomatology in the natural host and in experimental animals, with brief mention of macroscopic and microscopic lesions resulting from infection.

Ecology. Modes of transmission are described where these are known. Other factors are difficult to summarize briefly.

Control. Most attention is paid to specific prophylaxis.

References

To avoid overloading the book it has been necessary to be very selective in the matter of references. I have therefore included those likely to be most helpful, either because they afford the fullest account of the facts, or because they describe recent work not referred to in other books or reviews. I have accordingly frequently omitted reference to the first reported description of a new finding, though a few classical papers are mentioned.

Abbreviations

The following conventional abbreviations have been used:

CAM	= chorio-allantoic membrane
CE	= chick embryo
CF(T)	= complement fixation (test)
CNS	= central nervous system
CPE	= cytopathic effect
CSF	= cerebrospinal fluid
DNA	= desoxyribosenucleic acid
EM	= electron microscope (or microscopic)

EMC = encephalomyocarditis
HA = hæmagglutination
HAI = hæmagglutination-inhibition
IB = inclusion body
IC = intracerebral
IM = intramuscular
IN = intranasal
IP = intraperitoneal
IV = intravenous
MK = monkey kidney
NDV = Newcastle disease virus
RBC = red blood cell
RDE = receptor destroying enzyme
RNA = ribosenucleic acid
SV = simian virus
TC = tissue culture

PART I

RNA Viruses

TABLE 1

PROVISIONAL VIRUS CLASSIFICATION

Nucleic acid	RNA				DNA		RNA + DNA
Symmetry	Cubical		Helical	Uncertain	Cubical		? None
Presence of outer membrane	0 (ether stable)	+ (ether labile)	+ (ether labile)	+ (ether labile)	0 (ether stable)	+	+ (ether labile)
	Picornavirus Reovirus	Arbovirus (symmetry not certainly established and group may be heterogeneous)	Myxovirus Rabies	Fowl-leucosis complex Viruses associated with mouse tumours	Adenovirus Papovavirus	Herpes virus (ether labile) Poxvirus (ether stability varies within the group)	Psittacosis-Lymphogranuloma-Trachoma group

1

Picornaviruses

The group name Picornaviruses was suggested (Report, 1963), since a term was needed to cover the very small ether-resistant RNA viruses. "Pico" means "very small" and RNA indicates nucleic acid composition. It replaces the tentatively proposed name "nanivirus" (Andrewes *et al.*, 1961). It includes the enteroviruses (Committee, 1957), a term proposed to designate a group of related viruses of human origin: poliomyelitis, Coxsackie and ECHO. The term picornaviruses covers also the similar viruses of non-human origin, with those of foot-and-mouth disease, encephalomyocarditis (EMC), some others pathogenic for pigs, mice and chickens and the rhinoviruses causing common colds.

The characters of the group are as follows:

Morphology. Small spheres, 22–27 mμ in diameter, with a small number, perhaps 42, of regularly disposed surface capsomeres. Many virus particles are seen within the cytoplasm of infected cells in closely-packed crystalline arrangement. In most instances the antigen recognizable by the fluorescent antibody technique is only present in the cytoplasm.

Chemical composition. They are RNA viruses and in several instances infection has been initiated with RNA extracted from infected material.

Physico-chemical characters. Very resistant to ether, chloroform and bile salts. Survive well at −76° C or in 50 per cent. glycerol in the cold, but on the whole not very easily preserved by lyophilization. Most of the infectivity may be lost through this procedure, though the little remaining may thereafter survive well. Survival in drops is better under conditions of fairly high relative humidity.

Eggers & Tamm (1961a, b) have reported that 2(α-hydroxy benzyl) benzimidazole inhibits the CPE of some enteroviruses but not of others. Thus poliomyelitis Types I–III, Coxsackie B1–6, ECHO Types 1–9, 11–21, 24–27 are inhibited; there is no such effect on

3

ECHO 22, 23, 28, five Coxsackie A types, rhinoviruses (nor most viruses of other families). Further differentiation is possible if inactivation by guanidine hydrochloride is tested (Tamm & Eggers, 1962).

Enteroviruses pathogenic for man (but not all rhinoviruses) have increased stability at 50° in the presence of molar magnesium chloride. In this they resemble reoviruses but differ from those tested in other groups (Wallis & Melnick, 1962).

Cultivation. Most, although not all, grow in tissue culture causing a type of cellular damage which is fairly characteristic for the group (Pereira, 1962). It consists of formation of an eosinophilic mass in the cytoplasm, displacing the nucleus: such a change was, however, absent from cells infected with viruses of the EMC group (Barski, 1962).

Habitat. Most inhabit the intestinal tract, particularly of young hosts. They commonly cause no illness, but may spread from the gut and cause destructive lesions in the central nervous system. The rhinoviruses seem to represent a group adapted to live in the upper respiratory rather than the intestinal tract.

Viruses of this family fall into groups which are separated for convenience. They grade into each other: thus Coxsackie A7 forms a link between poliovirus and the other Coxsackies; the virus formerly known as ECHO 9 has been re-classified as Coxsackie A23 as it has close affinities with that group; "ECHO 28" stands between rhinoviruses and other ECHO'S . . . and so on. Nevertheless, the various groups having characters of clinical and other significance, form "constellations" (Andrewes, 1961), such that much would be lost if all the human enteroviruses were lumped together.

POLIOMYELITIS

Synonyms: Acute anterior poliomyelitis. Infantile paralysis. Heine-Medin disease. *Poliovirus hominis.*

Reviews. Howe & Wilson (1959) (Clinical and general).
Bodian (1959) (Pathogenesis and histopathology).
Schaffer & Schwerdt (1959) (Physical properties).

Morphology and development. Virus particles are about 25 mμ across (Sabin *et al.*, 1954) as are other picornaviruses. Finch & Klug (1959) considered on the basis of X-ray diffraction studies that the virus was an icosahedron with 60 protein subunits 6–6·5 mμ across, forming a shell around an RNA core. Horne & Nagington (1959) favoured a similar structure but thought there were 42 capsomeres arranged in 5 : 3 : 2 cubical symmetry. Steere & Schaffer (1958), on the other hand, considered that the subunits were arranged in close-packed cubic lattice—a view not generally accepted. There seems to be a central core 20 mμ in diameter (Taylor & McCormick, 1956). The development of virus within the cytoplasm has been analysed by Ackerman (1958): release of virus apparently takes place during several hours by a process described as cytotransudation. Virus regularly packed in microcrystals may be visible within cells; and purified virus has been crystallised in the test-tube (Schaffer & Schwerdt, 1959) forming crystals up to 0·05 mm in diameter.

Chemical composition. Virus particles contain 20–30 per cent. RNA (Schwerdt & Schaffer, 1955).

Physico-chemical characters. Density 1·56–1·62 (Schwerdt, 1957). Very resistant to ether, chloroform and bile salts. Survives well at −20° C, and for 8 years at −70° C. As with many other picornaviruses, not readily preserved by freeze-drying. Readily inactivated by heat—even 50° C for 30 minutes; but results vary according to strain and suspending medium; 30 minutes at 60° C seems always effective. The curve of inactivation by 0·1 per cent. formaldehyde has been studied by several workers.

The effect of many other chemicals has been reported; oxidizing agents seem particularly effective: data are reviewed by Gard (1955). UV radiation and high speed electrons have also been used for inactivating without destroying antigenicity.

Antigenic properties. Neutralization tests can be carried out in experimental animals, but recently this has been done much more conveniently in tissue-culture. A colorimetric test may be used since infected cultures do not become as acid as controls, metabolism of virus-infected cells having ceased. Plaque counting methods on monolayers are also used. There are three serological types, I, II and III, virtually distinct in neutralization tests but showing a little overlap in cross-immunity experiments and rather more in the CF test. Of four antigens separated by density gradient sedimentation, two, called C and D, were studied in complement fixation and gel-diffusion tests by Le Bouvier *et al.* (1957, 1959). D was type specific and was degraded by heat and other treatment to C, a smaller particle showing more cross-reactivity and probably devoid of nucleic acid. Very good CF antigens have been made from brains of baby mice, to which some strains have been adapted (Casals *et al.*, 1951; Selzer & van den Ende, 1956). Microflocculation (Smith *et al.*, 1956), micro-precipitin (Eggers & Sabin, 1961), and micro-ouchterlony (Selzer, 1962) tests have been described, giving mainly type-specific reactions.

Within the three main types, minor antigenic variants occur (Wecker, 1960; Plotkin *et al.*, 1961; Gard, 1960). These may be important in epidemiological studies especially in association with trials of attenuated virus: the antigenic characters are stable in culture but apparently less so in infected people or experimental animals.

Interference between poliomyelitis and other enteroviruses, also myxo- and arboviruses and rabies has been reported. An interfering agent appearing in cultures (Ho & Enders, 1959) is probably identical with interferon.

Cultivation. *In fertile eggs.* A Type II virus was adapted to growth in 6- to 9-day old chick embryos by Roca-Garcia *et al.* (1952), using yolk-sac inoculation or (Cabasso *et al.*, 1951) allantoic inoculation. Lesions of the nervous system, sometimes fatal, were produced (Love & Roca-Garcia, 1955).

In tissue culture the virus has been grown in many tissues of primates since the report by Enders, Weller & Robbins (1949). Cultures of kidney, from man, rhesus, patas and other monkey species, monkey fibroblasts, human amnion, Hela and other human cell lines have been widely used. Growth in non-primate tissues has mainly been unsuccessful. Although growth has been claimed in continuous cell lines of other origins, there is strong evidence that there may have been "pick-ups" of Hela or other cells. Curiously, the mouse-adapted strains have not been grown in mouse tissues.

Viruses can be attenuated by growth in eggs or in culture and used for immunization. Plaques are formed on monolayers of suitable primate cells. Several "marker" characters have been described, depending on the ability of virus to grow under differing conditions; these are useful for identifying particular strains, especially attenuated ones. These include the T (temperature) marker (Lwoff &

Lwoff, 1960), the d (bicarbonate) marker (Dulbecco & Vogt, 1958), MS (monkey stable cell line) and the A markers (stability in cations) (Melnick, 1962) and the intratypic antigenic structure (McBride, 1959; Gard, 1960).

Ackermann *et al.* (1958) describe changes in cultivated cells ascribed to an "extraviral toxin" produced by some strains. Cytological changes in relation to virus release are described by Dunnebacke (1956). It is reported (Holland *et al.*, 1959) that RNA extracted from virus will infect non-primate cells.

Pathogenicity. The viruses infect human pharynx and alimentary tract, reaching Peyer's patches and lymph-nodes. Thence they may, rather transiently, pass into the blood-stream and reach the nervous system, spreading further along nerve pathways. Invasion of the CNS is, however, exceptional. Two rather different views are contrasted by Bodian (1959). According to his own view, the primary site of multiplication is in lymphoid tissues, while according to Sabin (1956) it is in oropharyngeal and intestinal mucosa. Infection in man may be wholly inapparent; it may be a nondescript febrile illness, often called abortive poliomyelitis; or it may involve the nervous system causing non-paralytic and paralytic disease: paralysis usually affects the limbs but can involve the cranial nerves; an encephalitis affecting higher centres is rare. The incubation period is from 4 to 35 days with an average of 10 days.

Experimentally. A similar disease can be induced in many primates after inoculation by various routes but most readily by IC or IN inoculation. Chimpanzees and cynomolgus monkeys are readily infected *per os*, and chimpanzees, unlike lower primates, can readily be made into symptomless intestinal carriers. Type II was adapted by Armstrong (1939) to cotton-rats and, later, mice. Subsequently Types I and III were also adapted to mice by intraspinal injection (Li & Habel, 1951; Li & Schaffer, 1953). In contrast to the situation with many other viruses, suckling mice are less readily infected than adults, but adaptation of Type II to sucklings has been achieved (Casals *et al.*, 1951) and subsequently also Type I (Selzer & Butchart, 1959). Hamsters have also been infected.

Pathological lesions. The most important lesions are usually in the spinal cord particularly the anterior horns, where neurones are destroyed; cellular infiltration with mononuclear cells follows in the wake of this damage. Other parts of the CNS are involved to a varying extent. Eosinophilic inclusions are found in cytoplasm of infected cells (Beale *et al.*, 1956) but are not very characteristic. Very small intranuclear inclusions are also described (Hurst, 1931). Myocarditis may occur in man and in experimental animals.

Ecology. In countries with lower standards of hygiene, virus excreted in fæces is spread very readily, so that children are almost universally infected at an early age. The proportion of paralytic cases is very low, but paralysis is chiefly seen in children and the disease there deserves its name of "infantile paralysis". There is evidence that strains of low virulence have selective advantage under poor social conditions, and compete successfully with virulent strains. With better hygiene the virus spreads less readily and infections occur later in life, when paralysis is apt to be more serious. Virus has been recovered from flies in the field (Lucilia & Phormia); attempts to prove multiplication in flies have been suggestive but unconvincing. There has been much argument as to the relative importance of the oropharynx and intestine in spreading infection in man. Contact infection may take place amongst monkeys in the laboratory.

Control. This is not the place to review the great successes in preventing poliomyelitis with inactivated, formalinized virus (*cf.* Salk, 1959) or with the attenuated viruses first tested by Koprowski *et al.* (1952) and later developed by Sabin (1959). Use of the last seems to hold most promise of the ultimate elimination of the virus (Sabin, 1962). Hayflick *et al.* (1962) point out the advantages of a diploid line of human cells for growing virus for vaccine production.

Gamma-globulin has been used, with limited success, for giving temporary passive protection.

COXSACKIE VIRUSES

Synonym: C viruses (no longer used).
Reviews: Dalldorf, Melnick & Curnen (1959). Tobin (1953). Dalldorf (1955). Löffler (1958).

Named after a village in New York state where an outbreak occurred. These viruses are divided into two groups, A and B, on the basis of biological characters. They are similar in physico-chemical and other fundamental properties and these will be considered for the two groups together, with a bracketed (A) or (B) to indicate for which viruses particular information is available.

Morphology and development. Spheres of about 28 mμ diameter with a denser centre 15 mμ across (B). So far as is known, development is entirely within cytoplasm and here virus particles may be found closely packed in a crystalline arrangement (Morgan, Howe & Rose, 1959). From purified virus (A) crystals 100 mμ in diameter have been obtained (Mattern & DuBuy, 1956). A role for the nucleus, or at least nuclear membrane, in development cannot be excluded (Mattern & Chi, 1962).

Chemical composition. Contains about 4 per cent. RNA. Infection has been produced with virus RNA (A) (Sprunt et al., 1959).

Physico-chemical characters. As for poliomyelitis. Readily preserved at $-70°$ or $-20°$ C or in 50 per cent. glycerol in the cold, but not so easily by drying. Stable between pH 2·3 and 9·4 for 1 day, or between pH 4·0 and 8 for 7 days (Robinson, 1950). Inactivated in 30 minutes at 60° C. Ether resistant; also resistant to 5 per cent. lysol and 70 per cent. ethanol, but inactivated by 0·1 N HCl or 0·3 per cent. formaldehyde (Kaplan & Melnick, 1951). Coxsackie A but not B viruses, in general, are inhibited by 2(α-hydroxybenzyl) benzimidazole (Eggers & Tamm, 1961a) (cf. p. 3).

Hæmagglutination. Type A7 agglutinates those fowl RBC's which are sensitive to vaccinia hæmagglutinin (Grist, 1960); A21 and B3 will agglutinate human O cells. The hæmagglutinins apparently form part of the virus particle.

Antigenic properties. There are numerous serological types in each group. The 24 A-types and 6 B-types may be distinguished by neutralisation tests carried out in suckling mice or in tissue-culture, by gel-diffusion or by complement-fixation. Cross reactions in the CF test between different types are not very troublesome; however, sera of convalescent patients may show heterotypic responses. This may be due to presence of an antigen common to a number of types (Beeman & Huebner, 1952). Minor antigenic crossings may occur between some Coxsackie A and some ECHO viruses. Schmidt et al. (1963) separated group and specific antigens from Coxsackie B and A9 viruses.

Interference. Interference may be demonstrated between Coxsackie and numerous other enteroviruses, in particular between

Coxsackie and poliomyelitis. Dalldorf (1955) has drawn attention to epidemiological evidence suggesting that poliomyelitis is less prevalent when there is much Coxsackie B infection.

Cultivation. *In fertile eggs.* A few isolates of several A types have been adapted to grow in yolk-sacs or on the CAM (Huebner *et al.*, 1950; Godenne & Curnen, 1952); skeletal muscle of infected embryos may almost disappear.

In tissue cultures of monkey kidneys, B-types grow readily. A large number of B strains fail to produce cytopathic changes in human amnion or diploid cells, but have been grown occasionally in other tissues of man and various monkey species; also in cultures of hamster kidney (Barron & Karzon, 1959), pig kidney (Guérin & Guérin, 1957), calf and lamb (Lenahan & Wenner, 1960) and mouse interscapular fat (Stulberg *et al.*, 1952). CPE similar to that of poliovirus. Although several serotypes of A viruses grow readily in primate mouse and other cultures, the majority do not readily do so; ability to grow varies from one isolate to another (Dalldorf, 1957).

When we come to pathogenicity, the A and B Coxsackies have to be considered separately. The following table is modified from that published by Tobin (1953).

TABLE 2

THE PATHOGENICITY OF A AND B COXSACKIES

Characteristic	Group A	Group B
Optimum age of mice for inoculation	48 hrs.	24 hrs.
Incubation period in suckling mice	2–6 days	4–12 days
Type of paralysis	Flaccid	Spastic
Myositis in suckling mice	Generalized	Focal or absent
Panniculitis in suckling mice	Absent	Marked
Encephalitis in suckling mice	Absent	Often present
Pancreatitis in weaned mice	Absent	Often present
Growth in primate tissue cultures	Exceptional	Usually positive
Chief clinical picture produced in man	Herpangina	Epidemic myalgia, aseptic meningitis and myocarditis in infants

Coxsackie A Viruses

Pathogenicity. May be present in stools, especially in children in summer months without association with disease. Frequently associated with herpangina, a short febrile illness with sore-throat, in which are seen small papules or vesicles around the fauces, soon breaking down into shallow ulcers. Aseptic meningitis may also be caused, particularly by Type A9. One type, A21 or Coe Virus, may give rise to the picture of a common cold (see below). Infection of laboratory staff working with A-virus is not infrequent.

Experimentally the viruses characteristically infect suckling mice, producing paralysis as a result of acute necrotic myositis, infrequently also myocarditis or hepatitis. Further details are shown in the table above. Suckling mice are readily infected intramuscularly or by any other route, ground-up whole carcasses being used for passage. The viruses occasionally require adaptation to produce typical symptoms. The virus multiplies after injection into baby rabbits; myositis is produced but there are usually no obvious symptoms (Bell & Hadlow, 1959). Verlinde & Versteeg (1958) produced pneumonia by inoculating pigs; and Verlinde & Ting (1954) produced fatal myositis in suckling ferrets. Lepine *et al.* (1952) found the merion, a North African rodent, very susceptible, new-born hamsters less so. Some strains show neuropathogenicity for monkeys (Dalldorf, 1957).

Pathological lesions of muscles of baby mice consist of an eosinophilic hyaline necrosis.

Characteristics of particular Coxsackie A Viruses

A7. This type can cause paralytic disease in monkeys and cotton-rats. Russian workers have suggested that it be called a fourth type of poliovirus as it has been recovered from paralytic cases in man (Voroshilova & Chumakov, 1959).

A9 is in some ways intermediate between Coxsackie and ECHO ciruses. It resembles the ECHO's in being inactivated by 2(α-hydroxybenzyl)benzimidazole (Eggers & Tamm, 1961a). It has also been particularly associated with aseptic meningitis sometimes with an exanthem, and it shows some antigenic relation with A23–ECHO 9; it also produces CPE in rhesus kidney tissue cultures; A14 also is more neurotropic for monkeys than most A's. A16 has been associated in Canada (Robinson *et al.*, 1958) and elsewhere with a febrile illness with vesicular rash: "Hand, foot and mouth disease".

A21 is serologically identical with Coe virus (Lennette *et al.*, 1958) which produces common-cold-like symptoms, particularly amongst recruits. It is more commonly recovered from pharynx than fæces. It can be grown in embryo rabbit kidney, HeLa and other human cells and has a low pathogenicity for suckling mice. Its effects when given intranasally to volunteers have been described by Parsons *et al.* (1960). Recently isolated strains agglutinate human O RBC's.

A23 has been considered to be identical with ECHO 9 (Sickles *et al.*, 1959) and will be considered under that heading (*v.* p. 15).

Coxsackie B Viruses

Pathogenicity. Inapparent infections are common. Particularly associated with epidemic pleurodynia or myalgia (Bornholm disease); in this condition fever is associated with severe thoracic or abdominal pain. Orchitis occurs as a complication. Aseptic meningitis may be caused, more commonly than with Coxsackie A's. A serious, often fatal, myocarditis due to Coxsackie B's occurs in newborn infants (Gear, 1958). Myocarditis and pericarditis appear much more rarely in older children or adults. Upper respiratory involvement may be the only sign of infection, especially with B5.

Experimentally. Suckling mice can be infected by injection by various routes, but preferably IC. The lesions are predominantly in the brain. In contrast to the flaccid paralysis caused by the A-viruses, B-infected ones show spasticity or spastic paralysis and tremors. Necrosis of muscles, if it occurs, is focal. Myocarditis, hepatitis, parotitis and pancreatitis occur, particularly in older mice. Necrosis in the interscapular brown fat pad may be visible with the naked eye and is generally the most prominent lesion microscopically. Mice recovering from encephalitis may develop cerebral cysts.

Baby hamsters may also be infected and myocarditis has been produced by inoculating young cynomolgus monkeys (Lou *et al.*, 1961). Gravid mice are more susceptible than normally. B viruses, as well as As, have caused infections in laboratory workers.

The lesions in brain and elsewhere are mainly those of acute cell-necrosis. Lepine *et al.* (1952) found degenerative and inflammatory lesions in muscle removed by biopsy from two human infections.

Ecology. (A and B strains.) Viruses are widespread, usually in the summer and autumn months in the alimentary tracts especially of children and of those living under poor social-economic conditions. Their presence in the gut is probably transient—a week or less. Virus passes out in the urine and fæces and has been recovered from sewage and from flies. Infections causing myocarditis in infants have been contracted from mothers.

ECHO VIRUSES

The initials ECHO stand for "enteric cytopathic human orphan" (orphan implies lack of association with disease). However, many viruses in the group are now known to cause aseptic meningitis and other troubles; so the O of ECHO is not always relevant. Typically they are less neuropathogenic than poliovirus, do not produce disease in suckling mice as do Coxsackies nor cause common colds like rhinoviruses; they produce a CPE in rhesus kidney cultures. As will be seen, some are intermediate in character between typical ECHO's and other picornaviruses.

Reviews: Committee (1957).
Melnick and Sabin (1959).
Melnick (1960).
Müller (1961).

Morphology and development. Spheres 24–25 mμ across, not differing, so far as known, from polio- and Coxsackie-viruses. The diameter of a central nucleoid is estimated as 13 mμ, or 6 mμ for ECHO 4. May (ECHO 9) be packed in a hexagonal lattice within the cytoplasm, to be later dispersed in the cytoplasm and liberated from the cell either through rents in the plasma membrane or through the cell's disruption (Rifkind et al., 1960). Fibrils may be seen in association with the crystals. Duffy et al. (1962) suggest that ECHO 4 is not more than 20 mμ across.

Chemical composition. RNA viruses. Infectious RNA has been described for Types 1 and 8 by Sprunt et al. (1959).

Physico-chemical characters. Different sero-types and even strains of one type differ in their rate of inactivation at 37°, 22°, 4° and −20° C. In general, they are inactivated in 30 minutes at 65° C, survive well at −70° but lose much activity on drying. They are ether stable and also stable over a wide pH range. ECHO 1, at least, is very resistant to the photodynamic action of toluidine blue (Hiatt et al., 1960).

Hæmagglutination. Human O RBC's are agglutinated by many strains of Types 3, 6, 7, 10, 11, 12, 13, 19 (Goldfield *et al.*, 1957, Lahelle 1958). The hæmagglutinin is not separable from the virus particle. Receptor-destroying enzyme does not affect agglutinability of cells.

Antigenic properties. Neutralization tests in tissue culture and complement-fixation tests separate the ECHO viruses into different serological types. The hæmagglutination inhibition test is less specific. Twenty-eight serotypes were recognised in 1962 but others have been described. Some types, e.g. ECHO 6, exist in two phases, one reacting poorly with homologous antibodies (Karzon *et al.*, 1959). Cross-neutralization tests against prototype viruses may be "one-way", so that new isolates may mistakenly be thought to represent new types. Cross-reactions may occur in the neutralization or CF test between types 1, 8, 12 and 13 and there may even be evidence of a slight antigenic relation between ECHO viruses and poliovirus (ECHO 6) or Coxsackies (*v.* ECHO 9, p. 15). Lim & Benyesh-Melnick (1960) have proposed a scheme for testing with pools of antisera designed to facilitate the rapid typing of unidentified strains.

Interference is reported between ECHO and other enteroviruses; also with Newcastle disease virus.

Cultivation in fertile eggs is not reported. Although most strains grow well, with characteristic CPE, in cultures of rhesus, cynomolgus or cercopithecus kidneys, some strains grow better in human amnion cell cultures. Types 7, 8 and 12, but not the others reported on, grow well in kidney cultures from *Erythrocebus patas* monkeys (Hsiung & Melnick, 1957). Plaques formed on monolayers in culture are of different sizes and appearance and are not necessarily always the same for a particular type. Many strains have been adapted to grow in HeLa and other lines of human cells, also (ECHO 4 and 9) in calf or pig cells (Lenahan & Wenner, 1960). Growth may be poorer when the pH of the medium becomes more acid, in contrast to what occurs with rhinoviruses (Barron & Karzon, 1957).

Habitat. In intestinal tracts of many persons, especially children, in the summer and under poor social-economic conditions. Most isolations of virus have been from stools or rectal swabs, some from throat or CSF.

Pathogenicity. Most infections are inapparent. Many of the serotypes, however, have caused fever accompanied by signs of aseptic meningitis, sometimes with an exanthem. Exceptionally there may be paresis, usually transient (Types 9 and 16). The same serotypes have been associated with mild gastro-enteritis. Features of infection with some of the more important types are recorded below. In addition to these, Types 2, 3, 5, 7 and 14 have been associated with sporadic cases of aseptic meningitis, and Types 2, 7, 12, 14, 19 and 24 with gastro-enteritis. Types 1, 13, 15 and 17 have not as yet been incriminated as agents of disease. Some types appear to cause mild respiratory disease.

Experimentally ECHO viruses have rarely caused disease in experimental animals. Some epidemic strains of ECHO 9 have been adapted to suckling mice in which they have behaved like Coxsackie A viruses. Focal lesions have been found in the CNS of occasional monkeys inoculated in the brain or cord with Types 1, 2, 3, 4, 6, 7, 8, 9, 10, 12, 14 and 17; at times such lesions have appeared following intramuscular injections (Wenner & Chin, 1957). They have consisted of focal infiltration, less frequently neuronal destruction. Symptoms in the monkey are commonly absent but may occur after intraspinal injection (Lou & Wenner, 1962).

Characteristics of particular ECHO Viruses

ECHO 4 has caused at least two considerable outbreaks of aseptic meningitis, 70 per cent. of the patients having also gastro-intestinal symptoms (Chin et al., 1957; Johnsson, 1957).

ECHO 6 has also caused a number of similar outbreaks of aseptic meningitis in children and adults; gastro-intestinal disturbance was, however, less common (Kibrick et al., 1957). Localized muscle weaknesses have occurred and there were maculo-papular rashes in one outbreak. This type has rarely been isolated apart from association with disease.

ECHO 8 was recovered from patients with respiratory and intestinal symptoms (Rosen et al, 1958).

ECHO 9 was the cause of a widespread epidemic of aseptic meningitis occurring all over Europe in 1955 and 1956 and reaching North America in 1957. In many but not all outbreaks there was a maculo-papular rash. Familial infections were common. In contrast to the prototype ECHO 9 virus, many epidemic strains could be adapted to cause Coxsackie A-like disease in suckling mice (Tyrrell *et al.*, 1958). In other respects, also, the virus was intermediate between typical Coxsackie and typical ECHO viruses and Tyrrell *et al.* (1958) reported some antigenic relation with Coxsackie A9. It has been proposed (Sickles *et al.*, 1959) to rename it Coxsackie A23; it behaves, however, like an ECHO virus by Eggers & Tamm's (1961a) benzimidazole test. It can be grown in hamster kidney cultures (Barron & Karzon, 1957).

ECHO 10 has now been removed from the ECHO viruses and is considered under Reovirus (*v.* p. 45).

ECHO 11 under the name of U-virus was associated by Philipson & Wesslen (1958) with respiratory illness in children. In experiments on volunteers with this strain Buckland *et al.* (1959) produced no typical colds but rather gastro-intestinal disturbances.

ECHO 16 caused the so-called "Boston exanthem" (Neva & Enders, 1954). There were a very few cases of aseptic meningitis; many had a maculo-papular rash, not appearing till the fever was over.

ECHO 18 was recovered from fæces of numerous infants under 1 year old during an outbreak of diarrhœa in 1955 (Ramos-Alvarez, 1957) and it turned up in another outbreak in 1956. Evidence that it caused the diarrhœa was fairly good, but implication of other ECHO viruses as causative agents of infantile diarrhœa is still debatable. They do undoubtedly turn up more frequently than in normal children, as Coxsackie viruses do not (Ramoz-Alvarez & Sabin, 1958).

ECHO 20, first referred to as JV1, was recovered by Cramblett *et al.* (1958) from stools of children with fever, coryza and watery diarrhœa. Adult volunteers were infected with the virus by Buckland *et al.* (1961); 27 of 43 developed symptoms, chiefly constitutional, 2 had symptoms like those of a cold while 8 had abdominal symptoms.

ECHO 22 and 23 behaved unlike other ECHO's and resembled Coxsackie A viruses in their reaction to 2(α-hydroxybenzyl) benzimidazole (Eggers & Tamm 1961a). Nuclear changes produced in infected cultures also differed from those of other ECHO viruses (Shaver *et al.*, 1961).

ECHO 28 (JH or 2060 virus) is intermediate between ECHO and rhinoviruses, but lies nearer the latter and is referred to on p. 24.

Ecology. This is much as has been described for Coxsackie viruses (p. 12). Though the distribution of the viruses is world-wide, all the reported epidemics have occurred in the temperate zones, beginning in summer or autumn months. Sporadic isolations have been made throughout the year.

TESCHEN DISEASE

Synonyms: Infectious porcine encephalomyelitis or poliomyelitis (and similar names).
Ansteckende Schweinelähmung. Talfan disease.

Morphology and development. 25–30 mμ in diameter; estimates by several methods are in fair agreement. Specific antigen is detected by fluorescent antibody mainly in the cytoplasm, but some may be present at the periphery of the nucleus (Mussgay, 1958a).

Chemical composition. An infectious RNA has been extracted by cold phenol (Brown & Stewart, 1960).

Physico-chemical characters. Stable between pH 2·5 and 13. Inactivated in 20 minutes at 60° C but more readily—20 minutes at 50° C—after partial purification with protamine sulphate. Ether-stable. Inactivated by 0·15 per cent. formaldehyde. Survives well at 4° C or −79° C but is not readily preserved by drying (Patočka *et al.*, 1951; Armbruster & Zimmermann, 1958).

Hæmagglutination has been looked for, but not as yet demonstrated.

Antigenic properties. Antibodies are demonstrable by neutralization tests in tissue-culture or, less readily, by agar-gel diffusion (Wittman, 1958). Betts (1960) and Greig *et al.* (1962) have described immunologically distinct strains causing paralysis in pigs, but in general virulent strains are serologically similar, as are the mild British strain (Talfan disease) and the Danish "poliomyelitis suum" (Chaproniere, Done & Andrewes, 1958).
Strains can, however, be separated into at least three antigenic subtypes (Mayr, 1961; Huck *et al.*, 1962; Cartwright & Huck, 1963).

Cultivation. The virus can be readily cultivated in pig kidney cells, causing a CPE like that which poliomyelitis causes in monkey kidney cultures; it also produces plaques on monolayers. Rapid passage in culture attenuates its virulence for piglets.

Distribution. The virus is widespread in Europe but has only caused serious losses in Eastern Europe, especially Poland and

Czechoslovakia; also in Madagascar (Lepine & Atanasiu, 1950). Mild strains are probably present in Canada (Richards & Savan, 1960; Greig *et al.*, 1962) the United States (Koestner *et al.*, 1962) and Australia.

Pathogenicity. The disease may occur sporadically or in outbreaks. In the severe form, with a mortality averaging 70 per cent., there is a mild fever, soon followed by convulsions, prostration, stiffness and paralysis. Residual paralysis occurs in animals which survive. With milder strains, infection may be inapparent. Mild British strains are more apt to cause ataxia than paralysis (Done, 1961). In Czechoslovakia wild boars are affected.

The disease has been transmitted to young pigs by IC, IN, IM or IP inoculation, also by feeding but not by SC inoculation. Viræmia occurs early in the incubation period, which varies between 4 and 28 days, and may precede paralysis by 10–12 days (Horstmann, 1952).

Other species are insusceptible—except for *Potamochærus*, the wild Madagascan boar.

Pathological lesions are more widespread than in human poliomyelitis, as there is a diffuse encephalomyelitis. Cytoplasmic eosinophilic masses occur in nerve-cells. Myocardial lesions are reported.

Ecology. As with enteroviruses of man, the virus is normally a harmless inhabitant of the intestinal tract; it is probably only virulent strains which cause epizootics. Infected animals liberate virus both in mouth secretions and in stools.

Control. Effective vaccines have been made, particularly with virus cultivated in tissues. Virus may be given SC either living, attenuated in culture, or inactivated by formaldehyde. Both types gave 80–86 per cent. protection (Mayr & Correns, 1959).

OTHER ENTEROVIRUSES OF SWINE

Synonym: ECSO viruses (enteric cytopathic swine orphan).
Review: Kalter (1960).

Morphology. Diameter 28 mμ (McFerran, 1961). Bögel & Mayr (1961) estimated the size as 25–30 mμ. Singh *et al.* (1961), perhaps working with a different strain, found 36 mμ particles packed regularly in the cytoplasm of infected cells. Lamont & Betts (1958) also report a 35 mμ diameter.

Physico-chemical characters. Ether and chloroform stable. Bögel & Mayr (1961) find chloroform resistance easier to measure accurately than ether-resistance. Inactivated in 2 minutes at 56°. Survived freeze-drying and also storage for 3 weeks at room temperature (Lamont & Betts, 1958).

Antigenic properties. Serological types can be separated by means of neutralization tests in tissue culture. Betts *et al.* (1961) in Britain, differentiated 5 groups, including Teschen virus as one. On the other hand Beran *et al.* (1958) found that 121 of 123 strains isolated in the United States were serologically alike. Antibodies to this strain were present in pig sera from 27/29 herds.

Cultivation. The viruses grow well, producing a CPE in pig kidney cultures; one strain (Moscovici *et al.*, 1959) also grew in monkey cell cultures. Growth in cells from other species is not reported; nor would viruses grow in fertile eggs. Plaques are formed on monolayers.

Pathogenicity. Though Moscovici and others have isolated viruses from outbreaks of enteritis, there is little evidence that these viruses are naturally pathogenic for pigs. Beran *et al.* (1960) did, however, produce fatal infections with diarrhœa and some nervous symptoms in new-born pigs deprived of colostrum. The viruses are non-pathogenic for other species also, including suckling mice.

Ecology. Beran *et al.* (1958) isolated viruses with increasing frequency in pigs up to the age of 9–10 weeks. Moscovici *et al.* (1959) did not obtain their virus from rectal swabs of adult pigs. Beran *et al.* (1958) made no isolations during the winter months and suggested that virus-shedding was seasonal. Some virus was excreted throughout a month (Wenner *et al.*, 1960).

BOVINE ENTEROVIRUSES

Synonym: ECBO viruses (enteric cytopathic bovine orphan).
Review: Kalter (1960).

Morphology. Size estimated as 25–30 mμ (Bögel & Mayr, 1961), or 34 mμ (Luginbuhl *et al.*, 1961).

Physico-chemical characters. Moll & Finlayson's (1957) agents were not inactivated in 30 minutes at 56° C; they survived for over 2 months at −10° to −22° C and for four days at 37° C. All reported strains are ether-, and where tested, chloroform-resistant.

Hæmagglutination. 5/11 strains tested by Moscovici & Maisel (1958) agglutinated bovine RBC's at 5–8° C, not at room temperature. Three of them also clumped guinea pig cells. Elution was rather rapid. Strains isolated by Inaba *et al.* (1959) agglutinated horse and sheep RBC's at 4°. Viruses of one serotype agglutinate rhesus RBC's (La Placa *et al.*, 1963).

Antigenic properties. Neutralization tests in tissue culture reveal that there are numerous sero-types. McFerran (1958) found three types in Northern Ireland, one corresponding to an American type. Klein (quoted by Kalter, 1960) separated six types. On the other hand 8 viruses isolated by Kunin & Minuse (1958) were all alike. No certain cross-reactions with human enteroviruses have been established. On the other hand some bovine strains are neutralized by certain "normal" human, monkey and rabbit sera. Further some human enteroviruses, particularly Type II poliovirus are inactivated by "normal" cattle sera; Klein (1958) felt that true antibodies were concerned.

Cultivation. *In fertile eggs.* Kunin & Minuse's (1958) strain could be isolated by amniotic inoculation and also produced pocks on the CAM.

In tissue culture of calf kidney cells, the viruses produce CPE and at least those of Moll & Finlayson (1957) and Moll & Davis (1959) grow also in cell cultures from pig, guinea pig, rhesus and patas monkeys and man, but not in HeLa cells nor cat cells and poorly in those from swine, dog and rabbit. Several other workers have isolated these viruses in monkey kidney cultures. Formation of plaques of several types permits the separation of different agents.

Pathogenicity. Not known to be naturally pathogenic for cattle, but one strain caused bloody diarrhœa in colostrum-deprived calves. It also led to abortion in pregnant guinea pigs (Bögel & Mussgay, 1960). The Kunin strain produced lesions in suckling mice and hamsters like those due to Coxsackie-A viruses (*v.* p. 11).

Ecology. Viruses have been isolated most frequently from younger calves.

The van den Ende Strain

This virus was at one time associated with Lumpy skin disease of South African cattle: such a relation now seems very improbable. It has been classified as a "cytopathogenic bovine orphan virus" by Kipps *et al.* (1961), but its properties make it equally likely that it was of avian origin. The circumstances of its origin permit no decision about this. It grows to high titre in fertile eggs inoculated amniotically, allantoically or into the yolk sac. Four or five days after inoculation, the amniotic fluid has almost gone (van den Ende *et al.*, 1949) and the amnion is shrunk round a small featherless embryo. It grows well in chick-embryo tissue culture. It is neutralized by many "normal" bovine sera, also by those from man, rat and guinea pig. It is not pathogenic for cattle or laboratory rodents.

AVIAN ENCEPHALOMYELITIS

Synonym: Epidemic tremor.
Reviews: Jungherr & Minard (1942).
　　　　　　Calnek *et al.* (1961)—immunization.

Morphology. 20–30 mμ in diameter (Olitsky & Bauer, 1939).

Physico-chemical characters. Survives well at $-20°$ or in 50 per cent. glycerol in the cold. Stated also to be readily preserved by freeze-drying (Olitsky, 1939).

Antigenic properties. Neutralizing antibodies, most readily titrated in tissue-culture, are present in sera of recovered birds (Hwang *et al.*, 1959). Antigenically similar viruses were recovered from rectal swabs from normal chicks (Burke *et al.*, 1959—*v.* p. 22).

Cultivation. *In fertile eggs:* grows after inoculation into amnion, allantoic or yolk sac; infected embryos are atrophied and show neuronal degeneration, often hydrocephalus (Casorso & Jungherr, 1959). Some have encountered erratic results, attributable to using eggs from an infected flock, antibodies having passed from an immune hen into the yolk.

The virus grows also in chick embryo *tissue cultures*, better in monolayers than in whole minced embryo (Hwang *et al.*, 1959).

Distribution. Formerly thought to be confined to the Western hemisphere but now recognized in other continents including Australia.

Pathogenicity. Characteristic symptoms in chicks are ataxia, followed by tremors of head and neck, later somnolence and death. Mortality up to 50 per cent., average 10 per cent. The disease occurs only in young chicks, especially those 2–3 weeks old; also in pheasant and guinea-fowl chicks. Cataracts and other ocular lesions may occur as sequelæ (Peckham, 1957).

It may be readily transmitted IC; other routes give erratic results. The incubation period is from 6 to 10 days. Experimental infection of young ducks, turkeys and pigeons is possible, but mammals are insusceptible. No viræmia has been detected.

Pathological lesions are those of neuronal degeneration especially of Purkinje cells, with masses of mononuclear cells around blood-vessels. There is hyperplasia also of lymphatic tissue elsewhere.

Ecology. Not readily transmitted by contact. Commoner in winter and spring: arthropod transmission is unlikely. Circumstantial evidence suggests that transmission through the egg is probable.

Control. Schaaf & Lamoreux (1955), however, suggest immunization of older birds with live virus in wing webs so that their offspring are resistant. Later, Schaaf (1959) suggested a vaccine made from brain tissue, virus having been inactivated by β-propiolactone. Calnek et al. (1961) discuss the appropriate circumstances for use of live and inactivated vaccines.

AVIAN PICORNAVIRUSES

Viruses isolated from rectal swabs of chickens by Burke et al. (1959) and by Taylor & Calnek (1962) seem to fall into the category of avian entero- or picornaviruses.

One strain (EV-89) resisted heating for 22 hours at 56°, was not shown to hæmagglutinate any RBC's and grew well with CPE in chick kidney tissue cultures, not in those from calf or monkey (Burke et al., 1959). It also produced plaques on monolayers.

Taylor & Calnek (1962) found that 45 strains they isolated fell into 15 sero-types by neutralization tests in tissue-culture. One was identical with the CELO (Chick embryo lethal orphan) virus of Yates & Fry (1957), isolated by them from hens' eggs; this seems to be identical with a quail bronchitis virus (Dubose & Grumbles, 1959). Burke's EV-89 strain was closely related serologically to avian encephalomyelitis virus (p. 21). This strain was pathogenic, often lethal, for inoculated chick embryos, many showing dwarfing and heart nodules. It produced nervous symptoms when inoculated intracerebrally into newly hatched chicks.

Taylor & Calnek (1962) isolated viruses most readily from chicks 4 to 12 weeks old.

The van den Ende strain of enterovirus (Kipps *et al.*, 1961) (p. 21) may prove to be an avian virus of this group rather than of bovine origin.

SIMIAN ENTEROVIRUSES

Synonym: ECMO (enteric cytopathogenic monkey orphan).
Review: Kalter (1960).

The extensive use of monkeys for work on poliomyelitis and other viruses has led to the discovery of many "orphan" viruses present in monkey kidneys or stools. These have been given numbers in an SV (simian virus) series by Hull and his collaborators (1956, 1957, 1958). Some of them, SV2, 6, 16, 18 and 19 seem to be enteroviruses; also P13 of Cheever (1957). Still more isolated by Riordan and others are probably enteroviruses but await further study. The viruses concerned have come from rhesus and cynomolgus monkeys (see also section on simian viruses, p. 348).

Physico-chemical characters. SV2 and 6, unlike some of the others, were not inactivated by heating for 30 minutes to 65° C. All those tested have been susceptible to 1 : 4000 formaldehyde.

Antigenic properties. The viruses are antigenically distinct from human enteroviruses, so far as they have been tested.

Cultivation. All have been isolated in rhesus kidney cultures in which they produce a CPE, granulation or rounding-up occurring in 4–5 days. They do not produce changes in human amnion or HeLa cells. SV2, 16, 18 produce large plaques on rhesus and patas cultures, SV6 and S19 (= Cheever's P2) do so on rhesus cultures only (Hsiung & Melnick, 1958).

Pathogenicity. Though SV2 and 6 were isolated from monkeys with diarrhœa, there is no proof that any of them are natural monkey pathogens. Most have been grown from monkey kidneys. SV16, however, produced paralysis and death after IC inoculation into monkeys. S19 and P13 produce lesions in suckling mice like those due to Coxsackie A viruses.

RHINOVIRUSES

Synonyms: Common cold viruses., Coryza viruses.
Review: Andrewes (1960, 1962).

Morphology. Spheres about 31 mμ in diameter. Development probably all in cytoplasm.

Chemical composition. Probably RNA viruses (Ketler *et al.*, 1962) as indicated by tests with fluoro-deoxyuridine.

Physico-chemical characters. Survive well at $-76°$; more readily preserved by freeze-drying than many other picornaviruses. Ether-stable. Differ from enteroviruses in greater acid-lability, being quickly inactivated at pH 5·3; also in not being effectively stabilized against inactivation at 50° by 1M Mg Cl$_2$ (Dimmock & Tyrrell, 1962; Ketler *et al.*, 1962). 2(α-hydroxybenzyl) benzimidazole, which inactivates Coxsackie B and most ECHO viruses fails to do so with rhinoviruses or Coxsackie As (Eggers & Tamm, 1961). "Common Cold Virus" dried in air does not survive well (Lovelock *et al.*, 1952).

Hæmagglutination. None reported.

Antigenic properties. Neutralization tests can be carried out in tissue-culture by plaque-inhibition and other methods. There are numerous serotypes—at least 4 or 5 of the strains cultivable in rhesus kidney cultures (M strains), perhaps as many as 40 of the H strains growing only in human tissues (Taylor-Robinson & Tyrrell, 1962). One M strain, B362, shows antigenic overlap with a virus which has been classified as ECHO 28 (*v.* p. 16) but has greater claims to be considered an atypical rhinovirus. There is correlation between level of neutralizing antibody to a serotype of rhinovirus and resistance to that serotype (Bynoe *et al.*, 1961).

Interference occurs in tissue-culture between rhinoviruses and ECHO 11 and para-influenza 1, Sendai strain. This finding first permitted recognition of the growth of rhinoviruses in culture (Hitchcock & Tyrrell, 1960).

Cultivation. Several claims to have cultivated Common Cold viruses in *fertile eggs* remain unconfirmed.

Rhinoviruses can be grown with varying success in *cultures* of *primate tissues*. It is preferable for all of them, and essential for most, at least on first isolation, to cultivate at lower temperatures (about 33°) and lower pH than is conventional for virus-culture and to maintain good oxygenation by rotation (Tyrrell *et al.*, 1960). The M strains grow and produce CPE in rhesus kidney cultures as well as those of human embryonic kidney and the cancer lines HeLa and HEp-2, and other human cells (Taylor-Robinson *et al.*, 1962). The majority of strains (H strains) are best isolated in human embryonic kidney, but many of these grow also in lines of diploid cells from human embryonic lung and some in KB and HeLa cells (from human cancer) (Hayflick & Moorhead, 1961; Taylor-Robinson *et al.*, 1962). The DC strain, the one first cultivated (Andrewes *et al.*, 1953), in human embryonic lung, could subsequently only be isolated in diploid lines, though still later adapted to grow in other cultures (Tyrrell *et al.*, 1962). Cytopathic effects resemble those caused by enteroviruses. "Microplaques" produced on cell-sheets may be counted for purposes of assay (Parsons & Tyrrell, 1961) and macroscopic plaques may also be obtained (Porterfield, 1962).

Distribution. World-wide except in small isolated communities.

Pathogenicity. Rhinoviruses produce typical common colds, especially in adults, with profuse nasal discharge often preceded by sore throat and followed by cough; they are usually afebrile. The incubation period is usually about 48 hours, but some strains take 3 or 4 days to produce symptoms. Secondary bacterial invaders may cause sinusitis and other complications.

Experimentally washings or cultures produce the typical disease when given intranasally to volunteers. The colds occurring naturally or experimentally induced in chimpanzees (Dochez *et al.*, 1930) are probably, but not certainly, caused by rhinoviruses.

Ecology. Virus is present in the nose and throat, not, or rarely, in fæces; and infection is via the respiratory tract. Colds are commoner in winter but reasons for seasonal variation are obscure (Andrewes, 1962). An alleged effect of chilling in inducing colds has not been experimentally demonstrable (Andrewes, 1950; Dowling *et al.*, 1958). Repeated colds in individuals can be at least partly explained by existence of numerous serotypes.

Control. No effective virus vaccines are available, though experiments suggest that specific immunity to a particular strain may be produced (Price, 1957; Doggett *et al.*, 1963). Bacterial vaccines, directed against secondary invaders, are widely used but are of doubtful value. Attempts at control by air-hygiene are unpromising.

Bovine Rhinoviruses

Bögel and Bohm (1962) have isolated from a calf with acute rhinitis a virus with properties like those of human rhinoviruses. It was resistant to chloroform, less than 35 mμ in diameter and unstable at pH 5·2. It grew in calf kidney cultures, better at 33·5° than 37°. It caused some nasal discharge when inoculated into calves.

A Rhinovirus of Horses

Plummer (1962) recovered a virus from the respiratory tracts of horses with pharyngitis and nasal discharge. It grew well in monkey kidney tissue-cultures and had an apparent diameter, by electron-microscopy, of 30 mμ. Its acid stability resembled that of rhinoviruses (personal communication from Dr. A. P. Goffe, 1963). It was unrelated serologically to the many enteroviruses tested: neutralizing antibodies were detected in sera of 3 of 12 stable workers in contact with the horses, but in none of 159 other persons. A human subject inoculated intranasally developed severe pharyngitis with fever and viraemia (Plummer, 1963).

Common Cold Viruses of Man

Many colds yield filtrates which will produce colds in volunteers, though no agents have been cultivable. They may be due to rhinoviruses with more exacting cultural requirements or to quite different agents. Such colds have not been clinically separated from rhinovirus colds nor, apart from difficulty in cultivation, have the properties of the agents been defined. Clinical colds may also be caused naturally or experimentally by respiratory syncytial virus (p. 146,) Para-influenza viruses (p. 123), Coxsackie A21 (p. 11) or by the *Mycoplasma* causing atypical pneumonia.

ENCEPHALOMYOCARDITIS VIRUS (EMC)

Synonym: Parapoliomyelitis (not now used).
Well-known strains are Col-SK, MM and Mengo; these are alike antigenically but show certain differences in biological behaviour.
Reviews: Jungeblut (1958).
Melnick (1950).

Morphology and development. Diameter probably 25–29 mμ —about the same as poliomyelitis; earlier estimates probably underestimated its size (Jungeblut & Bourdillon, 1943). Though the earliest changes produced are in the nucleus, development is probably in the cytoplasm; the first antigen is detectable near the nucleus (Franklin, 1962).

Chemical composition. Infection has been produced by purified virus RNA (Colter *et al.*, 1957; Huppert & Sanders, 1958).

Physico-chemical characters. Survives well at $-76°$ C or in 50 per cent. glycerol in the cold; it may be lyophilized though is less readily preserved thus than are many viruses. The virus is unusually heat-stable. In 0·1 per cent. bovine albumin it was inactivated in 30 minutes at 60° but not at 56°; but in 20 per cent. monkey sera it survived 30 minutes at 80° C and 96° C for twenty minutes. It is ether-stable and rather resistant also to phenol, formalin and ethanol. Formalin 0·5 per cent. inactivated in 6 hours but not in 1 hour (Dick, 1948). When held in distilled water or in molar NaCl at 37° C it was much more resistant than strains (FA and GD VII) of mouse encephalomyelitis (Speir *et al.*, 1962). It was also fairly stable when held 2 hours at 37° between pH 3 and pH 9 (Speir *et al.*, 1962).

Hæmagglutination. Shown by Hallauer (1951) to agglutinate sheep RBC's in the cold, being adsorbed and then eluted at higher temperatures. RDE destroys the receptors on the sheep cells. Some strains also agglutinate human O cells; and Craighead & Shelokov (1962) isolated a stable agglutinin active for human and guinea pig cells. Hæmagglutination is inhibited by specific antisera. Hæmagglutinin was lost after 30 passes in a mouse ascites tumour (Furusawa & Cutting, 1962).

Antigenic properties. The various strains (MM, Mengo, Col-SK, etc.) are identical when compared by neutralization, CF or hæmagglutinin-inhibition tests (Warren *et al.*, 1949; Dick, 1949). Neutralizing antibodies have been found in the sera of wild rats and other species; hæmagglutinin inhibitors found in various animal sera may be non-specific substances rather than true antibodies.

Interference in experimental animals is reported between EMC and the poliomyelitis, Coxsackie, Eastern equine encephalomyelitis and lymphocytic choriomeningitis viruses.

Cultivation. *In fertile eggs*, the virus will grow when inoculated on the CAM or into the allantoic or amniotic cavities or yolk-sac. Infected embryos usually die, particularly if incubated at 35° C (Schultz & Enright, 1946). Maximum titres are obtained in 48 hours. Embryos show widespread degenerative changes and hæmorrhages (Dick, 1950).

In tissue culture it grows in embryonic and other tissues of chick, mouse, man, monkey, hamster and cattle: also in HeLa and other human cell-lines and in certain mouse tumours, though not all strains do equally well in all these tissues. The cytopathic effects (Barski & Lamy, 1957) differ from those of poliomyelitis and related viruses; there are retraction of nucleus and cytoplasm and nuclear fragmentation resulting in a basophilic mass. Cytoplasmic inclusions are not seen. With the aid of appropriate buffers, plaque development on monolayers is obtained (Bellett, 1960). Ellem & Colter (1961) isolated variants from plaques of 3 types: one of these formed cresentic plaques, following the lines of cell architecture.

Habitat. The virus has been isolated from the blood and from stools of human beings; from captive chimpanzee, gibbon, monkeys of several genera, a wild mongoose, pigs and several kinds of rodents —rats, a water-rat (*Hydromys*), cotton-rats and a squirrel. Serological evidence suggests that other rodents are probably infected in nature.

Pathogenicity. Infection is probably inapparent in rodents infected in nature. Not all the viruses isolated from human sources were necessarily the cause of disease. It seems, however, that infection can occasionally cause febrile illness in man with symptoms of CNS involvement and lymphocytic pleocytosis in the cerebrospinal fluid (Dick *et al.*, 1948; Gajdusek, 1955). Myocarditis in man is not recorded. In captive chimpanzees (Helwig & Schmidt, 1945), monkeys and pigs (Murnane *et al.*, 1960) illness has been accompanied by myocarditis, often fatal. Experimentally, the virus will infect a wide host range. Mice and hamsters commonly die with CNS involvement after inoculation by any route. Guinea pigs and rabbits are more resistant but the former develop myocarditis or become paralysed. Baby rats die after inoculation but in adults there is a chronic inapparent infection. Inoculated wild African rats and mongooses have died, apparently of myocarditis (Kilham *et al.*, 1956). Fatal encephalitis is produced by inoculating monkeys; different species show differing susceptibilities to various virus strains. Several species have contracted infection *per os*.

By passage in mice in different ways, virus was adapted to cause predominantly lesions of nervous system or of muscles (Kuwata, 1956–7).

Pathological lesions in infected animals are those of encephalitis with scattered focal necrosis; or, particularly near the site of intramuscular inoculation, necrosis of muscle fibres with inflammation and œdema. Similar necrotic lesions occur in the myocardium.

Ecology. The natural reservoir is probably in rodents, other species contracting infection from them. Cage infection has been recorded amongst cotton-rats and mice. Virus is present in urine and fæces. Though it has been recovered from wild-caught mosquitoes (*Tæniorhynchus*) in Uganda, there is no evidence that insects can act as vectors.

Control. A formolized virus vaccine protected mice experimentally (Kauffmann & Frantzer, 1948); so did that attentuated by passage in a mouse tumour (Furusawa & Cutting, 1962).

VESICULAR EXANTHEMA
(of pigs)

This is provisionally placed among the picornaviruses, but its position is uncertain.

Reviews: Madin & Traum (1955). Hagan (1958).

Morphology and development. According to Madin & Traum (1953) this is a very small virus comparable with that of foot-and-mouth disease, about 14–22 mμ across. However, Brooksby (1954) failed to filter it through a membrane of 37 mμ average pore diameter: and Newton and Bevis (1959) published electron-micrographs of bodies 55 mμ across, obtained after purification with zinc hydroxyde.

Physico-chemical characters. Resistance much like that of foot-and-mouth virus. Inactivated in 60 minutes at 62° C or 30 minutes at 64° C. Survived 6 weeks at room temperature, 2 years in the cold in 50 per cent. glycerol. Two per cent. NaOH is recommended for killing (Mott et al., 1953).

Hæmagglutination. Tests against cells of many species have all been negative.

Antigenic properties. Up to 13 serological types have been separated by neutralization, complement fixation or agar-gel diffusion tests; they have been identified by lettering: A, B, C, etc. Until recently only the B type had been identified outside California but 2 new ones were lately reported from New Jersey.

Cultivation. The viruses grow with varying ease in kidney, skin, or embryonic tissue cultures of swine, horse, dog and cat producing CPE (Madin, 1958). On monolayers of pig kidney plaques of two sizes develop, virus from larger plaques being more virulent for swine (McClain et al., 1959).

Distribution. The virus was first recognized in California in 1932 and did not spread thence until 1952 when it suddenly invaded most of the United States. By slaughter and other means it was thought to have been eliminated in 1956, but has occasionally been isolated since.

Pathogenicity. Only pigs are naturally infected. It is important mainly because of the close similarity to foot-and-mouth disease. It is much milder, but may be fatal in suckling pigs. Vesicles appear on snouts, tongue, feet and teats. There are fever, loss of weight and difficulty in walking.

Experimentally, the incubation period after intradermal inoculation is usually about 48 hours. Some strains will produce local lesions when inoculated on to the tongues of horses and dogs, and, very exceptionally, guinea pigs. Madin & Traum (1953) infected hamsters. Virus is present in all tissues of infected pigs with traces in urine and fæces.

Ecology. The virus passes by contact amongst pigs but much less readily than does foot-and-mouth disease. Infection is probably spread largely through uncooked garbage.

Control is by quarantine and slaughter, and by enforcement of laws on cooking garbage. A formolized vaccine has been found effective experimentally (Madin & Traum, 1953).

FOOT-AND-MOUTH DISEASE

Synonym: Aphthous fever.
Review: Brooksby (1958).

Morphology and development. Most workers agree that the diameter is between 20 and 25 mμ and that it is roughly spherical or hexagonal. Electron-microscopy reveals a granular structure and a central region of lower density (Bradish *et al.*, 1960). The granular appearance may be due to the 7 mμ non-infectious component associated with antigenic reactivity. Of the 25 mμ particles, probably only a very small number are infectious. Studies with fluorescent antibodies (Mussgay, 1958b) indicate that viral development takes place in the cytoplasm: this finding accords better with what is known of other picornaviruses than Guillot's (1958) description of viral development within the nucleus.

Chemical composition. RNA extracted from virus preparations with phenol is infective; it can be obtained in the latent phase of infection, when only a trace of complete virus is present (Brown & Stewart, 1959, 1960) and thus may come from virus precursor material. It is likely that infective RNA is liberated also by heating or acidification (Brown & Cartwright, 1961).

Physico-chemical characters. The specific gravity is estimated as between 1·3 and 1·43. The area sensitive to X-radiation is similar to that of the whole particle (Bonet-Maury & Frillay, 1946). The virus is resistant to ether, chloroform, bile salts; also to detergents (Cartwright & Thorne, 1959). Under controlled conditions it is inactivated in 30 minutes at 56° C but in presence of protective colloids may resist 85° C for 4 hours (Dimopoulos, 1960). Virus is stable at pH 7·4–7·6, readily destroyed on the acid side of pH 6 but more stable again in the region of pH 3. In the field its stability is a source of great trouble. It may survive for several weeks on hay and other materials (Bedson *et al.*, 1927). Disinfection is commonly carried out with 2 per cent. commercial NaOH or KOH or 4 per cent. Na_2CO_3, but the virus is even more sensitive to acids. In carcasses and meat, rigor mortis is accompanied by acid-formation which destroys the virus in muscles. In glandular organs and bone-marrow, on the other hand, less acid is formed and virus may persist for long periods. For preparing vaccines 0·05 per cent. formaldehyde acting at room temperature for 4 days is effective (Sellers *et al.*, 1959). Details of inactivation by formaldehyde, pH and temperature are given by Bachrach *et al.* (1957).

Hæmagglutination. A claim that rat RBC's are agglutinated remains unconfirmed.

Antigenic properties. Neutralization tests can be carried out in guinea pigs or, more accurately, on bovine tongues; or in tissue culture. Detailed techniques are described by Brooksby (1949) and he also (1952) describes the complement fixation techniques applicable to this infection. There are seven serological types known as A and O (Vallée), C (Waldmann), S.A.T. 1, S.A.T. 2, S.A.T. 3 (South African) and Asia 1. They can be distinguished by various serological tests, though with CF there are various degrees of overlapping. Within the main types there are variants and subtypes, differing sufficiently to affect the results of vaccination and to confuse diagnosis. Davie (1962) describes classification of sub-types. The Institute at Pirbright, Surrey, is recognised by F.A.O. as a World Reference Laboratory for typing strains. Freshly isolated virus is apt to be antigenically unstable but reports of transformation of one major type into another are now discredited. In the CF test, two antibodies are concerned: the 25 mμ virus particle combines with both, the non-infective 7 mμ component with one only (Cartwright, 1962). The agar-gel precipitin test (Brown & Crick, 1958) reveals two lines, due to the same two components.

Cultivation. *In fertile eggs.* Virus was adapted to growth in eggs by Skinner (1954) who inoculated the embryos IV and incubated them at 35° C.

In tissue-culture it grows in embryonic guinea pig tissues (Maitland & Maitland, 1931) and in bovine, porcine and ovine kidney. Mouse- and egg-adapted strains do not do as well as others (Sellers *et al.*, 1959). Cytopathic effects are much more marked in porcine than in bovine tissues, and it is possible to titrate virus in them by enumerating plaques (Sellers *et al.*, 1959) or by a colour-test depending upon changes in pH (Martin & Chapman, 1961). The course of development of virus in cultures of cattle-tongue epithelium was described by Cartwright *et al.* (1957). Changes produced in such cultures are described by Pay (1957): cells growing in membrane-like sheets rapidly rounded up and nuclei became pycnotic; in cells with a polygonal type of growth, however, though virus multiplied, CPE was minimal. A cell-line derived from baby hamster kidney has lately shown promise of usefulness (Mowat & Chapman, 1962).

Distribution. It has been possible to keep Australia, New Zealand, United States and Canada free from the disease. Infection is endemic in continental Europe, Asia, Africa and South America. The O, A and C sero-types are widespread; Asia 1 has been found only in Asiatic countries. The S.A.T. 1, 2 and 3 strains were confined to Africa until, at the end of 1961, S.A.T. 1 spread to the Middle East, reaching European Turkey in 1962.

Pathogenicity. The disease in naturally affected cattle is usually not fatal but leads to serious loss of condition and consequent economic loss. There occur fever and vesicular eruptions on mouth, tongue, muzzle, hooves, udder, sometimes elsewhere; the lesions lead to salivation and lameness. Secondary bacterial infections of denuded areas commonly occur, especially on the feet. Myocardial damage is severe in some outbreaks and may be fatal to calves. Lesions in pigs are similar; lameness is a prominent symptom. Sheep and goats are less severely affected. Deer, antelopes, and other ruminants may also be infected. The incubation period after contact is 2 to 4 days or less. Some strains in nature infect pigs better than cattle (Brooksby, 1950). Hedgehogs may contract infection naturally and are infectious for other species (McLauchlan & Henderson, 1947).

Experimentally infected cattle show lesions in 10–12 hours at the site of inoculation, which is usually the tongue. Generalization to the feet and elsewhere follows in 2 to 4 days.

Guinea pigs are susceptible to inoculation into the foot-pad and were for long the animal chiefly used experimentally; adaptation of strains is necessary before they grow well. Techniques for quantitative studies in cattle and guinea pigs are described in a monograph by Henderson (1949). Suckling mice were shown (Skinner, 1951) to be highly susceptible; they develop spastic paraplegia after IP inoculation, and virus passed in them will later infect older mice also. Some neurotropic strains have been developed by IC passage in weaned mice (Hofmann, 1941). Hamsters are very susceptible up to 60 days old (Eunes, 1955). Newborn rabbits may also be infected. Birds are fairly resistant, but Skinner (1959) infected fowls and other poultry: local vesicular lesions and occasional generalization occurred. A very few cases of a mild infection in human beings are reported: there were local vesicles, usually on the hands.

Pathological lesions. The vesicular lesions are associated with swelling, ballooning degeneration and necrosis of cells in the lower layer of epithelium. The lesions in guinea pigs have been described by Platt (1958); pancreatitis was common. Platt (1956) also reported on those in 7-day mice; these showed widespread necrosis of skeletal muscles with some myocardial necrosis. In 3–4-week-old mice, there was more myocardial and often pancreatic necrosis. In older mice there was frequently damage to suprascapular fat-pads.

Ecology. The disease is extremely contagious. Infective saliva and excreta contaminate the environment, so that animals are very readily infected either directly or indirectly. In Britain where the disease is not endemic, virus has repeatedly been introduced from South America, sometimes through uncooked garbage fed to pigs. There is circumstantial evidence that it may also reach Britain through the agency of migrating birds, particularly starlings (Wilson & Matheson, 1952). Virus has been isolated from the urine of recovered cattle during several months (Waldmann et al., 1931).

Control. Where the disease is not endemic a policy of quarantine, slaughter and disinfection of infected premises has proved efficient and best on the whole economically. For endemic areas vaccination is widely used; formolized vaccine adsorbed on to alum has been mainly used. It was previously made from epithelium of tongues of infected cattle, more recently from bovine epithelium infected and grown in tissue culture. Still more recently living virus has been attenuated by passage either in adult mice or in eggs (Skinner, 1960) and these attenuated strains have given encouraging results when tested in the field in South and East Africa (Mowat & Prydie, 1962).

MOUSE ENCEPHALOMYELITIS

Synonym: Mouse poliomyelitis.
Description: von Magnus *et al.* (1955).

Several viruses are included under this name. On the one hand are those related to the TO (Theiler original) strain; on the other, are the FA, GD VII and related strains. The last have biological, but not antigenic, characters intermediate between TO virus and the EMC viruses (*cf.* p. 27). The mouse encephalomyelitis (ME) strain studied by Franklin *et al.* (1959) and others is in fact EMC. The FA and GD VII viruses were originally thought to be virulent variants of TO: this now seems more than doubtful.

TO Strain

Some statements in the literature about this virus refer in fact to the other strains.

Morphology. Diameter probably about 25 mμ. Earlier estimates giving a size of 9–19 mμ are probably too low.

Physico-chemical characters. Ether and chloroform resistant. Survives well at −76° C or in 50 per cent. glycerol but is preserved by drying with difficulty, at least not at high titre. Inactivated at 50° C (Theiler & Gard, 1940).

Hæmagglutination. Unlike GD VII, does not agglutinate human RBC's.

Antigenic properties. Can be studied by neutralization tests in mice or, more readily, in tissue-culture (Pette, 1959). Gard (1956–7) has described an immuno-inactivation test more sensitive than conventional tests. Several workers report some cross-neutralization between the TO and GD VII strains (Olitsky, 1945; Shaw, 1956); there are also said to be minor antigenic differences amongst TO-like viruses.

Cultivation. The virus usually fails to grow in eggs, but has been adapted by Shaw (1953) to grow in yolk sacs and in "Maitland-type" chick embryo tissue culture. It will grow (Falke, 1957) in mouse kidney cultures, and in these, after adaptation, cytopathic effects appear.

Pathogenicity. Normally an inapparent infection occurring in the intestines of laboratory mice all over the world. Similar viruses have been recovered from wild mice, cotton-rats and kangaroo rats (Dipodomys), but there is a possibility that these had been infected from laboratory mice. The virus produces flaccid paralysis usually of hind limbs in a very small proportion of infected mice—a few amongst thousands. It is not necessarily fatal. Exceptionally, a number of paralytic cases may occur together (Gard, 1944).

Experimentally, response to inoculation is irregular; the incubation period after IC inoculation is 12–29 days. Very young mice may die without definite symptoms, older ones may have progressive flaccid paralysis, and still older ones an inapparent infection. Several workers have obtained mouse-colonies free from infection (von Magnus & von Magnus, 1949), and mice from such colonies are more regularly susceptible. In them, virus multiplies at the site of an intramuscular inoculation and may also cause paralysis when given *per os* or by other routes (von Magnus, 1951, Dean, 1951). Golden hamsters have also been infected but symptoms may be absent unless mice are interpolated in the transmission series (Dean & Dalldorf, 1948).

Pathological lesions in the CNS resemble those of poliomyelitis in man. There is destruction of anterior horn cells especially of the cord, with associated inflammatory reaction.

Ecology. Newborn and suckling mice enjoy passive protection from maternal antibody. Soon after weaning they are found to be carriers and become increasingly resistant to infection. The carrier rate becomes progressively less as they grow older: at $7\frac{1}{2}$ months it was only 54 per cent. and fell further thereafter.

FA and GD VII Strains

One spontaneous occurrence of disease due to an FA strain is recorded; otherwise these viruses have come to light after inoculation of mice with materials such as other viruses. It appears (Smithburn, 1952) that several ostensibly new arthropod-borne viruses do in fact belong in this group, having presumably come from the mice used for inoculation.

Morphology: does not, so far as known, differ from that of the TO virus. Leyon (1951) described spherical particles 28 mμ across packed in a hexagonal pattern.

Chemical composition. An infective RNA was extracted from the GD VII virus by Ada & Anderson (1959).

Physico-chemical characters also resemble those of TO. The virus is largely inactivated by drying but is readily preserved when frozen or in 50 per cent. glycerol. The effects of physical and chemical agents are fully reviewed by Gard (1955). The half-life at 50° C is 8·5 minutes. It survives better when suspended in milk. The virus is stable between pH 3 and pH 10; resistant to ether, chloroform and detergents and fairly resistant to phenol. Hypochlorite inactivates quickly in the absence of organic matter.

Hæmagglutination. The GD VII strains agglutinate human O cells at 0° C, being eluted at higher temperatures (Lahelle & Horsfall, 1949). After trypsin-treatment, virus preparations agglutinate at room temperature also (Morris, 1952).

Antigenic properties. Positive CF tests are reported but neutralization tests have been chiefly used. As already mentioned, several authors report some antigenic cross-reactions between TO and GD VII; GD VII and FA are also antigenically related.

Cultivation. The FA virus has been cultivated on CAM, yolk sac and allantoic cavity of fertile eggs (Riordan & Sá-Fleitas, 1947). GD VII has also been grown in eggs; also in tissue cultures of mouse-brain (Parker & Hollender, 1945). Both strains have been cultivated in chick and mouse embryo tissue cultures and in cultures of mouse tumour cells, GD VII more readily (Shean & Schultz, 1950).

Pathogenicity. When first isolated GD VII caused mostly flaccid paralysis, on passage generalized encephalitis. FA has always caused widespread encephalitis, flaccid paralyses only being seen after IP inoculation. Neither virus regularly appears in fæces. Intramuscular inoculation of either strain produces local myositis and GD VII at least apparently multiplied in the muscle (Rustigian & Pappenheimer, 1949). Some strains infect cotton-rats (Committee, 1948).

Pathological lesions. The changes due to diffuse encephalitis do not recall those of poliomyelitis in man closely, as do those of the TO virus.

4

Ecology. Presumably exist as latent infections of numerous mouse-stocks, occasionally activated by various injections (Melnick & Riordan, 1947). The viruses are not normally contagious amongst mice. Thompson *et al.*, however (1951), report an outbreak in young mice in a colony; a virus like GD VII was isolated.

Control. Mandel (1951) reports that a carbohydrate with inhibiting properties for GD VII (but not for FA or TO) can be extracted from intestines of adult mice and guinea-pigs.

REFERENCES

Ackermann, W. W. (1958) *Bact. Rev.*, **22**, 223.
Ackermann, W. W., Payne, F. E., & Kurtz, H. (1958) *J. Immunol.*, **81**, 1.
Ada, G. L., & Anderson, S. G. (1959) *Aust. J. Sci.*, **21**, 259.
Andrewes, C. H. (1950) *New Engl. J. Med.*, **242**, 235.
Andrewes, C. H. (1960) *Sci. Amer.*, **203**, 88.
Andrewes, C. H. (1962) *J. Roy. Inst. publ. Hlth*, **25**, 31, 55, and 79.
Andrewes, C. H., Burnet, F. M., Enders, J. F., Gard, S., Hirst, G. K., Kaplan, M. M., & Zhdanov, V. M. (1961) *Virology*, **15**, 52.
Andrewes, C. H. (1961) *Yale J. Biol. Med.*, **34**, 200.
Andrewes, C. H., Chaproniere, D. M., Gompels, A. E. H., Pereira, H. G., & Roden, A. T. (1953) *Lancet*, **2**, 546.
Armbruster, O., & Zimmermann, Th. (1958) *Z. Hyg. Infekt.–kr.*, **145**, 123.
Armstrong, C. (1939) *Publ. Hlth Rep. (Wash.)*, **54**, 1719 and 2302.
Bachrach, H. L., Breese, S. S., Cullis, J. J., Hess, W. R., & Patty, R. E. (1957) *Proc. Soc. exp. Biol. (N.Y.)*, **95**, 147.
Barron, A. L., & Karzon, D. T. (1957) *Proc. Soc. exp. Biol. (N.Y.)*, **94**, 393.
Barron, A. L., & Karzon, D. T. (1959) *Proc. Soc. exp. Biol. (N.Y.)*, **100**, 316.
Barski, G. (1962) *Virology*, **18**, 152.
Barski, G., & Lamy, M. (1955) *Ann. Inst. Pasteur*, **89**, 318.
Beale, A. J., Stevens, P. F., Davis, N., Stackiw, W., & Rhodes, A. J. (1956) *Canad. J. Microbiol.*, **2**, 298.
Becker, W. B. (1963) *Virology* **20**, 318.
Bedson, S. P., Maitland, H. M., & Burbury, Y. M. (1927) *J. comp. Path.*, **40**, 1
Beeman, E. A., & Huebner, R. J. (1952) *J. Immunol.*, **68**, 663.
Bell, J. F., & Haddow, W. J. (1949) *J. infect. Dis.*, **105**, 54.
Bellett, A. J. D. (1960) *Virology*, **10**, 285.
Beran, G. W., Wenner, H. A., Werder, A. A., & Underdahl, N. R. (1960) *Amer. J. vet. Res.*, **21**, 723.
Beran, G. W., Werder, A. A., & Wenner, H. A. (1958) *Amer. J. vet. Res.*, **19**, 545.
Betts, A. O. (1960) *Res. vet. Sci.*, **1**, 296.
Betts, A. O., Kelly, D. F., Lamont, P. H., & Sheffy, B. E. (1961) *Res. vet. Sci.*, **2**, 752 and 755.
Bodian, D. (1959) *Viral and Rickettsial Infections of Man*, Ed. Rivers & Horsfall. 3rd Ed. p. 479. London: Pitman Medical.
Bögel, K., & Böhm, H. (1962) *Zbl. Bakt. I. Abt. Orig.*, **187**, 2.
Bögel, K., & Mayr, A. (1961) *Zbl. Vet.-Med.*, **8**, 908.
Bögel, K., & Mussgay, M. (1960) *Zbl. Vet.-Med.*, **7**, 534.
Bonet-Maury, P., & Frilley, M. (1946) *Ann. Inst. Pasteur*, **72**, 432.

Bradish, C. J., Henderson, W. M., Kirkham, J. B. (1960) *J. gen. Microbiol.*, **22**, 379.
Brooksby, J. B. (1949) *Spec. Rep. Ser. agric. Res. Coun. (Lond.)*, no. 9 (H.M. Stationery Office, London).
Brooksby, J. B. (1950) *J. Hyg. (Camb.)*, **48**, 184.
Brooksby, J. B. (1952) *Spec. Rep. Ser. agric. Res. Coun. (Lond.)*, no. 12 (H.M. Stationery Office, London).
Brooksby, J. B. (1954) *Bull. Off. int. Épiz.*, **42**, 368.
Brooksby, J. B. (1958) *Advanc. Virus Res.* **5**, 1.
Brown, F., & Cartwright, B. (1961) *Nature (Lond.)*, **192**, 1163.
Brown, F., & Crick, J. (1958) *Virology*, **5**, 133.
Brown, F., & Stewart, D. L. (1959) *Virology*, **7**, 408.
Brown, F., & Stewart, D. L. (1960) *Nature (Lond.)*, **187**, 714.
Buckland, F. E., Bynoe, M. L., Philipson, L., & Tyrrell, D. A. J (1959) *J. Hyg. (Camb.)*, **57**, 274.
Buckland, F. E., Bynoe, M. L., Rosen, L., & Tyrrell, D. A. J. (1961) *Brit. med. J.*, **1**, 397.
Burke, C. N., Luginbuhl, R. E., & Jungherr, E. L. (1959) *Avian Diseases*, **3**, 412.
Bynoe, M. L., Hobson, D., Horner, J., Kipps, A., Schild, G. G., & Tyrrell, D. A. J. (1961) *Lancet*, **1**, 1194.
Cabasso, V. J., Burkhart, R. I., & Leaming, J. D., (1951) *Vet. Med.*, **46**, 167.
Calnek, B. W., Luginbuhl, R. E., McKercher, P. D., & van Roekel, H. (1961) *Avian Diseases*, **5**, 456.
Cartwright, B. (1962) *J. Immunol.*, **88**, 128.
Cartwright, B., & Huck, R. A. (1953) *J. comp. Path.*, **73**, 27.
Cartwright, B., & Pay, T. W. F., & Henderson, W. M. (1957) *J. gen. Microbiol.*, **16**, 730.
Cartwright, B., & Thorne, H. V. (1959) *J. gen. Microbiol.*, **20**, 61.
Casals, J., Olitsky, P. K., & Anslow, R. O. (1951) *J. exp. Med.*, **94**, 123.
Casorso, D. R., & Jungherr, E. L. (1959) *Amer. J. vet. Res.*, **20**, 547.
Chaproniere, D. M., Done, J. T., & Andrewes, C. H. (1958) *Brit. J. exp. Path.*, **39**, 74.
Cheever, F. S. (1957) *Ann. N.Y. Acad. Sci.*, **67**, 427.
Chin, T. D. Y., Beran, G. W., & Wenner, H. A. (1957) *Amer. J. Hyg.*, **66**, 76.
Colter, J. S., Bird, H. H., & Brown, R. A. (1957) *Nature (Lond.)*, **179**, 859.
Committee on Enteroviruses (1957) *Amer. J. publ. Hlth*, **47**, 1556.
Committee on Nomenclature of Nat. Found. for Infantile Paralysis (1948) *Science*, **108**, 701.
Craighead, J. E., & Shelokov, A. (1962) *Proc. Soc. exp. Biol. (N.Y.)*, **108**, 823.
Cramblett, H. G., Rosen, L., Parrott, R. H., Bell, J. A., Huebner, R. J., & McCullough, N. B. (1958) *Pediatrics*, **21**, 168.
Dalldorf, G. (1955) *Ann. Rev. Microbiol.*, **9**, 277.
Dalldorf, G. (1957) *J. exp. Med.*, **106**, 69.
Dalldorf, G. Melnick, J. L., & Curnen, E. (1959) *Viral and Rickettsial Diseases of Man*. Ed. Rivers & Horsfall. 3rd Ed. p. 519. London: Pitman Medical.
Davie, J. (1962) *Bull. Off. int. Épiz.*, **57**, 962.
Dean, D. J. (1951) *J. Immunol.*, **66**, 347.
Dean, D. J., & Dalldorf, G. (1948) *J. exp. Med.*, **88**, 645.
Dick, G. W. A. (1948) *Brit. J. exp. Path.*, **29**, 559.
Dick, G. W. A. (1949) *J. Immunol.*, **62**, 375.
Dick, G. W. A. (1950) *Proc. Soc. exp. Biol. (N.Y.)*, **73**, 77.
Dick, G. W. A., Smithburn, K. C., & Haddow, A, J. (1948) *Brit. J. exp. Path.*, **29**, 547.
Dimmock, N. J., & Tyrrell, D. A. J. (1962) *Lancet*, **2**, 536.

Dimopoullos, G. T. (1960) *Ann. N. Y. Acad. Sci.*, **83,** 706.
Dochez, A. R., Shibley, G. S., & Mills, K. C. (1930) *J. exp. Med.*, **52,** 701.
Doggett, J., Bynoe, M. L., & Tyrrell, D. A. J. (1963) *Brit. med. J.*, **1,** 34.
Done, J. T. (1961) *Bull. Off. int. Épiz.*, **56,** 117.
Dowling, H. F., Jackson, G. G., Spiesman, I. G., & Inoue, T. (1958) *Amer. J. Hyg.*, **68,** 59.
Dubose, R. T., & Grumbles, L. C. (1959) *Avian Diseases*, **3,** 321.
Duffy, F. E., Bell, A., & Menefee, M. G. (1962) *Virology*, **16,** 350.
Dulbecco, R., & Vogt, M. (1958) *Virology*, **5,** 220.
Dunnebake, T. H. (1956) *Virology*, **2,** 399 & 811.
Eggers, H. J. & Sabin, A. B. (1961) *Arch. ges. Virusforsch.*, **11,** 120 & 152.
Eggers, H. J., & Tamm, I. (1961a) *J. exp. Med.*, **113,** 657.
Eggers, H. J., & Tamm, I. (1961b) *Virology*, **13,** 545.
Ellem, K. A. O., & Colter, J. S. (1961) *Virology*, **15,** 340.
Enders, J. F., Weller, T., & Robbins, F. (1949) *Science*, **109,** 85.
Eunes, E. S. (1955) *Bull Off. int. Épiz.*, **43,** 756.
Falke, D. (1957) *Z. Hyg. Infekt.-Kr.*, **143,** 645.
Finch, J. T., & Klug, A. (1960) *Biochem. biophys. Acta*, **41,** 430.
Franklin, R. M., Wecker, E., & Henry, C. (1959) *Virology*, **7,** 220.
Franklin, R. M. (1962) *J. Cell. Biol.*, **12,** 1.
Furusawa, E., & Cutting, W. (1962) *Proc. Soc. exp. Biol. (N.Y.)*, **109,** 417.
Gajdusek, C. (1955) *Pediatrics*, **16,** 819.
Gard, S. (1944) *Yale J. Biol. Med.*, **16,** 467.
Gard, S. (1955) *Wld. Hlth Org. Monogr. Ser.*, **26,** 215.
Gard, S. (1956–57) *Arch. ges. Virusforsch.*, **7,** 449.
Gard, S. (1960) *Bull. Wld Hlth. Org.*, **22,** 235.
Gear, J. H. S. (1958) *Progr. med. Virology*, **1,** 106.
Godenne, M. O., & Curnen, E. C. (1952) *Proc. Soc. exp. Biol. (N.Y.)*, **81,** 81.
Goldfield, M., Srihongse, S., & Fox, J. P. (1957) *Proc. Soc. exp. Biol. (N.Y.)*, **96,** 788.
Greig, A. S., Mitchell, D., Corner, A. H., Bannister, G. L., Meads, E. B., & Julian, R. J. (1962) *Canad. J. comp. Med.*, **26,** 49.
Grist, N. R. (1960) *Lancet*, **1,** 1054.
Guérin, I. F., & Guérin, M. M. (1957) *Proc. Soc. exp. Biol. (N.Y.)*, **96,** 322.
Guillot, P. (1958) *Ann. Inst. Pasteur*, **94,** 571.
Hagan, W. A. (1958) *Ann. Rev. Microbiol.*, **12,** 140.
Hallauer, C. (1951) *Arch. ges. Virusforsch.*, **4,** 224.
Hayflick, L., & Moorhead, P. S. (1961) *Exp. Cell Res.*, **25,** 585.
Hayflick, L., Plotkin, S. A., Norton, T. W., & Koprowski, H. (1962) *Amer. J. Hyg.*, **75,** 240.
Helwig, F. C., & Schmidt, E. C. H. (1945) *Science*, **102,** 31.
Henderson, W. M. (1949) *Spec. Rep. Ser. agric. Res. Coun. (Lond.)*, no. 8 (H.M. Stationery Office, London).
Hiatt, C. W., Kaufman, E., Helprin, J. J., & Baron, J. (1960) *J. Immunol.*, **84,** 480.
Hitchcock, G., & Tyrrell, D. A. J. (1960) *Lancet*, **1,** 237.
Ho, M., & Enders, J. F. (1959) *Proc. nat. Acad. Sci. (Wash.)*, **45,** 385.
Hofmann, W. (1941) *Zbl. Bakt., I. Abt. Orig.*, **148,** 69.
Holland, J. J., McLaren, L. C., & Syverton, J. T. (1959) *Proc. Soc. exp. Biol. (N.Y.)*, **100,** 843.
Horne, R. W., & Nagington, J. (1959) *J. molec. Biol.*, **1,** 333.
Horstmann, D. M. (1952) *J. Immunol.*, **69,** 379.
Howe, H. A., & Wilson, J. L. (1959) *Viral and Rickettsial Infections of Man*. 3rd Ed. p. 432. Ed. Rivers & Horsfall. London: Pitman Medical.
Hsiung, G. D., & Melnick, J. L. (1957) *J. Immunol.*, **78,** 137.
Hsiung, G. D., & Melnick, J. L. (1958) *Ann. N.Y. Acad. Sci.*, **70,** 342.

Huck, R. A., Martin, W. B., Davies, E. B., & Chapman, W. G. (1962) *J. comp. Path.*, **72**, 374.

Huebner, R. J., Ransom, S. E., & Beeman, E. A. (1950) *Publ. Hlth. Rep. (Wash.)*, **65**, 803.

Hull, R. N., & Minner, J. R. (1957) *Ann. N.Y. Acad. Sci.*, **67**, 413.

Hull, R. N., Minner, J. R. & Mascoli, C. C. (1958) *Amer. J. Hyg.*, **68**, 31.

Hull, R. N., Minner, J. R., & Smith, J. W. (1956) *Amer. J. Hyg.*, **63**, 204.

Huppert, J., & Sanders, K. (1958) *Nature (Lond.)*, **182**, 515.

Hurst, E. W. (1931) *J. Path. Bact.*, **34**, 331.

Hwang, J., Luginbuhl, R. E., & Jungherr, E. L. (1959) *Proc. Soc. exp. Biol. (N.Y.)*, **102**, 429.

Inaba, Y., Omori, T., Kodama, M., Ishii, S., & Matumoto, M. (1959) *C.R. Soc. Biol. (Paris)*, **153**, 1653.

Johnsson, T. (1957) *Lancet*, **1**, 590.

Jungeblut, C. W. (1958) *Handbuch der Virusforsch*, **4**, 459. Vienna: Springer.

Jungeblut, C. W., & Bourdillon, J. (1943) *J. Amer. med. Ass.*, **123**, 399.

Jungherr, E. L., & Minard, E. L. (1942) *Amer. J. vet. Res.*, **5**, 125.

Kalter, S. S. (1960) *Bull. Wld. Hlth Org.*, **22**, 319.

Kaplan, A. S., & Melnick, J. L. (1952) *Amer. J. publ. Hlth.*, **42**, 525.

Karzon, D. T., Pollock, B. F., & Barron, A. L. (1959) *Virology*, **9**, 564.

Kauffmann, F., & Frantzer, A. (1958) *Acta path. microbiol. scand.*, **25**, 356.

Ketler, A., Hamparian, W., & Hilleman, M. R. (1961) *Proc. Soc. exp. Biol. (N.Y.)*, **110**, 821.

Kibrick, S., Meléndez, L., & Enders, J. F. (1957) *Ann. N.Y. Acad. Sci.*, **67**, 311.

Kilham, L., Mason, P., & Davies, J. N. P. (1956) *Amer. J. trop. Med.*, **5**, 647.

Kipps, A., Turner, G. S., & Polson, A. (1961) *J. gen. Microbiol.*, **26**, 405.

Klein, M. (1958) *Ann. N.Y. Acad. Sci.*, **70**, 362.

Koestner, A., Long, J. F., & Kasza, L. (1962) *J. Amer. vet. med. Ass.*, **140**, 811.

Koprowski, H., Jervis, G. A., & Norton, T. W. (1952) *Amer. J. Hyg.*, **55**, 108.

Kunin, C. M., & Minuse, E. (1958) *J. Immunol.*, **80**, 1.

Kuwata, T. (1956–7) *Arch. ges. Virusforsch.*, **7**, 333.

Lahelle, O., & Horsfall, F. L. (1949) *Proc. Soc. exp. Biol. (N.Y.)*, **71**, 713.

Lamont, P. H., & Betts, A. O. (1958) *Nature (Lond.)*, **182**, 608.

La Placa, M., Portolani, M., & Lamieri, C. (1963) *Arch. ges. Virusforsch.*, **13**, 587.

Le Bouvier, G. L., Schwerdt, C. E., & Schaffer, F. L. (1957) *Virology*, **4**, 590.

Le Bouvier, G. L. (1959) *Brit. J. exp. Path.*, **40**, 452.

Lenahan, M. F., & Wenner, H. A. (1960) *J. infect. Dis.*, **107**, 203.

Lennette, E. H., Fox, V. L., Schmidt, N. J., & Culver, J. O. (1958) *Amer. J. Hyg.*, **68**, 272.

Lepine, P., & Atanasiu, P. (1950) *Ann. Inst. Pasteur*, **79**, 3.

Lepine, P., Desse, G., & Sautter, V. (1952) *Bull. Acad. nat. Méd. (Paris)*, **136**, 66.

Leyon, H. (1951) *Exp. Cell Res.*, **2**, 207.

Li, C. P., & Habel, K. (1951) *Proc. Soc. exp. Biol. (N.Y.)*, **78**, 233.

Li, C. P., & Schaeffer, M. (1953) *Proc. Soc. exp. Biol. (N.Y.)*, **82**, 477.

Lim, K. A., & Benyesh-Melnick, M. (1960) *J. Immunol.*, **84**, 309.

Löffler, H. (1958) *Handbuch der Virusforsch.*, **4**, 631. Vienna: Springer.

Löffler, H., & Wenner, H. A. (1962) *Arch. ges. Virusforsch.*, **12**, 241 and 303.

Lou, T. Y., Wenner, H. A., & Kamitsuka, P. S. (1961) *Arch. ges. Virusforsch.*, **10**, 451.

Love, R., & Roca-Carcia, M. (1955) *Amer. J. Path.*, **31**, 901.

Lovelock, J. E., Porterfield, J. S., Roden, A. T., Sommerville, T., & Andrewes, C. H. (1952) *Lancet*, **2**, 657.

Luginbuhl, R. E., & Black, F. L. (1961) *Yale J. exp. Biol. Med.*, **33**, 339.

Lwoff, A., & Lwoff, M. (1960) *Ann. Inst. Pasteur*, **98**, 173.
McBride, W. D. (1959) *Virology*, **7**, 45.
McClain, M. E., Hackett, A. J., & Madin, S. H. (1958) *Science*, **127**, 1391.
Macferran, J. B. (1958) *Vet. Rec.*, **70**, 999.
Macferran, J. B. (1961) *Res. vet. Sci.* **2**, 185.
McLauchlan, J. D., & Henderson, W. M. (1947) *J. Hyg. (Camb.)*, **45**, 474.
Madin, S. H. (1958) *Diseases of Swine*. Ed. Dunne, Ames, Iowa: Iowa State
    Univ. Press. London: Baillière, Tindall and Cox.
Madin, S. H., & Traum, J. (1953) *Vet. Med.*, **48**, 395 and 443.
Madin, S. H., & Traum, J. (1955) *Bact. Rev.*, **19**, 6.
Maitland, M. C., & Maitland, H. B. (1931) *J. comp. Path.*, **44**, 106.
Mandel, B. (1951) *Bull. N.Y. Acad. Med.*, **27**, 583.
Martin, W. B., & Chapman, W. G. (1961) *Res. vet. Sci.*, **2**, 53.
Mattern, C. F. T., & Chi, L. L. (1962) *Virology*, **18**, 257.
Mattern, C. F. T., & Dubuy, H. G. (1956) *Science*, **123**, 1037.
Mayr, A. (1961) *Bull. Off. int. Épiz.*, **56**, 106.
Mayr, A., & Correns, H. (1949) *Zbl. Vet.-Med.*, **6**, 416.
Melnick, J. L. (1950) *Bact. Rev.*, **14**, 233.
Melnick, J. L. (1960) *Viral Infections of Infancy and Childhood*. p. 55. Ed. Rose.
    New York: Hoeber-Harper.
Melnick, J. L. (1962) *Amer. J. publ. Hlth.*, **52**, 472.
Melnick, J. L. & Riordan, J. T. (1947) *J. Immunol.*, **57**, 331.
Melnick. J. L., & Sabin, A. B. (1959) *Viral and Rickettsial Diseases of Man*.
    Ed. Rivers & Horsfall. 3rd Ed. p. 547. London: Pitman Medical.
Moll, T., & Davis, A. D. (1959) *Amer. J. vet. Res.*, **20**, 27.
Moll, T., & Finlayson, A. V. (1957) *Science*, **126**, 401.
Morgan, C., Howe, C., & Rose, H. M. (1959) *Virology*, **9**, 145.
Morris, M. C. (1952) *J. Immunol.*, **68**, 97.
Moscovici, C., Ginevri, A., & Mazzaracchio, V. (1957) *Amer. J. vet. Res.*,
    20, 625.
Moscovici, C., & Maisel, J. (1958) *Virology*, **6**, 769.
Mott, L. O., Patterson, W. C., Songer, J. R., & Hopkins, S. R. (1953) *N.
    Amer. Vet.*, **34**, 782.
Mowat, G. N., & Chapman, W. G. (1962) *Nature (Lond.)*, **194**, 253.
Mowat, G. N., & Prydie, J. (1962) *Res. vet. Sci.*, **3**, 368.
Müller, F. (1961) *Ergebn. Mikrobiol. Immunitätsforsch. Exp. Therap.* (1961).
    p. 275. Heidelberg: Springer.
Murnane, T. C., Craighead, J. E., Mondragon, H., & Shelokov, A. (1961)
    Science, **131**, 498.
Mussgay, M. (1958a) *Zbl. Bakt. I. Abt. Orig.*, **171**, 231.
Mussgay, M. (1958b) *Zbl. Bakt. I. Abt. Orig.*, **171**, 413.
Neva, F. A., & Enders, J. F. (1954) *J. Immunol.*, **72**, 307.
Newton, N., & Bevis, R. E. (1959) *Virology*, **8**, 344.
Olitsky, P. K. (1939) *J. exp. Med.*, **70**, 565.
Olitsky, P. K. (1945) *Proc. Soc. exp. Biol. (N.Y.)*, **58**, 77.
Olitsky, P. K., & Bauer, J. H. (1939) *Proc. Soc. exp. Biol. (N.Y.)*, **42**, 634.
Parker, R. C., & Hollender, A. J. (1945) *Proc. Soc. exp. Biol. (N.Y.)*, **60**, 88.
Parsons, R., Bynoe, M. L., Pereira, M. S., & Tyrrell, D. A. J. (1960) *Brit.
    med. J.*, **1**, 1776.
Parsons, R., & Tyrrell, D. A. J. (1961) *Nature (Lond.)*, **189**, 640.
Patočka, F., Kubelka, V., & Slavik, K. (1951) *Vestn. čsl. akad. Zeměd.*, **25**,
    461.
Pay, T. W. F. (1957) *Proc. roy. Soc. Med.*, **50**, 919.
Peckham, M. C. (1957) *Avian Diseases*, **1**, 247.
Pereira, H. G. (1962) *Advanc. Virus Res.*, **8**, 245.
Pette, J. (1959) *Zbl. Bakt. I. Abt. Orig.*, **175**, 212.

Philipson, L., & Wesslén, T. (1958) *Arch. ges. Virusforsch.*, **8**, 77.
Platt, H. (1956) *J. Path. Bact.*, **72**, 299.
Platt, H. (1958) *J. Path. Bact.*, **76**, 119.
Plotkin, S. A., Cohen, B. J., & Koprowski, H. (1961) *Virology*, **15**, 473.
Plummer, A. (1962) *Nature (Lond.)*, **195**, 519.
Plummer, A. (1963) *Arch. ges. Virusforsch*, **12**, 694
Porterfield, J. S. (1962) *Nature (Lond.)*, **194**, 1044.
Price, W. H. (1957) *Proc. nat. Acad. Sci. (Wash.)*, **43**, 790.
Ramos-Alvarez, M. (1957) *Ann N.Y.. Acad. Sci.*, **67**, 326.
Ramos-Alvarez, M. & Sabin, A. B. (1956) *Amer. J. Publ. Hlth.*, **46**, 295.
Report of International study groups (1963) *Virology*, **19**, 114.
Richards, W. P. C., & Savan, M. (1960) *Cornell Vet.*, **50**, 132.
Rifkind, A. A., Godman, G. C., Howe, C., Morgan, C., & Rose, H. M. (1960) *Virology*, **12**, 331.
Riordan, J. T., & Sá-Fleitas, M. J. (1947) *J. Immunol.*, **56**, 263.
Robinson, C. R., Doane, F. W., & Rhodes, A. J. (1958) *Canad. med. Ass. J.*, **79**, 615.
Robinson, L. K. (1950) *Proc. Soc. exp. Biol. (N.Y.)*, **75**, 570.
Roca-Garcia, M., Moyer, A. W., & Cox, H. R. (1952) *Proc. Soc. exp. Biol. (N.Y.)*, **81**, 519.
Rosen, L. Johnson, J. H., Huebner, R. J., & Bell, J. (1958) *Amer. J. Hyg.*, **67**, 300.
Rustigian, R., & Pappenheimer, A. M. (1949) *J. exp. Med.*, **89**, 69.
Sabin, A. B. (1956) *Science*, **123**, 1151.
Sabin, A. B. (1959) *Brit. med. J.*, **1**, 663.
Sabin, A. B. (1962) *Roy. Soc. Hlth. J.*, **82**, 51.
Sabin, A. B., Hennessen, W. A., & Warren, J. (1954) *Proc. Soc. exp. Biol. (N.Y.)*, **85**, 359.
Salk, J. E. (1959) *Viral and Rickettsial Infections of Man.* Ed. Rivers and Horsfall. 3rd Ed. p. 500. London: Pitman Medical.
Schaaf, K. (1959) *Avian diseases*, **3**, 245.
Schaaf, K. & Lamoreux, W. F. (1955) *Amer. J. vet. Res.*, **16**, 627.
Schaffer, F. L., & Schwerdt, C. E. (1959) *Advanc. Virus Res.*, **6**, 159.
Schmidt, N. J., Dennis, J., Frommhagen, L. H., & Lennette, E. H. (1963) *J. Immunol.* **90**, 654.
Schultz, E. W., & Enright, J. B. (1946) *Proc. Soc. exp. Biol. (N.Y.)*, **63**, 8.
Schwerdt, C. E. (1957) *Spec. Publ. N.Y. Acad. Sci.*, **5**, 157.
Schwerdt, C. E., & Schaffer, F. L. (1955) *Ann. N.Y. Acad. Sci.*, **61**, 740.
Sellers, R. F. (1960) *Arch. ges. Virusforsch.*, **9**, 621.
Sellers, R. F., Burt, L. M., Cumming, A., & Stewart, D. L. (1959) *Arch. ges. Virusforsch.*, **9**, 637.
Selzer, G., & Butchart, M. (1959) *J. Hyg. (Camb.)*, **57**, 285.
Selzer, G., (1962) *J. Hyg. (Camb.)*, **60**, 69.
Selzer, G., & van den Ende, M. (1956) *J. Hyg. (Camb.)*, **54**, 1.
Shaver, D. N., Barron, A. L., & Karzon, D. T. (1958) *Amer. J. Path.*, **34**, 943.
Shaw, M. (1953) *Proc. Soc. exp. Biol. (N.Y.)*, **82**, 547.
Shaw, M. (1956) *Proc. Soc. exp. Biol. (N.Y.)*, **92**, 390.
Shean, D. B., & Schultz, E. W. (1950) *Proc. Soc. exp. Biol. (N.Y.)*, **73**, 622.
Sickles, G. M., Mutterer, M., & Plager, H. (1959) *Proc. Soc. exp. Biol. (N.Y.)*, **102**, 742.
Singh, K. V., Greider, M. H., & Bohl, E. H. (1961) *Virology*, **14**, 372.
Skinner, H. H. (1951) *Proc. roy. Soc. Med.*, **44**, 1041.
Skinner, H. H. (1954) *Nature (Lond.)*, **174**, 1052.
Skinner, H. H. (1959) *Arch. ges. Virusforsch.*, **9**, 92.
Skinner, H. H. (1960) *Bull. Off. int. Épiz.*, **53**, 634.

Smith, W., Sheffield, F. W., Churcher, G., & Lee, L. H. (1956) *Lancet*, **2**, 163.

Smithburn, K. C. (1952) *J. Immunol.*, **68**, 441.

Speir, R. W., Aliminosa, K. V., & Southam, C. M. (1962) *Proc. Soc. exp. Biol. (N.Y.)*, **109**, 80.

Sprunt, K., Redman, W. M., & Alexander, H. E. (1959) *Proc. Soc. exp. Biol. (N.Y.)*, **101**, 604.

Steere, R. L., & Schaffer, F. L. (1958) *Biochim. biophys. Acta*, **28**, 241.

Stulberg, C. S., Schapira, R., & Eidam, C. R. (1962) *Proc. Soc. exp. Biol. (N.Y.)*, **81**, 642.

Tamm, I., & Eggers, H. J. (1962) *Virology*, **18**, 439.

Taylor, P. J., & Calnek, B. W. (1962) *Avian Diseases*, **6**, 51.

Taylor, A. R., & McCormick, M. J. (1956) *Yale J. Biol. Med.*, **79**, 296.

Taylor-Robinson, D., Hucker, R., & Tyrrell, D. A. J. (1962) *Brit. J. exp. Path.*, **43**, 189.

Taylor-Robinson, D., & Tyrrell, D. A. J. (1962) *Lancet*, **1**, 452.

Theiler, M., & Gard, S. (1940) *J. exp. Med.*, **72**, 79.

Thompson, R., Harrison, V. M., & Meyers, F. P. (1951) *Proc. Soc. exp. Biol. (N.Y.)*, **77**, 262.

Tobin, J. O'H. (1953) *Brit. med. Bull.*, **9**, 201.

Tyrrell, D. A. J., Bynoe, M. L., Buckland, F. E., & Hayflick, L. (1962) *Lancet*, **2**, 320.

Tyrrell, D. A. J., Bynoe, M. L., Hitchcock, G., Pereira, H. G., Andrewes, C. H., & Parsons, R. (1960) *Lancet*, **1**, 235.

Tyrrell, D. A. J., Clarke, S. K. R., Heath, R. B., & Curran, R. C. (1958) *Brit. J. exp. Path.*, **39**, 178.

van den Ende, M., Don, P. A., & Kipps, A. (1949) *J. gen. Microbiol.*, **3**, 174.

Verlinde, J. D., & Ting, L. K. (1954). Antonie van Leewenhoek, *J. Microbiol. Serol.*, **20**, 181.

Verlinde, J. D., & Versteeg, J. (1958) *T. Diergeneesk.*, **83**, 459.

von Magnus, H. (1951) *Acta path. microbiol. scand.*, **28**, 234 and **29**, 243.

von Magnus, H., Gear, J. H. S., & Paul, J. R. (1955) *Virology*, **1**, 185.

von Magnus, H., & von Magnus, P. (1949) *Acta. path. microbiol. scand.*, **26**, 175.

Voroshilova, M. K., & Chumakov, M. P. (1959) *Progr. med. Virology*, **2**, 106.

Waldmann, O., Trautwein, K., & Pyl, G. (1931) *Zbl. Bakt. I. Abt. Orig.*, **121**, 19.

Wallis, C., & Melnick, J. E. (1962) *J. Bact.*, **84**, 389.

Warren, J., Smadel, J. E., & Russ, S. B. (1949) *J. Immunol.*, **62**, 387.

Wecker, E. (1960) *Virology*, **10**, 376.

Wenner, H. A., Beran, G. W., & Wender, A. A. (1960) *Amer. J. vet. Res.*, **21**, 958.

Wenner, H. A., & Chin, T. D. Y. (1957) *Spec. Publ. N.Y. Acad. Sci.*, **5**, 384.

Wilson, W. W., & Matheson, R. C. (1952) *Vet. Rec.*, **64**, 541.

Wittman, G. (1958) *Zbl. Vet.-Med.*, **5**, 505.

Yates, V. J., & Fry, D. E. (1957) *Amer. J. vet. Res.*, **18**, 657.

2

Reoviruses

REOVIRUS (Respiratory Enteric Orphan Virus)

Synonyms: ECHO 10. Hepato-encephalomyelitis (Stanley *et al.*, 1953).
The viruses were previously included with ECHO viruses but have now been separated.

Description of group: Sabin (1959). There are 3 serological types.

Morphology and development. Diameter 60–90 mμ. According to Tournier & Plissier (1960) bodies 70 mμ across, enclosing nucleoids 35 mμ across, are arranged either in orderly or disorderly array in a paranuclear crescentic inclusion. There are 92 capsomeres (Jordan & Mayor, 1962); according to Vasquez & Tournier (1962) these are cylindrical and hollow. All evidence suggests that growth takes place in the cytoplasm. Tubular structures may also be present (Bernhard & Granboulan, 1962).

Chemical composition. Bodies in cytoplasmic inclusions give the staining reactions of RNA (Drouhet, 1960). Gomatos *et al.* (1962) cite other evidence that this is an RNA-virus. Moreover (Gomatos and Tamm, 1963) the RNA has unusual properties which are shared by the RNA of wound-tumour virus of clover; it appears to be 2-stranded (Langridge and Gomatos 1963).

Physico-chemical characters. Virus survives heating for 2 hours at 56° C or 30 minutes at 60° C. It is stable between pH 2·2 and 8 and is ether-resistant. It survived treatment for an hour at room temperature with 1 per cent. H_2O_2, 1 per cent. phenol, 3 per cent. formalin, 20 per cent. lysol, but was inactivated by 70 per cent. ethanol: also by 3 per cent. formalin at 56° C (Stanley *et al.*, 1953). Density 1·32 (Jordan & Mayor, 1962).

Hæmagglutination. Human O cells are agglutinated at room temperature by Type 2 (Rosen, 1960; Stanley, 1961). Type 3 agglutinates ox, not human, cells. The cell-receptor is sensitive to RDE but is distinct from that involved in agglutination by myxoviruses and other viruses (Gomatos & Tamm, 1962).

Antigenic properties. Neutralization tests can be carried out in baby mice inoculated IP or ID or in tissue-cultures. Complement fixation may also be used (Stanley *et al.*, 1954).

Reoviruses have been separated into three serological types by the hæmagglutinin-inhibition test (Rosen, 1960). A bovine strain may qualify as a fourth type (Moscovici *et al.*, 1961). Antisera can conveniently be made in guinea pigs or roosters. Infected persons and guinea pigs may show heterotypic antibody responses. Streissle and Maramorosch (1963) report a small degree of cross-reactivity in the complement-fixation test with wound-tumour virus of clover, a virus which is morphologically identical.

Cultivation. *In fertile eggs.* Some strains grow on the CAM or amniotically, but there may be difficulty in propagating them indefinitely (Stanley *et al*, 1953, 1954). Van Tongeren & Tiddens, however (1957), adapted a strain to chick embryos.

In tissue culture the viruses grow readily in cells, especially kidney cells, of various primates, swine, cat, dog and guinea pig (Hsiung, 1958). Rolling cultures on a drum is helpful. The CPE differs from that of enteroviruses, the formation of an RNA-containing cytoplasmic inclusion being characteristic (Tournier & Plissier, 1960). Plaques develop in monolayers of L cells (Franklin, 1961). It is best to use a serum-free overlay (Rhim & Melnick, 1961).

Pathogenicity. The relation of reoviruses to spontaneous disease is uncertain. Types 1 and 3 have been isolated from mild fevers in children, sometimes associated with diarrhœa, but whether they caused the illness is uncertain (Rosen *et al.*, 1960). Type 2 has been associated with coryza in chimpanzees and with an outbreak of steatorrhœic enteritis (Sabin, 1960). In addition, Type 1 has been isolated (Strain SV12 of Hull *et al.*, 1956), from rhesus kidney and from *Cercopithecus* kidney (Malherbe & Harwin, 1957). Type 2 has come also from chimpanzees, from a monkey which died of pneumonia (SV 59—Hull *et al.*, 1958) and from wild mice (Hartley *et al.*, 1961). Type 3 has been isolated from laboratory mice and cattle, apart from human sources (Hartley *et al.*, 1961; Rosen & Abinanti,

1960). Rosen *et al.* (1963) recovered all 3 types from cattle fæces. Two viruses of simian origin, SV 4 and SV 28 of Hull *et al.* (1958), seem to belong to the group but have not been typable by the hæmagglutinin inhibition test.

Experimentally Type 3 inoculated into suckling mice by various routes led to jaundice, alopecia, conjunctivitis, an "oily hair" effect (due to steatorrhœa) and death (Stanley *et al.*, 1953). A neurotropic strain was developed from the original hepatotropic one (Stanley *et al.*, 1954). The oily hair effect was lost after passage in eggs or in tissue culture (Stanley, 1961).

Inoculation of cattle strains into calves has not been followed by recognizable illness (Rosen & Abinanti, 1960). Guinea pigs develop an inapparent infection after inoculation. Type 2 Reovirus was isolated from a dog with a fatal respiratory infection. Inoculated puppies developed interstitial pneumonia (Lou and Wenner, 1963).

Pathological lesions. Infected mice show necrotic areas in the liver, along with lymphocytic infiltration and sometimes occlusion of ducts. Peritoneal exudate may occur (Stanley *et al.*, 1953).

Ecology. Infection, though an inapparent one, may spread amongst guinea pigs and cattle. Infection in man, and apparently also in monkeys, is more prevalent in winter and spring.

REFERENCES

Bernhard, W., & Granboulan, N. (1962) *Tumour Viruses of Murine Origin,* p. 36. Ed. Wolstenholme & O'Connor. London: Churchill.
Drouhet, V. (1958) *Ann. Inst. Pasteur,* **95,** 781.
Franklin, R. M. (1961) *Proc. Soc. exp. Biol. (N.Y.),* **107,** 651.
Gomatos, P. J., & Tamm, I. (1962) *Virology,* **17,** 455.
Gomatos, P. J., & Tamm, I. (1963) *Proc. nat. Acad. Sci. (Wash.),* **49,** 707.
Gomatos, P. J., Tamm, I., Dales, S., & Franklin, R. M. (1962) *Virology,* **17,** 441.
Hartley, J. W., Rowe, W. P., & Huebner, R. J. (1961) *Proc. Soc. exp. Biol. (N.Y.),* **108,** 390.
Hsiung, G. D. (1958) *Proc. Soc. exp. Biol. (N.Y.),* **99,** 387.
Hull, R. N., Minner, M. R., & Mascoli, C. C. (1958) *Amer. J. Hyg.,* **68,** 31.
Langridge, R., & Gomatos, P. (1963) *Science,* **141,** 694.
Jordan, L. E., & Mayor, H. D. (1962) *Virology,* **17,** 797.
Lou, T. Y., & Wenner, H. A. (1963) *Amer. J. Hyg.* **77,** 293.
Malherbe, H., & Harwin, R. (1957) *Brit. J. exp. Path.,* **38,** 539.
Moscovici, C., La Placa, M., Maisel, J., & Kempe, C. H. (1961) *Amer. J. vet. Res.,* **22,** 852.
Rhim, J. S., & Melnick, J. L. (1951) *Virology,* **15,** 80.
Rosen, L. (1960) *Amer. J. Hyg.,* **71,** 242.
Rosen, L., & Abinanti, F. B. (1960) *Amer. J. Hyg.,* **71,** 250.
Rosen, L., Evans, H. E., & Spickard, A. (1963) *Amer. J. Hyg.,* **77,** 29.

Rosen, L., Hovis, J. F., Mastrota, F. M., Bell, J. A., & Huebner, R. J. (1960) *Amer. J. Hyg.*, **71,** 258 and 266.

Sabin, A. B. (1959) *Science*, **130,** 1387.

Stanley, N. F. (1961) *Nature (Lond.)*, **189,** 687.

Stanley, N. F., Dorman, D. C., & Ponsford, J. (1953) *Aust. J. exp. Biol. med. Sci.*, **31,** 147.

Stanley, N. F., Dorman, D. C., & Ponsford, J. (1954) *Aust. J. exp. Biol. med. Sci.*, **32,** 543.

Streissle, G., & Maramorosch, K. (1963) *Science*, **140,** 996.

Tournier, P., & Plissier, M. (1960) *C.R. Acad. Sci. (Paris)*, **250,** 630.

van Tongeren, H. A. E., & Tiddens, H. A. W. M. (1957) *Ned. T. Geneesk.*, **101,** 579.

Vasquez, C., & Tournier, P. (1962) *Virology*, **17,** 503.

3

Arboviruses

"Arbovirus" and "Arborvirus" have both been widely used tele-scoped forms of "arthropod-borne virus". The virus sub-committee of the International Nomenclature Committee has recommended the use of Arbovirus (Sub-committee, 1963).

The term includes those viruses which not only are transferred by a biting arthropod to a vertebrate host but actually undergo a biological cycle involving multiplication in both arthropod and vertebrate. This cycle has not been proved to exist for all arbo-viruses: some are antigenically related to viruses for which the cycle has been proved and its occurrence in them also is inferred. For a few included viruses (Bat Salivary Virus and Modoc) an arthropod vector has not been demonstrated; these viruses are, however, closely related antigenically to the "B" group (see below). The group, thus based almost wholly on a biological character, cannot yet be regarded as equivalent to the groups Myxovirus, etc., described on the basis of more fundamental properties.

Reviews: Kissling (1960). W.H.O. (1961).

Morphology. The size reported for members of the group ranges from 20 mμ to more than 100 mμ, a fact supporting the idea that the group may be a heterogeneous one. The few examined by electron microscopy appear to be spheres with a surrounding membrane: vesicular stomatitis, if this were included, would be an exception.

Chemical composition. Nucleic acid composition has been demonstrated for only a few. It is apparently RNA for at least the A and B groups, very likely for all.

Physico-chemical characters. All are fairly labile at 56° C, readily preserved by lyophilization or at −76°, and inactivated by 20 per cent. ether or by 1 : 1000 desoxycholic acid (Theiler, 1957).

Hæmagglutination. Most arboviruses have a hæmagglutinin extractable from brains of infected suckling mice with acetone and ether or in other ways (Clarke & Casals, 1958). The most susceptible cells are those of newly-hatched chicks or (Porterfield, 1957) geese. Optimal conditions as regards temperature and pH vary from one virus group to another.

Antigenic properties. Arboviruses are divisible on the basis of immunological tests into groups of varying sizes. A recent analysis shows 15 in group A, 33 in group B, 7 in group C. Other groups are named from the first described member: there are at least 14 in the Bunyamwera group and 7 in the Guama group. Twelve other small groups contain in all more than 20 viruses and there are 40 "singleton", or "ungrouped" not yet related to any other virus.

The hæmagglutinin-inhibition test is in most groups the most useful for showing cross-relationships, while the CF test and IC neutralization tests are much more specific; an IP neutralization test often gives an intermediate result, as do active cross-immunity tests. For CF, avirulent antigens can be prepared by extracting lyophilized virus and irradiating with U.V.R. Acetone-ether extraction is also helpful (Casals, 1949). Hæmagglutinin and most of the complement-fixing antigen are associated with virus-particles. Smith & Holt (1961) have identified a second hæmagglutinin in group A and group B viruses.

Cultivation. Very many arboviruses have been grown in tissue culture, the most useful being hamster kidney and, using monolayers with agar overlay, chick-embryo. Many have been adapted to grow in HeLa cells (S. M. Buckley, personal communication, 1963).

Distribution. The A and B and Bunyamwera groups each have an almost world-wide distribution: but individual viruses are usually confined to one zoo-geographical region. The C, Guama and Capim groups are known only from neotropical areas. Numerous arboviruses have been isolated from patients with overt disease. Rather fewer are of veterinary interest. A large number have been obtained only from mosquitoes or ticks, directly, or through infection of "sentinel" animals, and are not known to be associated with disease in any species.

Pathogenicity. Nearly all these viruses will produce encephalitis when inoculated into suckling mice, especially IC; some go well

also in older mice. Some of them produce encephalitis, influenza-
like illness or other symptoms in man or domestic animals.

Ecology. There have been many able reviews of the ecology of
arboviruses: Eklund (1953), Gordon Smith (1959, 1960), Mattingly
(1960), Reeves (1958, 1961).

Control is by elucidation of ecology and destruction of vectors;
and in some instances by vaccination.

ARBOVIRUSES GROUP A

Every member of this important group of 15 viruses shows cross-
reactions in the hæmagglutinin-inhibition test with one or more,
usually numerous, others in the group. For this purpose one uses
sera from rabbits or other animals which have had multiple inoculations. Other available serological tests are more useful for revealing
differences between individual members. Active immunity tests
show considerable cross-protection between members of the group.
A plaque-inhibition test in cultures of chick fibroblasts (Porterfield,
1961a) is particularly useful in revealing relationships and differences.

The A viruses differ in some other characters, particularly from
the B viruses with which they have been mainly compared. Their
hæmagglutination is not inhibited by phospholipids (Porterfield &
Rowe, 1960). Their infectivity and their hæmagglutinins are unaffected by trypsin. Hæmagglutination occurs over a rather narrower
range of temperature and pH than with group B viruses.

They tend to kill inoculated chick-embryos, also infant mice,
within 48 hours.

EASTERN EQUINE ENCEPHALOMYELITIS (E.E.E.)

Review: Schaeffer & Arnold (1954).

Morphology. Estimates of size range from 20–30 mμ (Bauer
et al., 1935) to 39·6–58·8 mμ (Sharp *et al.*, 1943). Electron microscopy (Bang & Gey, 1949) indicates that particles are spherical.

Chemical composition. Probably an RNA virus. An infectious
RNA is reported (Wecker & Schäfer, 1957).

Physico-chemical characters. Specific gravity 1·13. Inactivated in 10′ at 60°, not 56°. Readily preserved at −20° or −70°. Not readily inactivated by freezing and thawing nor by exposure to CO_2. Inactivated by ether and desoxycholate. Less stable at pH 5·1 to 5·7 than on either side of that range (Finkelstein *et al.*, 1938).

Hæmagglutination as for other A arboviruses. A hæmolysin has also been demonstrated (Karabatsos, 1963).

Antigenic properties. In CF tests and in neutralization tests carried out by IC inoculation of mice or by plaque-inhibition in tissue culture the virus is antigenically distinct from others. By hæmagglutinin-inhibition there is shown crossing to varying degrees with the other A-viruses (Casals, 1958). Minor antigenic differences are demonstrable between strains of the virus coming from different areas.

Interference has been demonstrated between this and a number of other viruses, including other arboviruses, myxoviruses and picornaviruses. This is, in many instances at least, mediated by interferon, of the presence of which this virus is a good indicator (Wagner, 1961).

Cultivation. In eggs, the virus grows well after inoculation by various routes and is rapidly lethal for the embryos. It grows in tissue cultures of chick embryo, mouse, hamster, monkey, guinea pig and other mammals: also in HeLa cells. There is a rapid destructive effect. Chronic infection may be set up in some lines of human and rat cells at 31° (Bang *et al.*, 1957). Multiplication is even reported in fish (*Gambusia*) embryos.

Distribution. The virus' distribution covers Eastern United States with separate forms in Michigan and Wisconsin: also the Caribbean, parts of Central America, and eastern South America as far as Argentina. A surprising report is of occurrence of the virus in the Philippines (Livesay, 1949).

Pathogenicity. This is probably normally a harmless parasite of some wild birds, with man and horses infected incidentally by mosquito bite.

In infected horses there is a preliminary phase of fever and viræmia, followed by invasion of the CNS. There may be mild excitement, soon followed by other abnormal behaviour, somnolence, paralysis and death. Mortality is up to 90 per cent. and mortality has been heavy in the United States: in 1938, 184,000 horses were infected either by this virus or the Western strain.

In man, mortality is also high, up to 74 per cent., but incidence has never been high as in horses. It is likely that strains from different areas vary in virulence, since in some districts there is evidence of subclinical immunization in the absence of overt disease. As in horses, the disease tends to be diphasic; in the second phase of nervous involvement, there occur convulsions, rigidity and coma. Most survivors show paralytic or mental sequelæ. Laboratory infections are recorded. Outbreaks with high mortality also occur amongst pheasants (Jungherr & Wallis, 1958).

Experimentally the disease is more invasive than the Western virus (p. 54). Mice, guinea pigs, goats, newly-hatched chicks and several other species are readily infected by various routes; with older animals IC inoculation is usually necessary (Sabin & Olitsky, 1938). Monkeys may be infected IC or IN (Wyckoff & Tesar, 1939). Chamberlain *et al.* (1954) have described the usefulness of chicks, emphasizing that they should be not more than half a day old. Pheasants and some small passerine birds develop fatal infections but there may be only viræmia in egrets, ibises, pigeons and grackles. In birds the virus infects viscera, particularly liver, rather than CNS (Kissling *et al.*, 1954). Intra-ocular infection of rabbits produces a "toxic" corneal reaction (Evans & Bolin, 1946).

The virus multiplies after inoculation into various mosquitoes, ticks and even insects of other orders: Orthoptera, Heteroptera and larval Coleoptera and Lepidoptera (Hurlbut & Thomas, 1960).

Pathological lesions. In horses, destruction of grey matter in the cerebrum and elsewhere is evident (Kissling & Rubin, 1951). In man the main lesions are in the brain stem; pulmonary œdema also occurs.

Ecology. The virus spreads naturally amongst birds in a "sylvan cycle", the main vector being probably *Culiseta melanura*. Various other Culicine mosquitoes (*Aëdes, Culex* spp) may be involved in spread to man and horses; a number of these readily transfer infection experimentally. The extrinsic incubation period is from 3 to 12 days, varying with outside temperature (Chamberlain & Sudia, 1955). There is a definite association with salt-marshes. Stamm (1958) suggests that the normal endemic spread may at times become explosive and that only then are there infections of man and horses.

The disease is evident in late summer and the mechanism of virus survival through the winter is obscure (see Western Encephalomyelitis, p. 56).

Infection may spread amongst pheasants in the absence of an arthropod vector (Holden, 1955). Virus is shed from infected horses in nasal secretions, urine and milk and contact infection may occur (Kissling *et al.*, 1956). Cannibalism may spread infection amongst mice (Traub & Kesting, 1956).

Control. A living virus attenuated by passage through pigeons was used by Traub & Ten Broeck (1935). Formolized vaccines were proved to be effective in guinea pigs by Cox & Olitsky (1936). Similar vaccines made from infected chick embryos have been more recently and successfully used in horses (Beard *et al.*, 1938); also on a small scale to protect exposed laboratory workers (Maurer *et al.*, 1952).

WESTERN EQUINE ENCEPHALOMYELITIS (W.E.E.)

Morphology and development Estimates of size range from 25–48 mμ. Morgan *et al.* (1961) describe development of particles on membranes bordering cytoplasmic vacuoles; these acquire an outer membrane and are discharged into the vacuole or periphery without cell rupture. Their core is 30 mμ across and their outside diameter 45–48 mμ. Rubin *et al.* (1955) studied intracellular development and considered that each cell might yield 100 infective particles, but only a few at a time, particles apparently being released within 1 minute of gaining the property of infectiousness.

Chemical composition. Contains RNA (Sharp *et al.*, 1953). Infectious RNA is reported by Wecker (1959).

Physico-chemical characters. Readily preserved by lyophilization or at −20° or −76°: also in 50 per cent. glycerol in the cold. Maximum stability between pH 6·5 and 8·5. Filtrates withstood a temperature of 60° for 10′. 0·4 per cent. formalin inactivates in 2 days. The half-life in various media at 37° is reported by Lockart & Groman (1958).

Hæmagglutination. As for other A arboviruses. Recently isolated strains may have demonstrable hæmagglutinins while laboratory-adapted ones may not (Chanock & Sabin, 1954). A hæmolysin has also been demonstrated (Karabatsos, 1963).

Antigenic properties. Crossing with other A arboviruses in the HAI test is described by Casals (1958). Parks & Price (1958) using cross-protection tests and Porterfield (1961a) using a plaque-inhibition test find evidence that W.E.E. is more closely related to Sindbis than to others of the group; a fact also apparent from HAI tests. Neutralization, as with many other arboviruses, is improved by addition of fresh normal serum (Whitman, 1947). It may be demonstrated by tests in mice or by various tissue-culture techniques. In infected human beings neutralizing antibodies develop quickly and persist long: CF antibodies appear more slowly and are more transient.

Interference. Numerous papers describe interference in mice or infected eggs with various other arboviruses, myxoviruses and others.

Cultivation. As with E.E.E., the virus can be grown in eggs inoculated by various routes and is rapidly lethal for the embryo; it can similarly be grown in tissue cultures of cells from many species, hamster kidney cultures being especially useful; it will produce plaques on monolayers of chick embryo cells. A colour test depending on change of pH can be used as a visible means of titration (Brown, 1958). In the chick embryo it multiplies particularly in vascular endothelium (Nir et al., 1957). A chronic inapparent infection can be set up in a continuous line of mouse (L) cells (Chambers, 1957; Lockart, 1960).

Distribution. The virus is spread over most of the United States and Southern Canada but infections of horses and man are not reported from the eastern seaboard. It also extends to South America as far as Argentina.

Pathogenicity. Presumably an avian infection as in E.E.E., horses and man being attacked only incidentally. Symptoms in these species are as for E.E.E. but the mortality is considerably lower—usually 20–30 per cent. for horses (rarely 50 per cent.) and 10 per cent. for man, on the average. Sequelæ are uncommon. Many inapparent infections apparently occur in man. Virus has been recovered from naturally infected birds, chiefly passerines, also from squirrels, cow, deer and pig.

Experimentally the virus, given IC, will produce meningo-encephalo-myelitis in a large range of laboratory and wild rodents, monkeys, rabbits, young dogs, deer, pigs, calves, goats and some birds. Hamsters of all ages and young mice and guinea pigs can be infected by IM, IP and SC injection. As with E.E.E., half-day old chicks are highly susceptible (Chamberlain *et al.*, 1954). Virus given IV to rabbits or young mice or intra-ocularly to rabbits produces symptoms which are perhaps referable to a "toxin" which is not separable from the virus itself (Fastier, 1952; Evans & Bolin, 1945).

Virus multiplication in various arthropods is as described under E.E.E (p. 53).

Pathological lesions in the brain of fatal cases in man are those of diffuse encephalitis with scattered neuronal necrosis, accumulation of glial cells with only moderate cell infiltration of meninges or around blood vessels. Lesions in other viscera are not striking. Changes in other species are similar.

Ecology. Available evidence indicates that W.E.E. is a parasite of birds, in many of which it produces symptomless infections. During summer months it may be conveyed, especially by bites of *Culex tarsalis*, to horses and man. Other mosquitoes have been found naturally infected and may play a role. Several suggestions have been made as to how W.E.E. persists during the winter: (i) A possible role of bird-mites *Dermanyssus*, *Bdellonyssus* and *Liponyssus* no longer obtains support (Chamberlain & Sikes, 1955); (ii) Ticks, *Dermacentor andersoni*, could be infected (Syverton & Berry, 1941) and could transmit infection to their progeny. Their possible importance is not supported by epidemiological evidence; (iii) Virus might be re-introduced each summer by migrating birds having viræmia or carrying infected ectoparasites (studies by Kissling *et al.* (1957) tell against this view); (iv) Virus has been isolated from hibernating *Culex tarsalis* in all months except December (Reeves *et al.*, 1958); (v) Virus has been found to over-winter in garter snakes (*Thamnophis*) experimentally infected in the autumn and allowed to hibernate: viræmia occurred when they awoke in spring and infection could be transmitted to chicks by mosquito-bite (Thomas & Eklund, 1960).

Control. A formolized vaccine has been used, as with E.E.E. (p. 54).

Venezuelan Equine Encephalomyelitis (V.E.E.)

Morphology. In KB cells (human cancer) virus particles 40–50 mμ across appear to mature on membranes surrounding cytoplasmic vacuoles, then reaching the cell surface and escaping. Each cell was estimated to produce 2700 plaque-forming units. Other particles 25 mμ across may represent early stages (Mussgay & Weibel, 1962). A later paper (Mussgay & Weibel, 1963) describes particles 65–75 mμ across.

Physico-chemical characters. Survives well at −70°, in 50 per cent. glycerol or when lyophilized. Not readily inactivated by formalin. β-propiolactone vapour was better than formaldehyde for sterilizing infected rooms (Dawson et al., 1959).

Hæmagglutinin as for other A arboviruses.

Antigenic properties. Crosses with other A's in the HAI test but is not particularly close to any (Casals, 1958). Readily separable from the others by CF and neutralization tests.

Cultivation. Grows readily in *fertile eggs*, killing embryos in less than 48 hours; also in *cultures* of several primate tissues, chick embryo, L (mouse) and guinea pig cells. Chronic infections have been set up in L cells. In chick embryo, HeLa and guinea pig heart cultures, the virus is attenuated so that it no longer readily infects guinea pigs, rabbits or adult mice, when inoculated by peripheral routes (Koprowski & Lennette, 1946, and other authors). Virulence was soon restored by mouse-passage.

Distribution. Venezuela, Colombia, Equador, Panama, Trinidad, Brazil.

Pathogenicity. Infected horses and donkeys become ill, not necessarily with encephalitis. There may be only fever, depression and diarrhœa, but some develop nervous symptoms and may die (Kissling et al., 1956). In man, after an incubation period of 2–5 days, there is fever with severe headache but only a few cases show CNS involvement (tremors, diplopia and lethargy). Two fatal cases are recorded.

Laboratory infections occur much more readily than with other

A arboviruses and many are on record (Lennette & Koprowski, 1943; Slepushkin, 1960); infection is probably by inhalation.

Experimentally the disease is more virulent for laboratory rodents than W.E.E. or E.E.E.; it readily infects when given by peripheral routes. Besides horses, dogs, cats, sheep and goats are susceptible, but not cattle. Inoculated birds show no symptoms unless after very large doses: virus in their blood is of low titre. In contrast, there is viræmia at a high level in horses and other infected mammals. It is therefore suggested that the unknown natural reservoir is probably mammalian rather than avian.

Pathological lesions. The virus is more viscerotropic than neurotropic. Lesions in the brain affect vessels rather than neurones. In horses there is severe damage to blood-forming tissues—including spleen and lymph nodes—and necrotic foci in the pancreas occur regularly (Kissling *et al.*, 1956). "Lympho-myelopoietic necrosis" is seen also in infected rodents (Victor *et al.*, 1956).

Ecology. The natural reservoir, though suspected to be mammalian, is unknown. Nor do we know the important natural vector, though mosquitoes of the genera *Culex*, *Aëdes*, *Mansonia* and *Psorophora* will transfer infection experimentally. *Aëdes triseriatus* was particularly efficient. Virus was isolated from rafts of eggs laid by *Mansonia perturbans* (Chamberlain *et al.*, 1956).

Virus is present in nose, eye, mouth, urine and milk of infected horses and direct contact infection from horse to horse can occur (Kissling *et al.*, 1956). Contact infection also occurs between infected mice.

Control. Formolized vaccines have been prepared from infected chick embryos for protecting horses and exposed laboratory workers. However, 14 infections occurred in laboratory workers receiving ostensibly inactive vaccine (Sutton & Brook, 1954): possibly man is a more delicate indication of the presence of virus than the systems used for safety-testing the vaccine.

For Near East equine encephalomyelitis *v.* p. 303.

Sindbis Virus

Description: Taylor *et al.* (1955.)

Morphology. Size estimated at 40–48 mμ.

Physico-chemical characters. Survives well at 0° C and after lyophilization. Almost completely inactivated in 30′ at 56°.

Chemical composition. An RNA virus containing considerable amounts of phospholipid and cholesterol (Pfefferkorn & Hunter, 1963).

Antigenic properties. Several immunological tests indicate a closer relationship to Western Equine Encephalomyelitis (*v.* p. 54) than to other A arboviruses. There are minor antigenic differences between strains coming from different areas (Casals, 1961).

Interference. The activity of interferon in cultures of Sindbis has been studied by Gresser & Enders (1962) and Ho (1962).

Cultivation. Multiplies in fertile eggs and is very lethal to the embryos; grows also in cultures of chick, human and monkey cells with CPE in most of them (Frothingham, 1955). Plaques are produced on chick embryo monolayers (Shah *et al.*, 1960, Porterfield, 1961a). Frothingham (1963) found that plaque-size was larger in the presence of mumps virus.

Distribution. Egypt, South Africa, India, Malaya, Philippines, Australia (the only arbovirus occurring in each of four zoo-geographical regions).
Isolated from *Culex* spp. in Egypt and South Africa; also from several species of birds.

Pathogenicity. May be associated with fever in man (Report 1961–1962).
Experimentally the virus is lethal for suckling, not adult mice; in the infant mice it causes diffuse myositis and encephalitis. In inoculated monkeys of the genera *Macaca* and *Cercopithecus*, and in several species of birds, there was a low-grade viræmia, but no symptoms of disease were noted (Taylor *et al.*, 1955, Weinbren *et al.*, 1956).

Ecology. Probably an infection of birds transmitted by *Culex* spp.; but neutralizing antibodies have been found not only in birds but in sera from man and domestic ungulates in endemic areas.

Semliki Forest Virus

Description: Smithburn & Haddow (1944).
Synonym: Kumba virus.

Morphology. Non-rigid spheres or discs 50 mμ across (Cheng, 1961a). Gordon Smith (1960) described bodies 40–47 mμ across with a halo 55–70 mμ in diameter around them.

Chemical composition. Cheng (1958) infected 3-day-old mice with a preparation of RNA from brains of inoculated mice.

Physico-chemical characters. Inactivated in 1 hour at 60°, or in 30′ at 62°. Survival at various temperatures is described by Sanna & Angelillo (1957). Not inactivated by trypsin.

Hæmagglutination. The hæmagglutinating particle is identical with the virus. The properties of this and of CF particles are described by Cheng (1961b).

Antigenic properties. The virus shows the usual cross-reactivity with other A arboviruses in the HAI test; it crosses rather better with Mayaro and Chikungunya than with some others (Casals, 1958). Livers of recovered mice contain a protective substance (Shope, 1961).

Interference. Interference with rabbit fibroma and myxoma was reported by Ginder & Friedewald (1952).

Cultivation. Lethal to inoculated chick embryos (Smithburn, 1946). Grows in tissue cultures of many species. Henderson (1961) described plaque formation in cultures of Cebus, dog, pig, hamster, guinea pig and chick tissues.

Distribution. Only 3 isolations are reported—from *Aëdes* or *Eretmapodites* mosquitoes in Uganda, Mozambique and Cameroons respectively (the Kumba strain from the Cameroons is best considered as a Semliki virus). Serological studies (Smithburn *et al.*, 1954) suggest that the virus may occur in Malaya and North Borneo.

Pathogenicity. Not associated with any known illness.
Laboratory infection, presumably inapparent, can occur, as shown by development of antibodies (Clarke, 1961).

Experimentally the virus causes encephalitis when injected into adult mice by various routes, or IC into guinea pigs, rabbits, rhesus and red-tail monkeys. Apart from lesions of encephalomyelitis, most inoculated animals have shown kidney damage (Smithburn & Haddow, 1944). Viræmia lasting several days occurred in inoculated birds of several species; also in hamsters infected by various routes (Davies *et al.*, 1955).

Ecology. The natural hosts and vectors are unknown. Antibodies have been found in sera of human beings and 6/12 species of wild primates in Uganda (Smithburn *et al.*, 1944). The virus multiplies in *Aëdes ægypti* which could function as an efficient vector (Woodall & Bertram, 1959). Anopheline mosquitoes can transmit infection experimentally (Collins, 1963).

Control. An antibiotic (Helenine) was found to be of some value in experimentally infected mice (Shope, 1953).

Chikungunya

Description: Ross (1956).

The name is a native one meaning "that which bends up" from the contorted position of a sufferer and is not, as with most arboviruses, a place name. Most properties of the virus have not yet received much study.

Antigenic properties. By HAI tests it lies closer to Mayaro and Semliki viruses than to other A arboviruses. Rises in neutralizing antibody titres occur as a result of infection in man (Mason & Haddow, 1957).

Habitat. Tanganyika, Uganda, Congo, South Africa, Thailand.

Pathogenicity. An acute, dengue-like, fever, often biphasic; excruciating pains occur in joints and spine of affected persons. A maculo-papular rash commonly occurs in the second phase of fever. After recovery from fever, joint pains may recur for some months (Robinson, 1955). Closely related viruses have been recovered from patients with hæmorrhagic fever in Thailand (Hammon *et al.*, 1960); their relation to the disease is uncertain.

Experimentally, suckling mice die in a few days when inoculated

IC, but are less readily infected IP. Older mice are much more resistant. Guinea pigs and rabbits show no symptoms on inoculation.

A strain from Thailand produced multiple hæmorrhages in intestines and elsewhere in suckling mice, rats and hamsters (Halstead & Buescher, 1961); strains from Africa have also caused hæmorrhages in mice.

Pathological lesions in mice: encephalitis affecting especially Ammon's horn, myositis, myocarditis (Weinbren *et al.*, 1958b).

Ecology. There is no evidence of infection of species other than man. Virus was isolated in Tanganyika from *Anopheles* spp, *Aëdes ægypti* and *Culex fatigans* (Lumsden, 1955) and from *Aëdes africanus* in Uganda (Weinbren *et al.*, 1958b). Lumsden considers *A. ægypti* likely to be the most important vector. The virus was unknown until isolated from an epidemic in Tanganyika in 1952; at the height of this epidemic, the incidence in many villages was 60–80 per cent., all ages being attacked.

O'Nyong-Nyong

Description: Haddow *et al.* (1960). Williams & Woodall (1961).

Antigenic properties. Closely related in the HAI test to Chikungunya, but separable by the plaque-inhibition test (Porterfield, 1961a).

Cultivation. On chick embryo monolayers (Williams *et al.*, 1962).

Distribution. Uganda, Kenya, Congo.

Pathogenicity. Clinical features in man similar to those of Chikungunya (p. 61) with lymphadenitis as a differentiating feature. Similar severe joint pains and rash occur (Shore, 1961).

The virus is pathogenic for suckling mice when given IC; for primary isolation it is best to use diluted sera. Older mice are resistant. Infant mice which do not die show stunting of growth and patchy alopecia (Williams & Woodall, 1961).

Ecology. The infection began and spread through Northern Uganda in 1959. Tens of thousands of Africans were affected. Shore (1961) discusses the epidemiology. The vector appears to be *Anopheles (Gambiæ* and *funestus)*; this is thus the only arbovirus for which epidemic spread by Anophelines is known (Corbet *et al.*, 1961).

Other A Arboviruses

Information is scantier concerning 6 other viruses.

Mayaro virus caused an epidemic of fever and severe headache involving more than half a force of labourers working in quarries and forest in the state of Para in Brazil.

Uruma virus gave rise to a similar outbreak involving about half of 400 Okinawan pioneers making a settlement in Bolivia.

Middelburg virus was isolated in Cape province in South Africa from *Aëdes* captured during an epizootic amongst sheep. The virus was pathogenic for lambs but the relation of the virus to the epizootic is uncertain since Wesselsbron virus (p. 76) was also present.

The information available concerning these and 3 other A-viruses is presented in Table 3.

All the viruses in the table are pathogenic for suckling mice when given IC (usually IP also) but adult mice have symptomless infections.

Epidemic Exanthema and Polyarthritis

An epidemic disease occurring in Australia and having the characters indicated by the name was associated with a rise in antibodies to the A-group of arboviruses (Shope & Anderson, 1960).

B GROUP OF ARBOVIRUSES

This, the largest group of arboviruses, is delineated mainly on immunological grounds; its members differ also from the A group in the ways described on p. 51. Their mutual relations are best brought out by the HAI test, using sera obtained after several inoculations of rabbits or other species. Differences are revealed by the more specific neutralization and CF tests. Other properties are as described on p. 49 for arboviruses generally.

Review: covering most of the human pathogens (Olitsky & Clarke, 1959).

West Nile

Many papers refer to the Egypt 101 strain of this virus.
Original Description: Smithburn *et al.* (1940).

Morphology. Diameter 20–30 mμ. Studies with fluorescent antibodies show development of specific antigen in cytoplasm of infected neurones in mice (Noyes, 1955).

TABLE 3

MISCELLANEOUS A ARBORVIRUSES

Virus	MIDDELBURG	GETAH (SAGIYAMA)	MAYARO	URUMA	UNA	AURA	PIXUNA
Where isolated	South Africa	Japan Malaya	Brazil Trinidad	Bolivia	Brazil Trinidad	Brazil	Brazil
From what species	Aëdes spp. especially A caballus	Culex tritaeniorhynchus (1 from Aëdes)	Man Mansonia Venezuelensis (1)	Man	Psorophora spp. Aëdes serratus	Culex sp. Aëdes serratus	Anopheles
Association with disease	Isolated during epizootic in sheep	None	Epidemic of fever	None	None	None	None
Properties of virus	Passed 275 mμ membrane	Sensitive to ether and bile salts	Passed Seitz EK	17–26 mμ Sensitive to bile salts	Passed Seitz EK	Passed Seitz EK Sensitive to bile salts	
Related A arboviruses (HAI)	Possibly Semliki and Sindbis	Semliki (1-way)	Semliki	Mayaro	—	WEE and Sindbis	
Pathogenicity for animals, other than mice	Fever in lamb Viraemia in chicks	Viraemia in chicks	—	—			
Growth in eggs	—	Some strains lethal to embryos	Lethal (yolk-sac and amnion)	Lethal (yolk-sac)			
Growth in tissue culture	—	CPE in pig and hamster kidney	CPE in hamster kidney	CPE in hamster kidney			
Antibodies found naturally	Numerous sheep. Few man and rodents. Birds negative.	Pigs. Horses. A few men and birds	Man Monkeys in Trinidad	Men	Low per cent. in man, rodents, horse, cow. Birds negative	Very low per cent. in man, horse, cow, opossum, rodents. Birds negative.	
References	Kokernot et al. (1957)a	Scherer et al. (1962)	Casals & Whitman (1957) Causey & Maroja (1957)	Schaeffer et al. (1959) Schmidt et al. (1959)	Causey et al (1963)	Causey et al (1963)	Causey (1963) personal communication

Chemical composition. Colter *et al.* (1957) have described infectious RNA.

Physico-chemical characters. Inactivated in 30′ at 55°, not 50°; also by 0·2 per cent. formalin. Survives 2 weeks at 2–4° but less than 72 hours at 37°.

Hæmagglutination—as for other B arboviruses (Casals & Brown, 1954).

Antigenic properties. HAI tests reveal that this virus, together with Japanese B and Murray Valley and St. Louis viruses, forms a related sub-group within the B viruses. Ilhéus is also related though less closely. West Nile is more readily inactivated by sera made against these other viruses than are they by West Nile sera (Smithburn, 1942; Lennette & Koprowski, 1946). Clarke's (1960) studies with antibody absorption are particularly valuable.

Cultivation. Multiplies in *fertile eggs* forming plaques on the CAM and growing also after inoculation into yolk sac. Grows also in *tissue cultures* of chick embryo and many mammalian tissues, hamster kidney being especially useful. A CPE is best seen in this or in chick embryo, monkey kidney or human cancer lines. Plaques form on chick embryo or monkey kidney monolayers under appropriate conditions (Lavilloureix & Reeb, 1958; Bhatt & Work, 1957). Koprowski and Lennette (1946) record attenuation of the virus after cultivation, so that it no longer killed mice or hamsters when inoculated by peripheral routes.

Distribution. Egypt, Uganda, South Africa, probably other parts of Africa, Israel, India.

Pathogenicity. In Egypt and elsewhere it is endemic and infects man, chiefly children, as a usually silent infection. It may however be revealed, and especially in outbreaks in Israel, as a short febrile illness simulating dengue, sand-fly fever or rubella. Headache, adenopathy, maculo-papular rash, sore throat and limb pains occur (Bernkopf *et al.*, 1953). A laboratory infection is recorded. Inoculations into cancer patients usually produced only mild fever, but 11 per cent. had symptoms of mild encephalitis. Temporary regression of some cancers occurred (Southam & Moore, 1954).

Experimentally the virus causes encephalitis when inoculated IC into rodents of several species, chicks or rhesus monkeys, but only fever in *Cercopithecus* (Smithburn *et al.*, 1940). Mice and hamsters may be infected when inoculated by various routes; after 4 to 5 days they become excited, hunched-up, rough and may show paraplegia before death. Chicks infected by mosquito-bite show viræmia for several days.

Pathological lesions in mice resemble the encephalomyelitis caused by other arboviruses.

Ecology. Birds are probably the normal hosts, virus being transmitted by Culicine mosquitoes, chiefly, in Egypt, *Culex univittatus*. Secondary infection cycles may involve man, and, less certainly, domestic quadrupeds. *Culex pipiens* may play a role in carrying the infection through the winter (Taylor *et al.*, 1956). Hurlbut (1956) infected several species of *Culex*. Ticks (*Ornithodoros moubata*) can also be infected and will transmit infection, but their role in nature is uncertain (Whitman & Aitken, 1960). Antibodies to the virus occur to varying extents in different parts of Africa in sera of human beings, monkeys, domestic quadrupeds and birds (Kokernot *et al.*, 1956).

JAPANESE B

Synonyms: Japanese B encephalitis (J.B.E.).
Russian autumn encephalitis.

Morphology. Size 20–30 mμ by gradocol filtration. Studies with fluorescent antibody indicate that viral antigen is present in the cytoplasm, especially near the nucleus.

Chemical composition. Extraction of active RNA was reported by Nakamura (1961).

Physico-chemical characters. Survives at least 8 years at −76°. Inactivated in 30′ at 56°. Labile at pH 10 and 7; optimum stability at pH 8·5 (Duffy & Stanley, 1945). Much less stable at 25° than W.E.E. The more virulent strains are said to show greater heat stability (Huang 1957).

Hæmagglutination as for other B arboviruses. Old laboratory strains may lose their hæmagglutinins. Adsorption to red-cells is optimal at pH 6·5–6·8. Minute amounts of $ZnSO_4$ inhibit hæmagglutination (Sabin & Buescher, 1950). A hæmagglutinating particle 10 mμ across is described (Kitaoka & Nishimura, 1963).

Antigenic properties. By HAI falls into a sub-group of B arboviruses with Murray Valley, St. Louis and West Nile viruses (Smithburn, 1942; Lennette & Koprowski, 1946; Clarke, 1960). Minor antigenic differences exist between different Japanese B strains. Neutralizing and HAI antibodies appear within a week in affected persons and persist for years: CF antibodies appear much later and disappear sooner (Southam, 1956).

Interference in tissue culture or infected eggs is described between this virus and the W.E.E., poliomyelitis and influenza viruses.

Cultivation. Growth occurs in fertile eggs, best after inoculation into the yolk-sac; resulting embryo deaths could be used as a basis for titration (Howitt, 1946). Virus passed 50 times in 1-day-old chick embryos (Okuno, 1959) lost pathogenicity for mice.

Growth occurs in tissue cultures of chick embryo and various mammalian cells, sometimes without definite CPE, but strains have been adapted to produce CPE or plaques on monolayers of chick-embryo, pig, monkey or hamster kidney cells (Bhatt & Work, 1957; Inoue *et al.*, 1961).

Distribution. Particularly studied in Japan but apparently extends all over South East Asia from Siberia to Malaya and South-East India.

Pathogenicity. In Japan and elsewhere incidence may be very high especially in children, but only 0·1 to 0·2 per cent. of these may show encephalitis (Southam, 1956); the virus causes merely fever or inapparent infection in the others. Cases of encephalitis have varied symptoms including pareses; sequelæ are common. Encephalitis occurs also in horses, but in them also there are many infections without nervous symptoms (Hale & Witherington, 1953). It may cause abortions in pigs (Burns, 1950).

Experimentally the virus causes encephalitis, usually fatal, after IC inoculation into mice, hamsters and several species of monkey. Mice can be infected, especially young ones, by peripheral injections. Inoculated rabbits, guinea pigs, pigs, chicks and other birds usually develop inapparent infections with viræmia.

Pathological lesions in the brain are like those of other arbovirus encephalitides, but destruction of Purkinje cells in the cerebellum is particularly noteworthy.

Ecology. The virus is probably a parasite primarily of wild birds, especially night-herons. Nestlings of these seem to act as "amplifiers" to increase the amount of virus in an infected locality during summer months (Buescher *et al.*, 1959; Scherer *et al.*, 1959a). The main vector in Japan is *Culex tritæniorrhynchus*, but other culicines may play a role elsewhere, e.g. *C. vishnui* in India (Work & Shah, 1956). Hibernating mosquitoes (Hurlbut, 1950) or bats may permit virus to survive the winter. Domestic pigs are regularly infected, and have viræmia adequate to keep virus going in a secondary cycle (Scherer *et al.*, 1959b). Man, horses and other species are only infected incidentally.

Control. Formolized vaccines for protection of human beings have been widely used but are of dubious value. A new line of approach is to infect with one avirulent B arbovirus, e.g. West Nile, followed by a "booster" with inactivated Japanese B (Price *et al.*, 1961).

Murray Valley Encephalitis (M.V.E.)

Synonym: Australian X-disease.
Review: Anderson (1954).

Morphology. Diameter between 20 and 50 mμ probably about 25 mμ (Ada *et al.*, 1962).

Chemical composition. RNA. Ada *et al.* (1961) isolated an infectious RNA by treatment with cold phenol and a similar product has apparently been liberated from virus with desoxycholic acid (Anderson, 1959). There is also a lipid present in the virus (Anderson & Ada, 1960).

Physico-chemical characters. Inactivated in 15′ at 56°; also by phospholipase A (Anderson & Ada, 1961). Properties like those of Japanese B virus.

Hæmagglutination as for other B arboviruses. Activity against pigeon and day-old chick cells was described by Macdonald (1952).

Antigenic properties. A member, by HAI tests, of the subgroup of B arboviruses containing St. Louis, West Nile and Japanese B viruses, but more closely related to the last than to the others (McLean, 1956; Pond *et al.*, 1958). Presence of antibody in yolk of eggs laid by immune birds may prove useful in epidemiological surveys (Warner, 1957).

Cultivation. Fertile eggs can be infected by any route and die in consequence. French (1952) suggests that inoculation of the CAM with production of pocks may be the method of choice for primary isolation of virus.

Distribution. Australia, probably endemic in Northern Territory of Queensland, reaching Victoria and New South Wales at infrequent intervals; also endemic in Papua (New Guinea).

Pathogenicity. Encephalitis caused by this virus in man resembles Japanese B encephalitis, but the virus attacks predominantly children in the presumably non-endemic areas of South-Eastern Australia (Robertson & McLorinan, 1952). There may be troublesome sequelæ. Horses may be infected but do not develop encephalitis.

Experimentally the virus produces encephalitis when inoculated IC in mice, hamsters, monkeys, sheep and newly-hatched chicks. It infects suckling mice when given by peripheral routes and also, in contrast to Japanese B virus, does so in hamsters (Hammon & Sather, 1956). Rabbits, guinea pigs and birds, including older chicks, usually show only viræmia.

Pathological lesions resemble those due to Japanese B.

Ecology. Probably a bird-parasite endemic in New Guinea and Northern Australia. Epidemics of encephalitis in Australia in 1917, 1918, 1922 and 1925 (Australian X-disease) were almost certainly due to Murray Valley virus. A virus was isolated by Cleland & Bradley (1917) and subsequently lost. M.V.E. virus was recovered by Miles (1952) from the next (1951) outbreak. Australian workers suggest that after heavy spring rains in the north conditions are suitable for southward spread through the agency of migrating water-birds. The important vector is almost certainly *Culex annulirostris* (McLean, 1953; Reeves *et al.*, 1954).

St. Louis Encephalitis

Review: Olitsky & Clarke (1959).

Morphology. Size between 20 and 30 mμ by gradocol membrane filtration.

Physico-chemical characters. 30′ at 56° inactivates. Survival in various diluents at 0° and 37° was studied by Cook & Hudson (1937). Optimum pH for preservation was 8·8 (Duffy, 1946).

Hæmagglutination as for other B arboviruses. The pH range and other properties of the hæmagglutinin were studied by Chanock & Sabin (1953).

Antigenic properties. Falls in HAI tests in the sub-group of B arboviruses with Japanese B, Murray Valley and West Nile viruses.
Antigenic properties closely resemble those of these three viruses.

Interference is reported between this and other arboviruses.

Cultivation in *fertile eggs* is possible, inoculation being usually into yolk-sac or CAM; in the latter case there is a diffuse œdematous lesion with proliferative and necrotic elements. Embryos usually die.
Virus grows in *tissue cultures* of chick, mouse and other species. Plaques are produced on chick-embryo monolayers.

Distribution. United States, except the East, Panama, Trinidad.

Pathogenicity. Most infections of man only cause a brief febrile illness but encephalitis may occur in any age-group. More than a thousand cases of encephalitis occurred near St. Louis and Kansas City in 1932. Sequelæ are uncommon. One laboratory infection is recorded (von Magnus, 1950). Disease in horses is not reported, though they may have viræmia.
Experimentally mice, particularly those of certain susceptible strains, develop encephalitis after inoculation IC or IN. Inoculation IP is less certain except in sucklings. Intramuscular injection may cause local myositis. Young rats, hamsters and rhesus monkeys can be infected IC; infection in rhesus is rarely fatal. Guinea pigs, rabbits, chicks and other birds of several species inoculated by various routes develop symptomless viræmia. Young mice and hamsters can be infected by feeding. In partly resistant mice, challenge may cause a chronic infection (Webster & Clow, 1936) or a flaccid paralysis due to myelitis (Cook, 1938).
Pathological lesions in the brain resemble those caused by related viruses, but focal necroses are less commonly seen.

Ecology. Naturally an infection of birds transmitted by mosquito-bite. *Culex tarsalis* is the principal vector, at least in the western United States. In the mid-west *Culex quinquefasciatus* and *pipiens* may be more important (Chamberlain *et al.*, 1959). Virus has been isolated from several other mosquito species. How the virus over-winters is unknown (*cf.* W.E.E., p. 56); mites are no longer considered to be important.

Control. No effective vaccine is available for man. As with Japanese B, workers are investigating the possibility of using combinations of B arboviruses to obtain effective immunity (Hammon & Sather, 1956).

Ilhéus Virus

Description: Laemmert & Hughes (1947).
Koprowski & Hughes (1946).

Morphology. Diameter 18–26 mμ (Smithburn & Bugher, 1953).

Physico-chemical characters. Inactivated in 30' between 60° and 65°. Survived for several days at room temperature (20°–30°). Survives desiccation or in 50 per cent. glycerol in the refrigerator.

Hæmagglutination as for other B arboviruses. Potent hæmagglutinin is produced in tissue-cultures of hamster kidney (Diercks *et al.*, 1961).

Antigenic properties. Related, by HAI tests, to the St. Louis, West Nile, Japanese B sub-group, but less closely than these are to each other.

Cultivation. Grows well when inoculated on the CAM of *chick embryo*: most virus is present in the embryo itself; also in chick embryo *tissue cultures* (Koprowski & Hughes, 1946); and, in hamster kidney tissue culture, where cytopathic effects are produced (Diercks *et al.*, 1961).

Distribution. Brazil, Colombia, Central America and Caribbean.

Pathogenicity. Causes infection of man which is normally in-apparent, but a few cases of encephalitis are recorded. Three of these occurred amongst 9 infections of cancer patients in whom the virus was under test for possible oncolytic effects (Southam & Moore, 1951).

Experimentally the virus will cause encephalitis when injected into mice IC: the IP or SC routes are effective only in very young mice. Viræmia was produced after injection by various routes into several species of primates, rodents and marsupials. Of these marmosets (*Callithrix*) circulated virus for the longest period—up to 7 days. In chicks, pigeons and *Sicalis* (a Brazilian canary) no viræmia occurred more than three days after injection (Koprowski & Hughes, 1946).

Ecology. Virus has been isolated from several mosquito species, most of them in Trinidad from *Psorophora* spp. (Anderson *et al.*, 1956): also from birds in Panama (Galindo & Rodaniche, 1960). Antibodies have been found in sera of many persons in Brazil and Trinidad and in several species of mammals, including horses and birds. The important natural reservoir, however, is unknown.

YELLOW FEVER

Synonyms: Fiebre amarilla.
Reviews: Strode (1951). Theiler (1959).
                Dick (1953)—epidemiology.

Morphology. Diameter 17–28 mμ by filtration (Findlay & Broom, 1933) or 29–31 mμ by centrifugation (Polson, 1954). Spheres 38 mμ across and having dense centres are described by Bergold and Weibel (1962).

Chemical composition. Nielsen and Marquardt (1962) have extracted an infectious RNA.

Physico-chemical characters. Inactivated in 10' at 60° (Frobisher, 1930) but much more stable when dried. Iso-electric point: pH 6·9–7·3. Density 1·33. Inactivation by various chemicals described by Frobisher (1930). Readily preserved at −76° or after freeze-drying, but access of CO_2 to frozen specimens must be prevented.

Hæmagglutination as for other B arboviruses.

Antigenic properties. Several tests are available for serological study—the IP and IC neutralization tests in mice, CF, HAI and finally plaque-inhibition in cultures: they are of varying specificity, the HAI being least specific. In this test the virus shows the usual group reactions with other B arboviruses: Zika and Uganda S viruses seem to be its nearest relatives. Antibody absorption tests (Clarke, 1960) bring out differences between African and South American strains: the former contain an antigen lacking in the latter. The 17D strain contains an antigen absent from the strain (Asibi) from which it was derived. CF antibodies, as usual in the group, disappear sooner than neutralizing ones: they are commonly absent after vaccination (Perlowagora & Hughes, 1947). Neutralizing antibodies may persist in human sera for 75 years in the absence of opportunity for specific reinforcement (Sawyer, 1931). A precipitin may be present in sera of acutely ill monkeys (Hughes, 1933).

Interference between yellow fever and other arboviruses, also with influenza, is reported. That between yellow fever and Rift Valley fever was the first to be recorded where serologically unrelated viruses were concerned (Findlay & MacCallum, 1937).

Cultivation. *Fertile eggs* can be infected, usually only after previous adaptation of virus to mice or tissue culture. Inoculation is best done on to the CAM or directly into the embryo, in which highest titres of virus are found. Embryos under 11 days old commonly die. Virus will grow in *tissue cultures* of chick embryo and mouse embryo. The attenuated 17D strain used for vaccination was obtained by serial passage in chick embryo cultures of virus already partly attenuated by passage in mice IC and then in mouse embryo cultures (Theiler & Smith, 1937). Plaques appear on infected chick fibroblast monolayers (Porterfield, 1959).

Distribution. Endemic in tropical Africa south of the Sahara and south to Northern Rhodesia but barely reaching the Indian Ocean. Epidemics have occurred in the Sudan and Abyssinia, formerly in Europe. Endemic also in tropical South America, occasionally spreading to Central America and Trinidad and formerly to the United States.

Pathogenicity. The picture in man ranges from an inapparent infection in native Africans to a fulminating disease, with high fever, albuminuria, jaundice, black vomit and other hæmorrhages, and death. A number of laboratory infections have occurred, some fatal. Fatal epidemics may occur in wild South American monkeys, especially howlers (*Alouatta*).

Experimentally the infection was first transferred to Asiatic *Macaca* monkeys by Stokes, Bauer & Hudson (1928). In them the virus causes a fatal disease with hepatitis, though South American strains of virus tend to be less lethal. In most African primates it produces only viræmia with perhaps a little fever: one species of bush-baby, however, *Galago crassicaudatus*, is often killed. A number of South American monkeys including marmosets and howler monkeys may die after inoculation, though species of *Cebus* are more resistant (Davis, 1930).

The virus is fatal to hedgehogs (Findlay & Clarke, 1934). It has been adapted to cause encephalitis in mice by IC inoculation: a neurotropic variant thus derived causes encephalitis in rhesus monkeys. Infant but not adult mice can be infected IP. Guinea pigs infected IC develop encephalitis. "Fixed" neurotropic strains can be caused to revert to pan-tropism. Even 17D, which normally causes non-fatal encephalitis in rhesus, can have full neuro-virulence restored by repeated IC passage in mice.

Pathological lesions in yellow fever in man and rhesus monkeys include a fatty liver with mid-zonal necrosis, fatty degeneration in kidneys and multiple hæmorrhages. Necrotic hyaline cells in the liver are called Councilman bodies. Granular eosinophilic intra-nuclear inclusions, commonly surrounding nucleoli, may occur in human liver but are more regularly found in rhesus livers and in the brain and cord of mice (Cowdry & Kitchen, 1930). Use of the viscerotome to obtain samples of liver post-mortem is a valuable diagnostic measure. Histological changes in livers of Asiatic and African monkeys are described by Bearcroft (1960, 1962).

Ecology. Jungle yellow fever exists as an infection of wild primates in forests of Africa and South America. Many believe that yellow fever was originally an African disease introduced to America with the slave trade. In African forests the natural vector is probably *Aëdes africanus*, with *Aëdes simpsoni* acting as a link between monkeys in tree-tops and man in villages (Smithburn *et al.*, 1949). The ecology is not, however, wholly clear (Haddow, 1951). In South America *Hæmagogus* spp. are the main vectors in a sylvan cycle; men working in forests are only incidentally infected (Bugher *et al.*, 1944). Edentates, marsupials and rodents may also play a part as reservoirs. More important for man is urban yellow fever, with a cycle involving man and *Aëdes ægypti*, both in Africa and South

America. This has caused devastating epidemics. Some think that endemic prevalence of dengue and other B arboviruses may check the spread to Asia and elsewhere.

Control. Urban yellow fever is readily controlled by eliminating *Aëdes ægypti*, but jungle yellow fever cannot be easily dealt with. Yellow fever vaccines are very efficient and give immunity lasting for years. The 17D strain causes trivial reactions: vaccines are made from juice of chick embryos infected with tissue culture virus. It may be injected or given as a scratch vaccine, sometimes combined with vaccinia (Dick & Horgan, 1952). It may also be used after passage into mouse-brain, but not serially (Cannon & Dewhurst, 1955). The French neurotropic strain is considered as less safe; cases of encephalitis in man have followed its use (Stones & Mac-namara, 1955).

Turkey Meningo-encephalitis

Description: Komarov & Kalmar (1960).

Antigenic properties. Related to B arboviruses by the HAI test but distinct by the plaque inhibition test (Porterfield, 1961b).

Cultivation. Lethal for embryonated eggs, being best given into the yolk-sac. Produced plaques on chick embryo monolayers.

Habitat. Israel.

Pathogenicity. Caused progressive and fatal paralysis and enteritis in turkeys. There was 50 per cent. morbidity in the Israel outbreak; chicks and other birds were resistant. Adult mice developed encephalitis when inoculated IC and sucklings after injection IC or IM.

Ecology. Epidemiological evidence suggested mosquito transmission.

Control. Virus attenuated by passage in eggs could be used for immunising turkeys.

Wesselsbron Disease

Description: Weiss *et al.* (1956).
Review: Weiss (1957b).

Morphology. About 30 mμ in diameter (Polson, quoted by Weiss *et al.*, 1956).

Antigenic properties are those of a B arbovirus, but the virus is not particularly closely related to any other.

Cultivation. Readily passed in series in 8-day *fertile eggs* inoculated into the yolk sac, most virus being in the body of the embryo. Mortality low and irregular. Grows also in *tissue cultures* of lamb kidney.

Distribution. South Africa, Rhodesia, Mozambique.

Pathogenicity. Causes epizootics in sheep, particularly giving rise to abortions and to deaths of new-born lambs and pregnant ewes. Hæmorrhages and jaundice occur, and meningo-encephalitis in fœtuses. Probably causes abortions in cattle also. May infect man, giving rise to fever and muscular pains: has caused numerous laboratory infections.

Experimentally it causes abortions in ewes, and may kill lambs, the incubation period being 2 to 4 days. It causes fever in cattle, sheep and pigs. Infects suckling mice IC or IP, producing fatal encephalitis. Adult mice are only infected IC. Abortions are produced in pregnant rabbits and guinea pigs.

Pathological lesions are found mainly in the liver. There is necrobiosis of scattered hepatic cells with fatty infiltration, but lesions are variable (Le Roux, 1959).

Ecology. Transmission is by mosquito-bite, the two important vectors being *Aëdes caballus* and *circumluteolus* (Kokernot *et al.*, 1960). In endemic areas, antibodies are present in sera of human beings and various domestic quadrupeds.

DENGUE

Synonyms: Breakbone fever. Dandy fever.
Review: Sabin (1959a).

There are four serotypes. Nearly all the data concern Types 1 and 2 which have been studied much longer than Types 3 and 4.

Morphology. Diameter 17–25 mμ by filtration; 20 mμ by electron microscopy of partly purified virus (Hotta, 1953). The nature of elongated particles seen in some preparations is obscure. Virus is apparently located in cytoplasm of cells.

Chemical composition. An "infectious RNA" has been extracted by Ada & Anderson (1959) and Nakamura (1961).

Physico-chemical characters. Partly purified virus was inactivated by heating to 54° for 10' (Hotta, 1953). 0·05 per cent. formalin inactivates it. Other properties are as for other B arboviruses.

Hæmagglutination. Hæmagglutins for cells of newly-hatched chicks have been studied by Sweet & Sabin (1954); these were unstable except at pH 7–7·9. The optimum temperature and pH for hæmagglutination varied according to strain and passage level in mice.

Antigenic properties. The four serotypes are readily distinguished by neutralization and CF tests. They are related by HAI tests rather more closely amongst themselves than to other B arboviruses. Neutralization is considerably more effective if fresh unheated serum is added to the mixture of virus and specific antibody (Sabin, 1959a). For a time after recovery from an infection with one serotype, people may suffer from only a modified attack if infected with a second serotype. Some Type 1 and 2 strains from South-East Asia may have to be classified as distinct serotypes (Hammon *et al.*, in Symposium, 1962).

Interference. It has been suggested that the lack of geographical overlap between dengue and yellow fever (*q.v.*, p. 75) may be due to some form of interference. Such an interference is demonstrable to a limited extent in the laboratory (Sabin, 1952).

Cultivation. Type 1 virus has been adapted to grow in *fertile eggs* after previous adaptation to mice, but high titres were not obtained (Schlesinger, 1951).

Growth in *tissue culture* is reported for Types 1 and 2 in monkey kidney, hamster kidney, chick embryo and other tissues (Hotta, 1957; Hotta *et al.*, 1961), but again only after previous mouse-adaptation. With Types 3 and 4 cytopathic effects have been less readily measured. All four types produced good CPE in HeLa cells which had been fed with tryptose phosphate broth (Buckley, 1961).

Distribution. *Type 1*: Hawaii, South-East Asia from India to Japan. Temporary spread has occurred to Greece, South Africa and Australia.

Type 2: New Guinea, Thailand, Trinidad. Probably elsewhere in South-East Asia, Central America and Caribbean.

Type 3: Thailand, Philippines (Hammon *et al.*, 1960).

Type 4: Thailand, Philippines (Hammon *et al.*, 1960).

Some, at least, of the "dengue" in tropical Africa may be due to Chikungunya (p. 61) or other arboviruses.

Pathogenicity. Dengue in man is an acute fever, often lasting 5 or 6 days, with severe aches in head, back and limbs and often a scarlatiniform or maculo-papular rash. Mild or inapparent infections occur. Dengue viruses have also been recovered from hæmorrhagic fever in the Philippines and Thailand (Hammon *et al.*, 1959) but their relation to the infection is uncertain, as other arboviruses have been isolated also. This infection, in contrast to typical dengue, carries a considerable mortality (*v.* p. 95).

Experimentally volunteers have been infected by various routes. The incubation period is usually 5–8 days.

Types 1 and 2 have been adapted to mice by IC inoculation, sucklings being most susceptible; but adaptation has usually been difficult (Hotta, 1952; Sabin, 1959a). The most prominent symptom is flaccid paralysis of limbs. Chimpanzees and monkeys of several Asiatic, African or South American species normally undergo only inapparent infections; but mouse-adapted virus may produce paralytic disease in rhesus and cynomolgus (Sabin, 1955). Newborn hamsters are susceptible (Meiklejohn *et al.*, 1952). Other animal species in the laboratory have proved resistant.

Pathological lesions: In the rare fatal cases in man degenerative changes and hæmorrhages have been found in various organs.

Ecology. Infection is transmitted mainly by *Aëdes ægypti*, which has domestic habits; but *A. albopictus* apparently acts as a sylvan vector. Other species may be concerned at times. There is likely to be a reservoir amongst monkeys or other jungle animals in Malaya and elsewhere in Asia (Gordon Smith, 1956), but probably not in America (Rosen, 1958).

Control. Where *Aëdes ægypti* is the only vector, measures directed against this species should control dengue.

Types 1 and 2 have been attenuated by serial mouse-passage so that they can be used as living vaccines for protection of man. Rashes may result but no unpleasant symptoms (Sabin & Schlesinger, 1945; Sabin, 1955).

TICK-BORNE ENCEPHALITIS COMPLEX

There exists a family of tick-borne B arboviruses so closely inter-related antigenically that earlier work failed to differentiate sharply between them. Clarke (1962) using the tests of HAI, agar-gel precipitation and antibody absorption has now shown that they may be divided into six entities having discontinuous distributions:

(*a*) Louping ill (British Isles) (L.I.).

(*b*) Central European tick-borne (Central Europe, Scandinavia, Western U.S.S.R.) (C.E.T.).

(*c*) Omsk hæmorrhagic fever (Central U.S.S.R.) (O.H.F.).

(*d*) Kyasanur forest disease (India) (K.F.D.).

(*e*) Far Eastern Russian (Eastern U.S.S.R.) (F.E.R.).

(*f*) Langat (Malaya).

There are also related viruses; Powassan from North America and Negishi from Japan.

This account will deal first in a general section with properties known or likely to be common to the group and then with the separate viruses. The particular virus dealt with in the general section will be indicated by bracketed initials.

Reviews: Smorodintseff (1958).
Libikova (1962).

Morphology. Round bodies 25 mμ across with a central dense nucleoid. Some of the bodies were contained in vesicles up to 80 mμ across, in the cytoplasm, especially near the nucleus (C.E.T.) (Kovac *et al.*, 1961). Other reports give figures for diameters ranging from 15–45 mμ.

Chemical composition. An infectious RNA has been reported by Sokol *et al.* (1959).

Physico-chemical characters. Inactivated in 15' at 55° in saline, in 20' at 55° in 10 per cent. rabbit serum but survived in milk until heated 20' at 65° (C.E.T.) (Grešiková-Kohútová, 1959b). The optimal pH for survival was 7·6–8·2 but the virus survived throughout a wide range at 4° (Grešiková-Kohútová, 1959a). Silber & Soloviev (1946) quote figures for inactivation by various chemicals (F.E.R.).

Hæmagglutination—as for other B arboviruses. Adsorption and elution from rooster RBC's were studied by Salminen (1960) (C.E.T.). He obtained satisfactory results with cells from cocks but not hens (except as young chicks) (Salminen, 1959) (C.E.T.).

Antigenic properties. Crossing with other B arboviruses is seen in HAI tests, but the members of the complex are much more closely related to each other than to other B's. Their relations, as stated above, have been clarified by Clarke (1962) using agar-gel precipitation and antibody-absorption tests. CF tests may fail to separate members of the complex, and other tests, apart from those of Clarke, yield confusing results. Immunity tests may fail to show protection against other members of the complex.

Cultivation. The viruses grow in *fertile eggs* whether inoculated on the CAM, where discrete pocks appear (L.I.) (Burnet, 1936a) or into the yolk-sac or embryo (L.I.) (Edward, 1947).
   Growth also occurs in tissue cultures of mouse embryonic tissue (F.E.R.) (Takemori, 1949) and in HeLa and other continuous cell lines of primate origin (C.E.T.) (von Zeipel & Svedmyr, 1958; Libikova & Vilček, 1960), pig kidney (L.I.) (Williams, 1958), bovine, sheep, chick and other tissues. Cytopathic effects are not invariably seen, but were satisfactory in Libikova & Vilček's (1960) HeLa cells and in sheep embryo cultures (Gaidomovich & Obukhova, 1960).

Pathogenicity. All these viruses readily produce encephalitis when inoculated IC into mice, except for Omsk hæmorrhagic fever. Most of them are also pathogenic on IC inoculation into rhesus or cynomolgus monkeys: also (Silber & Soloviev, 1946) for sheep.

Ecology. The viruses are normally transmitted by ticks, and it is likely that there is a permanent reservoir in ticks; mammals and birds are only irregularly found infected in nature. There is evidence that transovarial transmission occurs in ticks (Silber & Soloviev, 1946) and virus may survive in hibernating ticks.

Louping-Ill

Synonym: Ovine encephalomyelitis.
Virus characters: as for others of the complex.

Distribution. Scotland, Ireland, N. and S.W. England.

Pathogenicity. Normally a disease of sheep, less often cattle. The disease has two phases, the first characterised by high fever and viræmia, the second, several days later, by inco-ordination, followed by paralysis and often death; the second phase may be absent; and probably the disease is normally almost inapparent. A few cases are reported in man having contact with sheep, larger numbers in laboratory workers (Rivers & Schwentker, 1934): these have suffered from serous meningitis with some evidence of encephalitis, but the disease has been much less serious than with the Russian viruses. Rodents and deer may be naturally infected, but so far as is known without symptoms.

Experimentally mice develop encephalitis after IC inoculation but much less readily when infected IP, IN or SC—at least in adult mice (Edward, 1950). Many other species can be infected IC but not guinea pigs or rabbits. Rats inoculated IN develop an inapparent infection (Burnet, 1936b).

Pathological lesions: destruction of Purkinje cells is a feature in fatal cases in sheep. Hurst (1931) found cytoplasmic inclusions in brain cells of mice but not of other species.

Ecology. *Ixodes ricinus* is the vector and may also act as the reservoir of infection. Concurrent infection with the rickettsiæ of tick-borne fever may favour invasion of the nervous system in sheep (Macleod, 1962).

Control. Formalinized vaccines made from sheep brain, mouse brain or chick-embryo have been used to protect sheep, cattle and exposed laboratory workers. The egg vaccines were not satisfactory (Edward, 1947, 1948).

Central European Tick-borne Fever

Synonyms: Russian spring-summer encephalitis (Western form), biundulant meningo-encephalitis, diphasic milk fever.

Virus characters: as for others of the complex.

Distribution. Central Europe from Scandinavia to the Balkans and from Germany to Western U.S.S.R.

Pathogenicity. The disease in man is biphasic. An afebrile period of 4 to 10 days intervenes between the first influenza-like fever and the second phase of meningitis or meningo-encephalitis. Mild or inapparent forms occur. In severe forms there is transient or permanent paralysis and the bulbo-spinal form is usually fatal. In severity the disease is intermediate between louping-ill and the Far East form. Virus may be present in the milk of infected goats and may thus infect man (van Tongeren, 1955–6).

Experimentally the virus behaves like louping-ill but peripheral inoculation into mice is more regularly fatal. Guinea pigs react with fever, rarely encephalitis. Young chicks may be infected IC; also lizards. Virus may localize in the mammary glands of infected goats, cows, sheep, and also mice, and appear in the milk. It may appear in the urine.

Pathological lesions are found in all parts of the CNS, the cervical cord being often affected (Grinschgl, 1955).

Ecology. The vector is *Ixodes ricinus* and this is likely to be also an important reservoir. Transmission through milk of goats has already been mentioned, but this is unlikely to be significant in a long-term view of the ecology. Virus has been recovered from *Aëdes* mosquitoes, though these are not considered important.

Control. Protection of exposed persons against ticks is the first line of defence. Formalinized vaccine has been widely used in the U.S.S.R. (Smorodintseff *et al.*, 1940). It has been made from mouse or suckling rat brains or from tissue cultures of chick embryo or cynomolgus heart (Levkovich, 1962). There is also work in progress on use of living attenuated virus for vaccination especially of cattle, sheep and goats (Blaškovič *et al.*, 1962).

Far East Russian Encephalitis

Synonym: Russian spring-summer encephalitis (Eastern form).
Review: Silber & Soloviev (1946).
Virus characters: as for others of the complex.

Distribution. Eastern U.S.S.R. (but two viruses isolated from *Ixodes ricinus* near Leningrad seem to belong in this group, D. H. Clarke, personal communication, 1963.)

Pathogenicity. This is the most serious form of the disease for man. Flaccid paralysis followed by atrophy is common; so are symptoms due to bulbar involvement. Mortality has been around 30 per cent.
Experimentally the virus causes encephalitis in laboratory mice inoculated by various routes, also fever in guinea pigs. Inoculated IC it produces encephalitis in rhesus monkeys, sheep, goats and some wild rodents but not in others; also in some finches (Silber & Soloviev, 1946).
Pathological lesions resemble those of related viruses, but, in contrast to louping ill, Purkinje cells are not particularly attacked.

Ecology. The vector is *Ixodes persulcatus* which replaces *I. ricinus* in the East, though their ranges overlap.

Control. As for the Central European virus.

Omsk Hæmorrhagic Fever

Review: Gajdusek (1956).

Distribution. Central U.S.S.R.

Pathogenicity. Commonly a diphasic illness in man with fever, enlargement of lymph nodes, gastro-intestinal symptoms and hæmorrhages from nose, stomach or uterus, but little or no CNS involvement. Mortality is 1–2 per cent.
Experimentally the virus causes fever after IP inoculation of rhesus monkeys. It does not, on first isolation, infect mice, but sucklings may not have been used.

Ecology. The vectors are *Dermacentor pictus* and *D. marginatus*. Transovarial transmission is recorded for these ticks.

Kyasanur Forest Disease

Review: Work (1958).

Distribution. Kyasanur forest, Mysore and possibly elsewhere in India.

Pathogenicity. Unknown until 1955; in 1957 an extensive epidemic occurred, chiefly amongst forest workers; numerous dead langurs (*Presbytis entellus*) and bonnet macacques (*Macaca radiata*) were picked up in the forests. Symptoms in man include headache, fever, back and limb pains and prostration, conjunctival inflammation, diarrhœa, vomiting and often bleeding from intestines and elsewhere. Symptoms due to CNS involvement are lacking. Leucopenia and albuminuria are found. Death may follow especially if the dehydration is not treated. A number of laboratory infections have occurred.

Experimentally mice develop encephalitis after inoculation by various routes. Adults are less susceptible to peripheral inoculation. Suckling hamsters are susceptible but other rodents were resistant. Rhesus and bonnet monkeys, injected IC, IP or SC, developed viræmia without symptoms.

Pathological lesions were similar in man and monkeys. Hæmorrhages were found in lungs or elsewhere, their histopathological basis being uncertain. There were tubular necrosis in kidneys, focal necroses in liver, more so in the monkeys, and also focal necroses in some monkey brains.

Ecology. The vector appears to be a tick, *Hæmaphysalis spinigera*, possibly also other *Hæmaphysalis* species. The disease may be spread by movements of monkeys, many of which probably have mild infections, and by birds. Antibodies have been found in small forest mammals—a squirrel, a shrew and some forest rats: also in jungle fowl and a woodpecker. It is possible that the disease was introduced through the agency of birds.

Negishi Virus

A virus of the tick-borne encephalitis complex has been isolated from two fatal cases in Japan and appears to be a new member (Okuno *et al.*, 1961).

Langat Virus

Another new member of the complex was isolated from a pool of *Ixodes granulatus* in Malaya by Gordon Smith (1956). This (strain TP21) was pathogenic for mice, and agglutinated cells of newly hatched chicks at a pH optimum of 6·8. Antibodies were found in sera of 6/51 forest ground-rats. Its low pathogenicity has suggested its possible use as a live vaccine for protection against other members of the complex.

Powassan Virus

This virus was isolated from the brain of a boy with fatal encephalitis in Ontario (McLean & Donohue, 1959). It infected newborn but not weaned mice, formed a hæmagglutinin and showed a serological relation to members of the tick-borne encephalitis group. It was, however, less closely related to the European and Asian strains than these are to each other (Casals, 1960). Antibodies were found in sera of squirrels and chipmunks caught locally (McLean & Larke, 1963). A closely related virus has been obtained from *Dermacentor andersoni* in Colorado (Thomas *et al.*, 1960).

B-arboviruses with no known Arthropod Vector

The *Modoc* virus was recovered from mammary glands of a mouse (*Peromyscus manicatus*) in California. It showed some antigenic relation to Rio bravo virus in cross-immunity tests (Casals, 1960).

Rio bravo (bat salivary) virus (Burns & Farinacci, 1956) from the salivary glands of a bat (*Tadarida brasiliensis*) caught in California is identical with others from Texas and Mexico. Related to Modoc virus.

Entebbe bat virus was obtained from salivary glands from a pool of bats (*Tadarida*) in Uganda (Lumsden *et al.*, 1961).

These three viruses behave in general like B-arboviruses, but the Rio bravo virus did not multiply in several mosquito species and when inoculated into mice peripherally showed tropism for kidneys, mammary and salivary glands. It was also responsible for 5 laboratory infections, 2 of them with orchitis (Sulkin *et al.*, 1962).

Lagos Bat Virus

Best mentioned here though not proved to be an arbovirus is the *Lagos bat virus* (Boulger & Porterfield, 1958) obtained from the brains of a pool of six forest bats (*Eidolon*) in Lagos. It was transmissible to mice by IC inoculation, not to rabbits or guinea pigs. It passed a 0·66 μ gradocol membrane and was ether-sensitive. No agglutinin for goose and day-old chick cells was obtained. No relation to known arboviruses was discovered.

Information about other B-arboviruses is summarised in Table 4.

GROUP C ARBOVIRUSES

Six viruses isolated in Belem, Brazil (Causey *et al.*, 1961) have been placed in a separate serological group by Casals & Whitman (1961). They have been recovered from sentinel mice or monkeys, from mosquitoes or from man. They form hæmagglutinins for goose cells, working best at pH 6·2 to 7. They produce encephalitis in suckling mice, some of them also in older mice, but not all colonies of mice are susceptible. At least two of them (Caraparu & Oriboca) produce plaques on monkey kidney monolayers. Infected persons have fever, headache and malaise. Antibodies are present in a proportion of people and forest mammals in the Amazon valley: and antibodies against Oriboca virus have been found in West and South Africa. The six Brazilian strains are inter-related as shown in the table.

Related by CF   *Related by HAI and*
                              Oriboca⎤   *neutralization*
                             ⎰Itaqui ⎰
                             ⎱Caraparu⎱
                             ⎰Apeu   ⎰
                             ⎱Marituba⎱
                             ⎰Murutucu⎰
                             ⎱with Oriboca   (Shope & Causey, 1962).

A seventh C arbovirus has been isolated in Trinidad and strains closely related to Caraparu have been found there and in French Guiana.

MISCELLANEOUS ARBOVIRUSES

A report by W.H.O. (1961) lists 37 other arboviruses, not considered elsewhere in this book. They fall antigenically into small groups of species or stand alone. Only brief mention is required and will be largely confined to those listed in the W.H.O. report.

TABLE 4
MISCELLANEOUS B ARBOVIRUSES

Virus	UGANDA S (= MAKONDE)	ZIKA	SPONDWENI	NTAYA	BUSSUQUARA	KUNJIN	KOKOBERA	EDGEHILL	STRATFORD
Where isolated	Uganda Possibly S.E. Asia	Uganda Tanganyika Possibly S.E. Asia	S. Africa Nigeria	Uganda	Brazil Colombia	Queensland	Queensland	Queensland	Queensland
From what species	Aëdes spp. (pool)	Aëdes africanus Sentinel rhesus	Culicine mosquitoes of 3 genera	Mosquitoes (mixed lot)	Sentinel howler monkey	Mosquitoes	Mosquitoes	Mosquitoes	Mosquitoes
Association with disease	None	None Nigerian "Zika" viruses are Spondweni	Probably hepatitis in Nigeria. Fever (lab. infection)	None	Hepatitis in howler monkey (Alouatta)				
Properties of virus	2 estimates of size 15–22 mμ 75–112 mμ (less probable)	18–26 mμ	—	81–122 mμ					
Related B arboviruses (HAI)	Zika Yellow Fever	Uganda S Yellow Fever	—			Murray Valley Kokobera	Murray Valley Kunjin	Murray Valley	
Pathogenicity for animals other than mice	Nil in monkeys	Fever in rhesus Nil in rabbits and various rodents	—	Nil in rhesus or hamster					
Growth in eggs	Easily propagated	Propagated	—						
Growth in tissue culture	Hamster kidney		—						
Antibodies found naturally	Man Cercopithecus	Man Cercopithecus	Man Possibly sheep and cattle						
References	Dick & Haddow (1952) Ross (1956)	Dick et al. (1952)	Kokernot et al. (1957b) Macnamara (1954)	Smithburn & Haddow (1951)	Gomes & Causey (1959)	Doherty et al. 1963			

Bunyamwera group (Casals & Whitman, 1960). Eight members are included, coming from North and South America, Africa, Europe and Asia (Bunyamwera, Cache Valley, Calovo, Chittoor, Germiston, Ilesha, Kairi and Wyeomyia). Of these Bunyamwera (S and E. Africa), Ilesha (Nigeria) and Germiston (S. Africa) have caused fevers in man. The Guaroa virus (S. America) is related to this group by CF but to the next group in HAI tests (Whitman and Shope, 1962). Several others have been added to the group recently.

The *Californian encephalitis* group contains 5 members: California and Trivittatus (N. America), Melao (Trinidad), Lumbo (Mozambique) and Tahyňa (Czechoslovakia). Only Tahyňa is known to cause fever in man.

Guama group (Whitman & Casals, 1961) has 3 members: Guama and Catu from Brazil, Bimiti from Trinidad. The first two were associated with fever in man. Four others have been added lately.

Simbu group contains Simbu (S. Africa), Sathuperi (India) and Oropouche (Brazil), the last one causing fever in man.

A group of three from Trinidad—no human disease.

Others are: Bwamba, from cases of fever in Uganda, related to Pongola from S. Africa. Available evidence suggests that it is larger (75–113 mμ) than other arboviruses (Smithburn *et al.*, 1941).

Turlock (California) related to Umbre (India).

Anophlees *A* (Colombia) related to Lukuni (Trinidad).

Quaranfil (Egypt) related to Chenuda and another, unnamed, virus from Egypt.

Other, singleton, viruses are Hart Park (California), Manzanilla (Trinidad), Tacaiuma (Brazil) and Witwatersrand (S. Africa). References concerning those mentioned above which are known to be human pathogens will be found in the W.H.O. report (1961).

W.H.O. arbovirus reference laboratories are aware of the existence of at least 40 other viruses mostly undescribed and many only known as yet by a number. Evidence that they properly belong in the arboviruses is for a number of them incomplete. It seems that altogether at least 150 arboviruses are known.

Phlebotomus Fever

Synonyms: Sandfly fever. Pappataci fever.
Reviews: Sabin (1951, 1959b).

Morphology. Diameter estimated at 17–25 mμ by filtration. In the light of recent interpretation of results of filtration, this estimated size is probably too low.

Physico-chemical characters. Survives storage in solid CO_2, or when lyophilized, for 8 or 9 years.

Hæmagglutination. A hæmagglutinin for chick cells was demonstrable when an alcohol-soluble inhibitor was first removed. Hæmagglutination was optimal at 37° and between pH 5·5 and 6·5. The hæmagglutinin, unlike those of B arboviruses was inactivated by merthiolate.

Antigenic properties. The two known viruses, the Sicilian and Naples strains, are antigenically distinct from other arboviruses and from each other. Convalescent persons develop antibodies which are of low titre or not demonstrable at all.

Cultivation. Reports of cultivation in *fertile eggs* are unconfirmed. Grows in tissue cultures of human, rhesus, mouse or hamster kidney. CPE may be seen in human cells only after adaptation. Virus growth is more readily demonstrated by plaque production (Henderson & Taylor, 1960; S. M. Buckley, personal communication, 1963).

Distribution. Middle East and Italy. The Sicilian virus occurs also in Yugoslavia, U.S.S.R. and India.

Pathogenicity. The viruses cause in man a short sharp fever, occasionally recurrent, with pains in the eyes, head, back and limbs and gastro-intestinal disturbances. There is leucopenia. Only man is known to be naturally affected.

Experimentally volunteers have been infected (Sabin, 1951), most readily by IV or intradermal injection. The normal incubation period of 3 or 4 days may be as short as 42 hours after IV inoculation. The viruses have been adapted to cause encephalitis in suckling mice inoculated IC; after numerous passages weaned mice also have been infected. Fully adapted Naples virus would also infect mice inoculated intranasally and produced fever after IC inoculation into rhesus monkeys. Mouse-adapted viruses inoculated intradermally into man produced immunity but no symptoms.

Pathological lesions in mice are like those caused by other arboviruses.

Ecology. The vector is *Phlebotomus papatasi*, often called sand-fly. There is an extrinsic incubation period in the fly of 7–10 days. There is conflict of evidence as to the possibility of transovarial transmission.

Control. The *Phlebotomus* because of their indoor biting habits are very easily controlled by D.D.T. Use of attenuated viruses for vaccination, though theoretically possible, has not been extensively adapted, except for a time in the U.S.S.R.

Colorado Tick Fever

Review: Cox (1959).

Morphology. Diameter 35–50 mμ (Koprowski & Cox, 1947).

Physico-chemical characters. Very stable in serum, surviving $3\frac{1}{2}$ years in an ordinary refrigerator and even at room temperature, but not always so stable at lower temperatures (Pickens & Luoto, 1958). Inactivated in 30′ at 60°.

Hæmagglutination of cells of day-old chicks is reported.

Antigenic properties. Distinct by neutralization, CF and other tests from other arboviruses including the other tick-borne ones. Antibodies develop slowly in convalescents but both neutralizing and CF antibodies persist for long periods.

Cultivation. Grows in fertile eggs when inoculated into the yolk-sac; virus reaches highest titre in the embryo's CNS in 4–5 days. In tissue cultures of human carcinoma KB cells it grows and produces CPE. No changes were seen in monkey kidney cells (Pickens & Luoto, 1958).

Distribution. North-Western states of the United States, but not reaching the Pacific coast.

Pathogenicity. Affected persons, 4–5 days after a bite by an infected tick, develop fever, usually of saddle-back type, with chills, aches in head and limbs and often vomiting. Rashes are absent. There is leucopenia. Encephalitis may occur, especially in children. Virus has been recovered from several species of wild rodent, most frequently from ground-squirrels: the disease in them is inapparent.

Experimentally hamsters can be infected IP and after adaptation the virus often kills them (Florio *et al.*, 1944). Rhesus monkeys develop viræmia. The virus has also been adapted to mice IC and up to 8 days of age they can also be infected IP. Other species are resistant.

Pathological lesions. Hamsters show changes mainly in the spleen, the follicles being full of large pale-staining mononuclear cells (Black *et al.*, 1947). Mice show destruction of Purkinje cells (Miller *et al.*, 1961). Cytoplasmic inclusions occur both in mice and hamsters. Suckling mice show also myocardial necrosis (Hadlow, 1957), and specific antigen is revealed with the aid of fluorescent antibody in the cytoplasm of myocardial and brain cells (Burgdorfer & Lackman, 1960).

Ecology. Infection is transmitted by the tick *Dermacentor andersoni* and the distribution of the disease and of the tick practically coincide. Ticks once infected retain the infection. It has been maintained that there is transovarial transmission (Florio *et al.*, 1950) but Eklund quoted by Cox (1959) doubts this. Possibly the cycle is maintained by a cycle between immature ticks and small rodents (Burgdorfer & Eklund, 1959).

Control depends largely on protection against ticks. Koprowski *et al.* (1950) used a living chick-embryo-adapted virus as a vaccine but the virus was not satisfactorily attenuated.

Rift Valley Fever

Original description: Daubney *et al.* (1931).

Review: Weiss (1957a).

Morphology. Diameter 23–35 mμ by filtration. By centrifugation the diameter was estimated at 50 mμ with smaller particles 30 mμ across present also in egg-passaged virus (Naudé *et al.*, 1954). Levitt *et al.* (1963) describe spheres 60–75 mμ across, their surfaces covered with hollow cylinders looking like short spikes.

Physico-chemical characters. 40′ at 56° inactivates. Survives well when frozen or lyophilized and in some circumstances is much more stable than other arboviruses. There is evidence (Francis & Magill, 1935) that infective virus persisted in a room for 3 months. It survived 1048 days in serum kept at −4° (Smithburn *et al.*, 1949): it also withstood 0·5 per cent. phenol for 6 months in the cold. 1 : 1000 formalin inactivated it. Density 1·23 (Levitt *et al.*, 1963).

Hæmagglutination. A hæmagglutinin for cells of day-old chicks worked best at pH 6·5 and 25°. An inhibitor present in normal mouse serum disappeared on storage in the cold. Natural hæmagglutinin was more potent than an acetone–ether extracted one and also agglutinated mouse, guinea pig and human group A cells (Mims & Mason, 1956).

Antigenic properties. Distinct from other arboviruses in all immunological tests. A CF antigen made from livers of infected mice is useful for diagnosis. The agar-gel-diffusion test is also applicable, as well as conventional neutralization and HAI tests. An atypical strain (Lunyo) is described by Weinbren *et al.* (1957).

Interference with yellow fever has already been mentioned (p. 73). UV inactivated virus acts as an interfering agent and neurotropic virus interferes with pantropic (Naudé & Polson, 1957). Greater activity of dilute as compared with concentrated virus has been noted by several workers and is attributed by Mims (1956) to presence of incomplete virus.

Cultivation. The virus produces thickening on inoculation on to the CAM of *fertile eggs* (Saddington, 1934) and grows also when inoculated into the yolk-sac. It grows in *tissue cultures* of chick, rat, mouse, human and other cells (Takemori *et al.*, 1955). Weiss (1956) found lamb kidney cells very suitable.

Distribution. Occurs naturally only in Africa—Kenya, Uganda, S. Africa and probably elsewhere in Central and Southern Africa.

Pathogenicity. A disease of sheep, goats and cattle causing abortions and many deaths in pregnant and newborn animals. An epizootic in South Africa in 1951 killed about 100,000 lambs. Lambs show fever, vomiting, mucopurulent nasal discharge and bloody diarrhœa. Cattle are less seriously affected. Many infections have occurred in man during these epizootics, especially in herdsmen and veterinary officers. In man it resembles dengue and is probably biphasic. It is ordinarily mild but cases of retinal damage have occurred in South Africa. The disease is very apt to spread to laboratory workers though people working with neurotropic virus often have mild or inapparent infections.

It may affect buffalo and camels; and antelopes in the field were reported to have died or aborted (Gear *et al.*, 1955).

Experimentally lambs are very susceptible and may die as early as 36 hours after infection. Mice, weaned or sucklings, can be infected by various routes. They ordinarily die with hepatitis within 3 days. A neurotropic strain was obtained by IC passage in mice (McKenzie & Findlay, 1936; Smithburn, 1949). This, given SC, can be used for immunising mice and sheep (see below), as it has largely lost its viscerotropic properties. Inoculated monkeys have a mild fever, African species being less susceptible than rhesus. The neurotropic virus, however, may kill rhesus when injected IC (Findlay *et al.*, 1936). Rats and other laboratory rodents, but not rabbits, are susceptible, and may die. Infected guinea pigs may abort. Ferrets infected IN (Francis & Magill, 1935) showed fever and lung consolidation. Birds are resistant.

Pathological lesions caused by pantropic virus are chiefly those of massive hepatitis in lambs and focal hepatitis in older sheep. Eosinophilic bodies resemble the Councilman bodies of yellow fever and there are intranuclear inclusions in livers. These are more homogeneous and more closely resemble Cowdry's Type A inclusions than do those of yellow fever. Blood-lakes are found in the liver. There is often damage to kidneys and there may be hæmorrhages in intestines and elsewhere. Lesions in other species are similar (Daubney *et al.*, 1931; Findlay, 1931).

Ecology. Infection is mosquito-borne. The most important vectors seem to be *Eratmopodites chrysogaster* in Uganda and *Aëdes caballus* in S. Africa. Contact infection probably occurs also: and infection of laboratory workers has presumably been by the respiratory route. There is probably a reservoir in some wild African animals, other than primates. Weinbren suggests that a forest rat, *Arvicanthis*, fulfils the requirements in Uganda, as virus circulates plentifully in it during an inapparent infection (Weinbren & Mason, 1957).

Control. Control involves protection of flocks from mosquitoes. Live neurotropic virus has been used on a large scale to immunize sheep: it is not safe to give it during pregnancy (Weiss, 1957a).

Nairobi Sheep Disease

Synonym: Kisenyi sheep disease from the Congo (Bugyaki, 1955) is probably the same.

Description: Montgomery (1917). Daubney & Hudson (1931).

Morphology. The virus passes a Berkefeld N filter.

Physico-chemical characters. Survives well when lyophilized.

Antigenic properties. Distinct from other arboviruses in neutralization tests. A report of crossing with B-arboviruses has not been confirmed.

Cultivation. No definite growth in fertile eggs. Attempted tissue culture not reported.

Distribution. Kenya and Uganda: probably also Congo and parts of South-East Africa.

Pathogenicity. A hæmorrhagic gastro-enteritis affecting sheep and goats with high fever and a mortality of 30–70 per cent. In the disease seen in Kenya splenic enlargement and involvement of the female genital tract were noted (Daubney & Hudson, 1931). These were not seen in an outbreak in Uganda by Weinbren *et al.* (1958a), who frequently encountered cardiac damage and pulmonary œdema. Virus is most abundantly present in spleen and liver. Goats may undergo subclinical infection.

Experimentally the disease is transmissible to sheep with blood or serum. It produces encephalitis in mice inoculated IC, and sucklings can also be infected IP. They die with characteristic tonic spasms. After 110 passages in adult mice the virus was attenuated for sheep, which had symptomless viræmia (Ansell, 1957; Weinbren *et al.*, 1958a).

Ecology. Transmitted by ticks, *Rhipicephalus appendiculatus*. There may well be a reservoir in a wild animal: Daubney & Hudson (1934) suggest that a rodent, *Arvicanthis*, may serve as such.

Control. Virus attenuated by mouse-passage is under trial as a vaccine.

HÆMORRHAGIC FEVERS

Review: Gajdusek (1956).

A number of serious illnesses accompanied by hæmorrhage are known or suspected to be arthropod-borne. In all there is a sudden onset with fever, often diphasic, purpuric rashes and hæmorrhages into lungs, gastro-intestinal tract, kidneys and elsewhere. There is considerable mortality. The following appear to be separate entities.

Crimean Hæmorrhagic Fever

Occurs in Bulgaria, the Crimea, Astrakhan and elsewhere in Central U.S.S.R. It has been experimentally transmitted to psychiatric patients, using virus from blood of acutely ill persons. Laboratory animals seem to be insusceptible, with the possible exception of rhesus monkeys. Complement-fixation tests have shown that it is distinct from the Omsk hæmorrhagic fever. It is transmitted by ticks of the genus *Hyalomma* (Chumakov, 1957).

Omsk hæmorrhagic fever is due to a virus related to tick-borne encephalitis and is considered on p. 83.

Hæmorrhagic Fevers of Thailand and Philippines

From these fevers Dengue viruses 2, 3 and 4 (p. 75) and also Chikungunya (p. 61) viruses have been isolated. Their causative role is in some doubt since some cases of the disease have yielded one or other of these four different viruses, while from others there is no direct evidence of participation of any known virus (Hammon *et al.*, 1960; Symposium, 1962). Similar findings are reported from Singapore by Lim *et al.* (1961).

Argentinian Hæmorrhagic Fever

A virus, now called Junin, has been isolated from this infection (Pirosky *et al.*, 1959; Mettler *et al.*, 1961). It has the properties of an arbovirus but is serologically distinct from others tested. A hæmagglutinin is active against RBC's of day-old chicks, man, dog, frog, mouse, rats, guinea pig and pigeon, between pH 6·5 and 8·5 and 37° to 0°. It causes encephalitis in suckling mice when inoculated IC or IP; also after IC injection into suckling guinea pigs (Mettler *et al.*, 1963). It produces pocks on the chorioallantoic membranes of fertile eggs and CPE in HeLa cells. It is believed to be transmitted by the mite *Echinolælaps echidninus*, which infests *Mus musculus*, *Hesperomys* and other small rodents.

Epidemic Hæmorrhagic Fever (Manchuria, Eastern Siberia and Korea)

Synonym: Hæmorrhagic nephroso-nephritis.
Reviews: Smadel (1959). Gajdusek (1956).

In this disease, which was a serious problem during the Korean war, there is particularly severe damage to kidneys and many died with shock or oliguria. Attempted transmission to experimental animals has been unsuccessful; so have attempts at growing in tissue-culture (Gey, 1954): this despite intensive work. The pathological lesions in man include retroperitoneal œdema and intense congestion of kidneys. Oliver & Macdowell (1957) have described the histopathology. The agent has been recovered from the mite *Lælaps jettmari* which normally infests field mice (*Apodemus agrarius*) but *Trombicula* spp. are more likely vectors (Traub *et al.*, 1954). What may be the same disease has been reported from Hungary and elsewhere in Europe (Trencséni & Keleti, 1960).

REFERENCES

Ada, G. L., Abbot, A., Anderson, S. G., & Collins, F. D. (1962) *J. gen. Microbiol.*, **29**, 165.
Ada, G. L., & Anderson, S. G. (1959) *Aust. J. Sci.*, **21**, 259.
Ada, G. L,. Anderson, S. G., & Abbot, A. (1961) *J. gen Microbiol.*, **24**, 177
Anderson, C. R., Aitken, T. H. G., & Downs, W. G. (1956) *Amer. J. trop. Med. Hyg.*, **5**, 621.
Anderson, S. G. (1954) *J. Hyg. (Lond.)*, **52**, 447.
Anderson, S. G. (1959) *Virology*, **8**, 270.
Anderson, S. G., & Ada, G. L. (1960) *Nature (Lond.)*, **188**, 876.
Anderson, S. G., & Ada, G. L. (1961) *J. gen. Microbiol.*, **25**, 451.
Ansell, R. H. (1957) *Vet. Rec.*, **69**, 410
Bang, F. B. (1957) *Virology*, **4**, 393.
Bang, F. B., & Gey, G. O. (1949) *Proc. Soc. exp. Biol. (N.Y.)*, **71**, 78.
Bauer, J. H., Cox, H. R., & Olitsky, P. K. (1935) *Proc. Soc. exp. Biol. (N.Y.)*, **33**, 378.
Bearcroft, W. G. C. (1960) *J. Path. Bact.*, **80**, 19 and 421.
Bearcroft, W. G. C. (1962) *J. Path. Bact.*, **83**, 49.
Beard, J. W., Finkelstein, H. Sealy, W. C., & Wyckoff, R. W. G. (1938) *Science*, **87**, 490.
Bergold, G. H., & Weibel, J. (1962) *Virology*, **17**, 554.
Bernkopf, H., Levine, S., & Nerson, R. (1953) *J. infect. Dis.*, **93**, 207.
Bhatt, P. N., & Work, T. H. (1957) *Proc. Soc. exp. Biol. (N.Y.)*, **96**, 213.
Black, W., Florio, L., & Stewart, M. O. (1947) *Amer. J. Path.*, **23**, 217.
Blaskovič, D. (1962) in *Symposium on Biology of Tick-borne Encephalitis Complex* p. 317. New York: Academic Press.
Boulger, L. R., & Porterfield, J. S. (1958) *Trans. roy. Soc. trop. Med.*, **52**, 421.
Brown, L. V. (1958) *Amer. J. Hyg.*, **67**, 214.
Buckley, S. M. (1961) *Nature (Lond.)*, **192**, 778.

Buescher, E. L., Scherer, W. F., McClure, H. E., Moyer, J. T., Rosenberg, M. Z., Yoshii, M., & Okada, Y. (1959) *Amer. J. trop. Med.*, **8**, 678.
Bugher, J. C., Boshell-Manrique, J., Roca-Garcia, M., & Osorno-Mesa, E. (1944) *Amer. J. Hyg.*, **39**, 16.
Bugyaki, L. (1955) *Bull. agric. Congo Belge*, **46**, 1455.
Burgdorfer, W., & Eklund, C. M. (1959) *Amer. J. Hyg.*, **69**, 127.
Burgdorfer, W., & Lackman, D. (1960) *J. Bact.*, **80**, 131.
Burnet, F. M. (1936a) *Brit. J. exp. Path.*, **17**, 294.
Burnet, F. M. (1936b) *J. Path. Bact.*, **42**, 213.
Burns, K. F. (1950) *Proc. Soc. exp. Biol. (N.Y.)*, **75**, 621.
Burns, K. F., & Farinacci, C. J. (1956) *Science*, **123**, 227.
Cannon, D. A., & Dewhurst, F. (1955) *Ann. trop. Med. Parasit.*, **49**, 174.
Casals, J. (1949) *Proc. Soc. exp. Biol. (N.Y.)*, **70**, 339.
Casals, J. (1958) *Proc. 6th int. Congr. trop. Med. Malaria*, **5**, 34.
Casals, J. (1960) *Canad. med. Ass. J.*, **82**, 355.
Casals, J. (1961) *Abstr. 10th Pacific Science Congress*. p. 458.
Casals, J., & Brown, L. V. (1954) *J. exp. Med.*, **99**, 429.
Casals, J., & Whitman, L. (1960) *Amer. J. trop Med. Hyg.*, **9**, 73.
Casals, J., & Whitman, L. (1961) *Amer. J. trop. Med. Hyg.*, **10**, 250.
Causey, O. R., Casals, J., & Shope, R. E. (1963) *Amer. J. trop. Med. Hyg.*, in the Press.
Causey, O. R., Causey, C. E., Maroja, O. M., & Macedo, D. G. (1961) *Amer. J. trop. Med. Hyg.*, **10**, 227.
Causey, O. R., & Maroja, O. M. (1957) *Amer. J. trop. Med.*, **6**, 1017.
Chamberlain, R. W., & Sikes, R. K. (1955) *Amer. J. trop. Med.*, **4**, 106.
Chamberlain, R. W., Sikes, R. K., & Kissling, R. E. (1954) *J. Immunol.*, **73**, 106.
Chamberlain, R. W., Sikes, R. K., & Nelson, D. B. (1956) *Proc. Soc. exp. Biol. (N.Y.)*, **91**, 215.
Chamberlain, R. W., & Sudia, W. D. (1955) *Amer. J. Hyg.*, **62**, 295.
Chamberlain, R. W., Sudia, W. D., & Gill, J. D. (1959) *Amer. J. Hyg.*, **70**, 221.
Chambers, V. C. (1957) *Virology*, **3**, 62.
Chanock, R. M., & Sabin, A. B. (1953) *J. Immunol.*, **70**, 271 and 286.
Chanock, R. M., & Sabin, A. B. (1954) *J. Immunol.*, **73**, 337 and 352.
Cheng, P. Y. (1958) *Nature (Lond.)*, **181**, 1800.
Cheng, P. Y. (1961a) *Virology*, **14**, 124.
Cheng, P. Y. (1961b) *Virology*, **14**, 132.
Chumakov, M. P. (1957) *Publ. Hlth. Monogr*. No. 50. U.S. Govt. Printing Office, Washington.
Clarke, D. H. (1960) *J. exp. Med.*, **111**, 21.
Clarke, D. H. (1961) *Amer. J. trop. Med. Hyg.*, **10**, 67.
Clarke, D. H. (1962) *Symposium on the Biology of Viruses of the Tick-borne Encephalitis complex.* p. 67. New York: Academic Press.
Clarke, D. H., & Casals, J. (1958) *Amer. J. trop. Med. Hyg.*, **7**, 561.
Cleland, J. B., & Bradley, B. (1917) *Med. J. Aust.*, **1**, 499.
Collins, W. E. (1963) *Amer. J. Hyg.*, **77**, 109.
Colter, J. S., Bird, H. H., Moyer, A. W., & Brown, R. A. (1957) *Virology*, **4**, 522.
Cook, E. A. (1938) *J. infect. Dis.*, **63**, 206.
Cook, E. A., & Hudson, N. P. (1937) *J. infect. Dis.*, **61**, 289.
Corbet, P. S., Williams, M. C., & Gillett, J. D. (1961) *Trans. roy. Soc. trop. Med.*, **55**, 463.
Cowdry, E. V., & Kitchen, S. F. (1930) *Amer. J. Hyg.*, **11**, 227.
Cox, H. R. (1959) in *Viral and Rickettsial Diseases of Man.* Ed. Rivers and Horsfall. 3rd Ed. p. 384. London: Pitman Medical.

Cox, H. R. & Olitsky, P. K. (1936) *J. exp. Med.*, **63**, 745.

Daubney, R., & Hudson, J. R. (1931) *Parasitology*, **23**, 507.

Daubney, R., & Hudson, J. R. (1934) *Parasitology*, **26**, 496.

Daubney, R., & Hudson, J. R., & Garnham, P. C. (1931) *J. Path. Bact.*, **34**, 545.

Davies, A. M., Fendrich, J., Yoshpe-Purer, Y., & Nir, Y. (1955) *J. trop. Med. Hyg.*, **58**, 12.

Davis, N. C. (1930) *Amer. J. Hyg.*, **11**, 321.

Dawson, F. W., Hearn, H. J., & Hoffmann, R. K. (1959) *Appl. Microbiol.*, **7**, 199.

Dick, G. W. A. (1953) *Trans. roy. Soc. trop. Med.*, **47**, 13.

Dick, G. W. A., & Haddow, A. J. (1952) *Trans. roy. Soc. trop. Med.*, **46**, 600.

Dick, G. W. A., Kitchen, S. F., & Haddow, A. J. (1952) *Trans. roy. Soc. trop, Med.*, **46**, 509.

Diercks, F. H., Kundin, W. D., & Porter, T. J. (1961) *Amer. J. Hyg.*, **73**, 164.

Doherty, R. L., Carley, J. G., Mackerras, M. J., & Marks, E. N. (1963) *Aust. J. exp. Biol. med. Sci.*, **41**, 17.

Duffy, C. E. (1946) *Proc. Soc. exp. Biol.* (*N.Y.*), **63**, 333.

Duffy, C. E., & Stanley, W. M. (1945) *J. exp. Med.*, **82**, 385.

Edward, D. G. ff. (1947) *Brit. J. exp. Path.*, **28**, 368.

Edward, D. G. ff. (1948) *Brit. J. exp. Path.*, **28**, 237, **29**, 367.

Edward, D. G. ff. (1950) *Brit. J. exp. Path.*, **31**, 515.

Eklund, C. M. (1953) *Ann. Rev. Microbiol.*, **7**, 339.

Evans, C. A., & Bolin, V. S. (1946) *Proc. Soc. exp. Biol.* (*N.Y.*), **61**, 106.

Fastier, L. B. (1952) *J. Immunol.*, **68**, 531.

Findlay, G. M., & Broom, J. C. (1933) *Brit. J. exp. Path.*, **14**, 391.

Findlay, G. M., & Clarke, L. P. (1934) *Trans. roy. Soc. trop. Med.*, **28**, 193 and 335.

Findlay, G. M., & MacCallum, F. O. (1937) *J. Path. Bact.*, **44**, 405.

Findlay, G. M., Mackenzie, R. D., & Stern, R. O. (1936) *Brit. J. exp. Path.*, **17**, 431.

Finkelstein, H., Marx, W., Bridgers, W. H., & Beard, J. W. (1938) *Proc. Soc. exp. Biol.* (*N.Y.*), **39**, 103.

Florio, L., Miller, M. S., & Mugrage, E. R. (1950) *J. Immunol.*, **64**, 257.

Florio, L., Stewart, M. O., & Mugrage, E. R., (1944) *J. exp. Med.*, **80**, 165.

Francis, T., & Magill, T. P. (1935) *J. exp. Med.*, **62**, 433.

French, E. L. (1952) *Med. J. Aust.*, **1**, 100.

Frobisher, M. (1930) *Amer. J. Hyg.*, **11**, 300.

Frothingham, T. E. (1955) *Amer. J. trop. Med.*, **4**, 863.

Frothingham, T. E. (1963) *Virology*, **19**, 583.

Gaidomovich, S. I., & Obukhova, V. R. (1960) *Probl. Virol.* (*N.Y.*), **5**, 331.

Gajdusek, D. C. (1956) *Klin. Wschr.*, **34**, 769.

Galindo, P., & Rodaniche, E. de (1960) *Amer. J. trop. Med. Hyg.*, **10**, 395.

Gear, J. H. S., de Meillon, B., Le Roux, A. F., Rofsky, R., Rose-Innes, R., Steyn, J. J., Cliff, W. D., & Schutz, K. H. (1955) *S. Afr. med. J.*, **29**, 514.

Gey, G. O. (1954) *Bull. Johns Hopk. Hosp.*, **94**, 108.

Ginder, D. R., & Friedwald, W. F. (1952) *Proc. Soc. exp. Biol.* (*N.Y.*), **79**, 615.

Gomes, G., & Causey, O. R. (1959) *Proc. Soc. exp. Biol.* (*N.Y.*), **101**, 275.

Gresíková-Kohútová, M. (1959a) *Acta virol.* (Eng. Ed.), **3**, 159.

Gresíková-Kohútová, M. (1959b) *Acta virol.* (Eng. Ed.), **3**, 215.

Gresser, I., & Enders, J. F. (1962) *Virology*, **16**, 428.

Grinschgl, G. (1955) *Bull. Wld. Hlth. Org.*, **12**, 535.

Haddow, A. J. (1951) *Ann. trop. Med. Parasit*, **46**, 135.

Haddow, A. J., Davies, C. W., & Walker, A. J. (1960) *Trans. roy. Soc. trop. Med.*, **54**, 517.

Hadlow, W. J. (1957) *J. infect. Dis.*, **101**, 158.
Hale, J. H., & Witherington, D. H. (1953) *J. comp. Path.*, **63**, 195.
Halstead, S. B., & Buescher, E. L. (1961) *Science*, **134**, 475.
Hammon, W. McD., Rudnick, A., & Sather, G. E. (1960) *Science*, **131**, 1102.
Hammon, W. McD., Rudnick, A., Sather, G. E., & Rogers, K. D. (1959) *Proc. 6th Internat. Congr. trop. Med. Malaria*, **5**, 107.
Hammon, W. McD., & Sather, G. E. (1956) *Proc. Soc. exp. Biol. (N.Y.)*, **91**, 521.
Henderson, J. R. (1961) *Yale J. Biol. Med.*, **33**, 350.
Henderson, J. R., & Taylor, R. M. (1960) *Amer. J. trop. Med. Hyg.*, **9**, 32.
Ho, M. (1962) *Virology*, **17**, 262.
Holden, P. (1955) *Proc. Soc. exp. Biol. (N.Y.)*, **88**, 607.
Hotta, S. (1952) *J. infect. Dis.*, **90**, 1.
Hotta, S. (1953) *Acta Sch. Med. Univ. Kyoto*, **31**, 7.
Hotta, S. (1957) *Ann. trop. Med. Parasit.*, **51**, 249.
Hotta, S., Ohyama, A., Yamada, T., & Awai, T. (1961) *Jap. J. Microbiol.*, **5**, 77.
Howitt, B. F. (1946) *Proc. Soc. exp. Biol. (N.Y.)*, **62**, 105.
Huang, C. H. (1957) *Acta virol.* (Engl. Ed.), **1**, 36.
Hughes, T. P. (1933) *J. Immunol.*, **25**, 275.
Hurlbut, H. S. (1950) *Amer. J. Hyg.*, **51**, 265.
Hurlbut, H. S. (1956) *Amer. J. trop. Med. Hyg.*, **5**, 76.
Hurlbut, H. S., & Thomas, J. I. (1960) *Virology*, **12**, 391.
Hurst, E. W. (1931) *J. comp. Path.*, **44**, 231.
Inoue, Y. K., Iwasaki, T., & Kato, H. (1961) *J. Immunol.*, **87**, 337.
Jungherr, E. L., & Wallis, R. C. (1958) *Amer. J. Hyg.*, **67**, 1.
Karabatsos, N (1963) *J. Immunol.*, **91**, 76.
Kissling, R. E. (1960) *Amer. Rev. Microbiol.*, **14**, 261.
Kissling, R. E., Chamberlain, R. W., Eidson, M. E., Sikes, R. K., & Bruce, M. A. (1954) *Amer. J. Hyg.*, **60**, 237.
Kissling, R. E., Chamberlain, R. W., Nelson, D. B., & Stamm, D. D. (1956) *Amer. J. Hyg.*, **63**, 274.
Kissling, R. E., & Rubin, H. (1951) *Amer. J. vet. Res.*, **12**, 100.
Kissling, R. E., Stamm, D. D., Chamberlain, R. W., & Sudia, W. D. (1957) *Amer. J. Hyg.*, **66**, 42.
Kitaoka, M., and Nishimura, C. (1963) *Virology*, **19**, 238.
Kokernot, R. H., de Meillon, B., Paterson, H. E., Heymann, C. S., & Smithburn, K. C. (1957a) *S. Afr. J. med. Sci.*, **22**, 145.
Kokernot, R. H., Smithburn, K. C., Muspratt, J., & Hodgson, B. (1957b) *S. Afr. J. med. Sci.*, **22**, 103.
Kokernot, R. H., Smithburn, K. C., Paterson, H. E., & de Meillon, B. (1960) *S. Afr. med. J.*, **34**, 871.
Kokernot, R. H., Smithburn, K. C., & Weinbren, M. P. (1956) *J. Immunol.*, **77**, 313.
Komarov, A., & Kalmar, E. (1960) *Vet. Rec.*, **72**, 257.
Koprowski, H., & Cox, H. R. (1947) *J. Immunol.*, **57**, 239 and 255.
Koprowski, H., Cox, H. R., Miller, M. S., & Florio, L. (1950) *Proc. Soc. exp. Biol. (N.Y.)*, **74**, 126.
Koprowski, H., & Hughes, T. P. (1946) *J. Immunol.*, **54**, 371.
Koprowski, H., & Lennette, E. H. (1946) *J. exp. Med.*, **84**, 181 and 205.
Kovac, W., Kunz, C., & Stockinger, L. (1961) *Arch. ges. Virusforsch.*, **11**, 544.
Lavilloureix, J., & Reeb, E. (1958) *Bull. Soc. Path. exot.*, **51**, 941.
Laemmert, H. W., & Hughes, T. P. (1947) *J. Immunol.*, **55**, 61.
Lennette, H., & Koprowski, H. (1943) *J. Amer. med. Ass.*, **123**, 1088.
Le Roux, J. M. W. (1959) *Onderstepoort J. vet. Res.*, **28**, 237.
Levitt, J., Naudé, W. du T., & Polson, A (1963) *Virology*, **20**, 530.

Levkovich, E. N. (1962) in *Symposium on the Biology of the Viruses of the Tick-borne Encephalitis Complex*. New York: Academic Press.

Libikova, H. (1962) (Ed.) *Symposium on the Biology of Viruses of the Tick-borne Encephalitis Complex*. New York, Academic Press.

Libikova, H., & Vilček, J. (1960) *Acta virol.* (Engl. Ed.), **4**, 165.

Lim, K. A., Rudnick, A., & Chan, Y. C. (1961) *Singapore med. J.*, **2**, 158.

Livesay, H. R. (1949) *J. infect. Dis.*, **84**, 306.

Lockart, R. Z. (1960) *Virology*, **10**, 198.

Lockart, R. Z., & Groman, N. B. (1958) *J. infect. Dis.*, **103**, 163.

Lumsden, W. H. R. (1955) *Trans. roy. Soc. trop. Med.*, **49**, 33.

Lumsden, W. H. R. Williams, M. C., & Mason, P. J. (1961) *Ann. trop. Med. Parasit.*, **55**, 389.

Macdonald, F. (1952) *Brit. J. exp. Path.*, **33**, 537.

Mackenzie, R. D., & Findlay, G. M. (1936) *Lancet*, **1**, 140.

McLean, D. M. (1953) *Aust. J. exp. Biol. med. Sci.*, **31**, 481.

McLean, D. M. (1956) *Aust. J. exp. Biol. med. Sci.*, **34**, 71.

McLean, D. M., & Larke, R. P. B. (1963) *Canad. med. Ass. J.*, **88**, 182.

McLean, D. M., & Donohue, W. L. (1959) *Canad. med. Ass. J.*, **80**, 708.

McLeod, J. (1962) *J. comp. Path.*, **62**, 411.

Macnamara, F. N. (1954) *Trans. roy. Soc. trop. Med.*, **48**, 139.

Mason, P. J., & Haddow, A. J. (1957) *Trans. roy. Soc. trop. Med.*, **51**, 238.

Mattingly, P. F. (1960) *Trans. roy. Soc. trop. Med.*, **54**, 97.

Maurer, F. D., Kuttler, K. L., Yager, R. H., & Warner, A. (1952) *J. Immunol.*, **68**, 109.

Meiklejohn, G., England, B., & Lennette, E. H. (1952) *Amer. J. trop. Med. Hyg.*, **1**, 59.

Mettler, N., Buckley, S. J., & Casals, J. (1961) *Proc. Soc. exp. Biol. (N.Y.)*, **107**, 684.

Mettler, N., Casals, J., & Shope, Robert E. (1963) *Amer. J. trop. Med. Hyg.*, **12**, 647.

Mettler, N., Macnamara, L. G., & Shope, R. E. (1962) *J. exp. Med.*, **116**, 665.

Miles, J. A. R. (1952) *Aust. J. exp. Biol. med. Sci.*, **30**, 341.

Miller, J. K., Tompkins, V. N., & Sieracki, J. C. (1961) *Arch. Path. (Chicago)*, **72**, 149.

Mims, C. A. (1956) *Brit. J. exp. Path.*, **37**, 129.

Mims, C. A., & Mason, P. J. (1956) *Brit. J. exp. Path.*, **37**, 423.

Montgomery, R. E. (1917) *J. comp. Path.*, **30**, 28.

Morgan, C., Howe, C., & Rose, H. M. (1961) *J. exp. Med.*, **113**, 219.

Mussgay, M., & Weibel, J. (1962) *Virology*, **16**, 52.

Mussgay, M., & Weibel, J. (1963) *Virology*, **19**, 109.

Nakamura, M. (1961) *Nature (Lond.)*, **191**, 624.

Naudé, W. du T., Madsen, T., & Polson, A. (1954) *Nature (Lond.)*, **173**, 1051.

Naudé, W. du T., & Polson, A. (1957) *J. gen. Microbiol.*, **16**, 491.

Nielsen, G., & Marquardt, J. (1962) *Arch. ges. Virusforsch.*, **12**, 335.

Nir, Y., Fendrich, J., & Goldwasser, R. (1957) *J. infect. Dis.*, **100**, 207.

Noyes, W. F. (1955) *J. exp. Med.*, **102**, 243.

Okuno, T. (1959) *Jap. J. med. Sci. Biol.*, **12**, 71.

Okuno, T., Oya, A., & Ito, T. (1961) *Jap. J. med. Sci. Biol.*, **14**, 51.

Olitsky, P. K., & Clarke, D. H. (1959) in *Viral and Rickettsial Infections of Man*. Ed. Rivers & Horsfall. 3rd Ed. p. 305. London: Pitman Medical.

Oliver, J., & Macdowell, M. (1957) *J. clin. Invest.*, **36**, 99.

Parks, J. J., & Price, W. H. (1958) *Amer. J. Hyg.*, **67**, 187.

Pfefferkorn, E. R., Hunter, H. S. (1963) *Virology*, **20**, 433.

Perlowagora, A., & Hughes, T. P. (1947) *J. Immunol.*, **55**, 103.

Pickens, E. G., & Luoto, L. (1958) *J. infect. Dis.*, **103**, 102.
Pirovsky, L., Zuccarini, J., Mollinelli, E. A., di Pietro, A., Barrera Oro, J. G., Martini, P., Martos, L., & d'Empaire, M. (1959) *Orientación med.*, **8**, 708.
Polson, A. (1947) *Onderstepoort J. vet. Sci.*, **22**, 41.
Polson, A. (1954) *Proc. Soc. exp. Biol .(N.Y.)*, **85**, 613.
Pond, W. L., Russ, S. B., Rogers, N. G.,& Smadel, J. E. (1958) *J. Immunol.*, **75**, 78.
Porterfield, J. S. (1957) *Nature (Lond.)*, **180**, 1201.
Porterfield, J. S. (1959) *Trans. roy. Soc. trop. Med.*, **53**, 458.
Porterfield, J. S. (1960) *Virology*, **11**, 765.
Porterfield, J. S. (1961a) *Bull. Wld. Hlth. Org.*, **24**, 735.
Porterfield, J. S. (1961b) *Vet. Rec.*, **73**, 392.
Porterfield, J. S., & Rowe, C. E. (1960) *Virology*, **11**, 765.
Price, W. H., Lee, R. W., Gunkel, W. F., & O'Leary, W. (1961) *Amer. J. trop. Med. Hyg.*, **10**, 403.
Reeves, W. C., Bellamy, R. E., & Scrivani, R. P. (1958a) *Amer. J. Hyg.*, **67**, 78.
Reeves, W. C. (1958b) *Handb. Virusforsch.*, **4**, 177. (Vienna, Springer.)
Reeves, W. C. (1961) *Progr. med. Virol.*, **3**, 59.
Reeves, W. C., French, E. L., Marks, E. N., & Kent, N. E. (1954) *Amer. J. trop. Med. Hyg.*, **3**, 147.
Report of East African Virus Research Institute (1961–2) pp. 13 and 17.
Rivers, T. M., & Schwentker, F. E. (1934) *J. exp. Med.*, **59**, 669.
Robertson, E. G., & McLorinan, H. (1952) *Med. J. Aust.*, **1**, 10.
Robinson, M. C. (1955) *Trans. roy. Soc. trop. Med.*, **49**, 28.
Rosen, L. (1958) *Amer. J. trop. Med. Hyg.*, **7**, 406.
Rosen, L., Evans, H. E., & Spickard, A (1963) *Amer. J. Hyg.*, **77**, 29.
Ross, R. W. (1956) *J. Hyg. (Lond.)*, **54**, 177.
Rubin, H., Baluda, M., & Hotchin, J. E. (1955) *J. exp. Med.*, **101**, 205.
Sabin, A. B. (1951) *Arch. ges. Virusforsch.*, **4**, 367.
Sabin, A. B. (1952) *Amer. J. trop. Med. Hyg.*, **1**, 30.
Sabin, A. B. (1955) *Amer. J. trop. Med. Hyg.*, **4**, 198.
Sabin, A. B. (1959a) in *Viral and Rickettsial Infections of Man.* Ed. Rivers and Horsfall. 3rd Ed. p. 361. London: Pitman Medical.
Sabin, A. B. (1959b) in *Viral and Rickettsial Infections of Man.* Ed. Rivers and Horsfall. 3rd Ed. p. 374. London: Pitman Medical.
Sabin, A. B., & Buescher, E. L. (1950) *Proc. Soc. exp. Biol. (N.Y.)*, **74**, 222.
Sabin, A, B., & Olitsky, P. K. (1938) *Proc. Soc. exp. Biol. (N.Y.)*, **38**, 595.
Sabin, A. B., & Schlesinger, R. W. (1945) *Science*, **101**, 640.
Saddington, R. S. (1934) *Proc. Soc. exp. Biol. (N.Y.)*, **31**, 693.
Salminen, A. (1959) *Ann. Med. exp. Fenn.*, **38**, 267.
Salminen, A. (1960) *Acta virol.* (Eng. Ed.), **4**, 17.
Sanna, A., & Angelillo, B. (1957) *Igiene mod.*, **50**, 693.
Sawyer, W. A. (1931) *J. prev. Med.*, **5**, 413.
Schaeffer, M., & Arnold, E. H. K. (1954) *Amer. J. Hyg.*, **60**, 231.
Schaeffer, M., Gajdusek, D. C., Lema, A. B., & Eichenwald, H. (1959) *Amer. J. trop. Med. Hyg.*, **8**, 372.
Schlesinger, R. W. (1951) *Proc. Soc. exp. Biol. (N.Y.)*, **76**, 817.
Scherer, W. F., Buescher, E. L., & McClure, H. E. (1959a) *Amer. J. trop. Med. Hyg.*, **8**, 689.
Scherer, W. F., Izumi, T., McCown, J., & Hardy, J. L. (1962) *Amer. J. trop. Med. Hyg.*, **11**, 269.
Scherer, W. F., Moyer, J. T., Izumi, T., Gresser, I., & McCown, J. (1959b) *Amet. J. trop. Med. Hyg.*, **8**, 698.

Schmidt, J. R., Gajdusek, D. C., Schaeffer, M., & Gorrie, R. H. (1959) *Amer. J. trop. Med. Hyg.*, **8**, 479.

Shah, K. V., Johnson, H. N., Rao, T. R., Rajagopalan, P. K., & Lamba, B. S. (1960) *Indian J. med. Res.*, **48**, 300.

Sharp, D. G., Taylor, A. R., Beard, D., & Beard, J. W. (1943) *Arch. Path.*, **63**, 167.

Shope, R. E. (1953) *J. exp. Med.*, **97**, 627.

Shope, R. E. (1961) *J. exp. Med.*, **113**, 511.

Shope, R. E., & Anderson, S. G. (1960) *Med. J. Aust.*, **1**, 156.

Shope, Robert E., & Causey, O. R. (1962) *Amer. J. trop. Med. Hyg.*, **11**, 283.

Shore, H. (1961) *Trans. roy. Soc. trop. Med.*, **55**, 361.

Silber, L. A., & Soloviev, V. D. (1946) *Amer. Rev. Soviet Med.*, supplement. p. 6.

Slepushkin, A. N. (1960) *Probl. Virol.*, **4**, 54.

Smadel, J. E. (1959) in *Viral and Rickettsial Diseases of Man*. Ed. Rivers and Horsfall. 3rd Ed. p. 400. London: Pitman Medical.

Smith, C. E. Gordon (1956) *Nature (Lond.)*, **178**, 581.

Smith, C. E. Gordon (1959) *Brit. med. Bull.*, **15**, 235.

Smith, C. E. Gordon (1960) *Trans. roy. Soc. trop. Med.*, **54**, 113.

Smith, C. E. Gordon, & Holt, D. (1961) *Bull. Wld. Hlth. Org.*, **24**, 749.

Smithburn, K. C. (1942) *J. Immunol.*, **44**, 25.

Smithburn, K. C. (1946) *J. Immunol.*, **52**, 309.

Smithburn, K. C. (1949) *Brit. J. exp. Path.*, **30**, 1.

Smithburn, K. C., Haddow, A. J., & Lumsden, W. H. R. (1949) *Ann. trop. Med. Parasit.*, **43**, 74.

Smithburn, K. C., & Bugher, J. C. (1953) *J. Bact.*, **66**, 173.

Smithburn, K. C., & Haddow, A. J. (1944) *J. Immunol.*, **49**, 141 and 159.

Smithburn, K. C., & Haddow, A. J. (1951) *Proc. Soc. exp. Biol. (N.Y.)*, **77**, 130.

Smithburn, K. C., Hughes, T. P., Burke, A. W., & Paul, J. H. (1940) *Amer. J. trop. Med.*, **4**, 471.

Smithburn, K. C., Kerr, J. A., & Gatna, P. B. (1954) *J. Immunol.*, **72**, 248.

Smithburn, K. C., Mahaffy, A. F., Haddow, A. J., Kitchen, S. F., & Smith, J. F. (1949) *J. Immunol.*, **62**, 213.

Smithburn, K. C., Mahaffy, A. F., & Paul, J. H. (1941) *Amer. J. trop. Med.*, **21**, 75.

Smorodintsev, A. A. (1940) *Arch. ges. Virusforsch.*, **1**, 468.

Smorodintsev, A. A. (1958) *Progr. med. Virol.*, **1**, 210.

Sokol, F., Libikova, H., & Jemla, J. (1959) *Nature (Lond.)*, **184**, 1581.

Southam, C. M. (1956) *J. infect. Dis.*, **99**, 155 and 163.

Southam, C. M., & Moore, A. E. (1951) *Amer. J. trop. Med.*, **31**, 724.

Southam, C. M., & Moore, A. E. (1954) *Amer. J. trop. Med. Hyg.*, **3**, 19.

Stamm, D. D. (1958) *Amer. J. publ. Hlth.*, **48**, 328.

Stokes, A., Bauer, J. H., & Hudson, N. P. (1928) *Amer. J. trop. Med.*, **8**, 103.

Stones, P. B., & Macnamara, F. N. (1955) *Trans. roy. Soc. trop. Med.*, **49**, 176.

Strode, G. K. (1951) (Ed.) *Yellow fever*. New York: McGraw Hill.

Sulkin, S. E., Burns, K. F., Shelton, D. F., & Wallis, C. (1962) *Texas Rep. Biol. Med.*, **20**, 113.

Subcommittee of International Nomenclature Committee (1963) *Virology*, **21**, 576 in the Press.

Sutton, L. S., & Brooke, C. C. (1954) *J. Amer. med. Ass.*, **155**, 1473.

Sweet, B. H., & Sabin, A. B. (1954) *J. Immunol.*, **73**, 363.

Symposium on Thai Haemorrhagic Fevers. (1962). Bangkok. SEATO Medical Research Monograph No. 2.

Syverton, J. T., & Berry, G. P. (1941) *J. exp. Med.*, **73**, 507.

Takemori, N., Nakano, M., & Hemmi, M. (1955) *Virology*, **1**, 250.

Takemori, N. (1949) *Jap. med. J.*, **2**, 231.
Taylor, R. M., Hurlbut, H. S., Work, T. S., Kingston, J. R., & Frothingham, T. E. (1955) *Amer. J. trop. Med. Hyg.*, **4**, 844.
Taylor, R. M., Work, T. H., Hurlbut, H. S., & Rizk, F. (1956) *Amer. J. trop. Med. Hyg.*, **5**, 579.
Theiler, M. (1957) *Proc. Soc. exp. Biol. (N.Y.)*, **96**, 380.
Theiler, M. (1959) in *Viral and Rickettsial Diseases of Man.* 3rd Ed. Rivers and Horsfall. p. 343. London: Pitman Medical.
Theiler, M., & Smith, H. H. (1937) *J. exp. Med.*, **65**, 767 and 787.
Thomas, L. A., & Eklund, C. M. (1960) *Proc. Soc. exp. Biol. (N.Y.)*, **105**, 52.
Thomas, L. A., Kennedy, R. C., & Eklund, C. M. (1960) *Proc. Soc. exp. Biol. (N.Y.)*, **104**, 355.
Traub, E., & Kesting, F. (1956) *Zbl. Bakt., I. Abt. Orig.*, **166**, 462.
Traub, E., & TenBroeck, C. (1935) *Science*, **81**, 572.
Traub, R., Hertig, M., Lawrence, W. H., & Harriss, T. T. (1954) *Amer. J. Hyg.*, **59**, 291.
Trencséni, T., & Keleti, B. (1960) *Acta med. (Budapest)*, **16**, 303.
Victor, J., Smith, D. G., & Pollack, A. B. (1956) *J. infect. Dis.*, **98**, 55.
van Tongeren, H. A. E. (1955) *Arch. ges. Virusforsch.*, **6**, 158.
von Magnus, H. (1950) *Acta path. microbiol. scand.*, **27**, 276.
von Zeipel, G., & Svedmyr, A. (1958) *Arch. ges. Virusforsch.*, **8**, 370.
Wagner, R. R. (1961) *Virology*, **13**, 323.
Warner, P. (1957) *Aust. J. exp. Biol. med. Sci.*, **35**, 327.
Webster, L. T., & Clow, A. D. (1936) *J. exp. Med.*, **63**, 827.
Wecker, E. (1959) *Virology*, **7**, 241.
Wecker, E., & Schäfer, W. (1957) *Z. Naturforsch.*, **12b**, 415.
Weinbren, M. P., Kokernot, R. H., & Smithburn, K. C. (1956) *S. Afr. med. J.*, **30**, 631.
Weinbren, M. P., Gourlay, R. N., Lumsden, W. H. R., & Weinbren, B. M. (1958a) *J. comp. Path.*, **68**, 174.
Weinbren, M. P., Haddow, A. J., & Williams, M. C. (1958b) *Trans. roy. Soc. trop. Med.*, **52**, 253.
Weinbren, M. P., & Mason, P. J. (1957) *S. Afr. med. J.*, **31**, 427.
Weinbren, M. P., Williams, M. C., & Haddow, A. J. (1957) *S. Afr. med. J.*, **31**, 951.
Weiss, K. E. (1957a) *Bull. epizoot. Dis. Afr.*, **5**, 431.
Weiss, K. E. (1957b) *Bull. epizoot. Dis. Afr.*, **5**, 459.
Weiss, K. E., Haig, D. A., & Alexander, R. A. (1956) *Onderstepoort J. vet. Res.*, **27**, 183.
Whitman, L. (1947) *J. Immunol.*, **56**, 97.
Whitman, L., & Aitken, T. H. G. (1960) *Ann. trop. Med. Parasit.*, **54**, 192.
Whitman, L., & Casals, J. (1961) *Amer. J. trop. Med. Hyg.*, **10**, 259.
Whitman, L., & Shope, Robert E. (1962) *Amer. J. trop. Med. Hyg.*, **11**, 691.
W.H.O. report. (1961) *Arthropod-borne Viruses*; technical report series 219 Geneva: Wld. Hlth. Org.
Williams, H. E. (1958) *Nature (Lond.)*, **181**, 497.
Williams, M. C., & Woodall, J. P. (1961) *Trans. roy. Soc. trop. Med.*, **55**, 135.
Williams, M. C., Woodall, J. P., & Porterfield, J. S. (1962) *Trans. roy. Soc. trop. Med.*, **56**, 166.
Woodall, J. P., & Bertram, D. S. (1959) *Trans. roy. Soc. trop. Med.*, **53**, 440.
Work, T. H. (1958) *Progr. med. Virol.*, **1**, 248.
Work, T. H., & Shah, K. V. (1956) *Indian J. med. Sci.*, **10**, 582.
Wyckoff, R. W. G., & Tesar, W. C. (1939) *J. Immunol.*, **37**, 329.

4

Myxoviruses

The following description is based on the original account (Andrewes *et al.*, 1955). There are two subgroups:

  I. *Myxovirus influenzæ-A, influenzæ-B, influenzæ-C.*
 II. *Myxovirus multiforme* (Newcastle disease), *M. parotitidis* (mumps) and *M. para-influenzæ 1, 2, 3 and 4,* and simian myxoviruses SV5 and SV41.

Certain other viruses will almost certainly have to be admitted to the group: those of measles, dog distemper, rinderpest, respiratory syncytial virus and African swine fever. It has been suggested that rabies may belong here also (*v.*, p. 152). The name "myxovirus" indicates a special affinity of the original members of the group for certain mucins.

Morphology and development. Virus particles consist of a nucleoprotein core surrounded by an outer membrane. The peripheral part of the virus is probably soft and easily deformed, especially by drying, so that to give precise dimensions for size is not very useful: diameters range from 60–200 mμ, sometimes more for the subgroup II. Filaments are often present in virus preparations of subgroup I. The core consists of a tightly coiled helix or double helix of nucleoprotein, 9 to 18 mμ in diameter, with a periodicity in the structure dependent on the spacing of the coils; there is a hollow centre within the coil. Host-cell constituents, particularly lipids (Kates *et al.*, 1961) take part in forming the outer membrane; this also contains radially disposed rods probably composed of hæmagglutinin. When virus is disrupted by ether, the nucleoprotein coil breaks up into short lengths, and pieces of membrane may curl up into star-shaped rosettes (Horne & Waterson, 1960; Horne *et al.*, 1960; Hoyle *et al.*, 1961). Nucleoprotein may be formed in the nucleus (subgroup I) or cytoplasm (subgroup II); hæmagglutinin is formed in the cytoplasm and virus particles are gradually released from the cell-surface practically as they are completed.

Chemical composition. All are RNA viruses. Very stable at −76°, less so at −10°. Infectivity is readily destroyed by treatment with 20 per cent. ethyl ether in the cold (Andrewes & Horstmann, 1949).

Hæmagglutination. Most myxoviruses are adsorbed on to the surface of red cells of fowls and some other vertebrates, causing their agglutination. Subsequently they elute more or less completely, having produced by an enzyme-like action irreversible changes in mucoprotein receptors on the red cell surface. Their action on a substrate on the cell surface releases neuraminic acid (Gottschalk, 1959). The adsorption and hæmagglutination are inhibited by certain mucoproteins present in mammalian sera and other biological fluids (different in the case of *influenzæ-C*). Red cells fully treated with receptor-destroying enzyme of *V. choleræ* (RDE) are not agglutinated by myxoviruses. Where hæmagglutination is demonstrable with difficulty or not at all, adsorption of RBC's to cells infected in tissue-culture (hæmadsorption) may occur. Although hæmagglutination was written into the definition of myxoviruses in 1959 and is implied in the name, it now appears that some, e.g. respiratory syncytial and rinderpest viruses, belong naturally to the group, though neither hæmagglutination nor hæmadsorption have been recorded.

Antigenic characters. Members of the group are antigenically different from one another as judged by complement-fixation, hæmagglutination-inhibition and neutralization tests though there may be overlapping especially in subgroup II. Infected tissues contain a nucleoprotein antigen (soluble antigen) of smaller dimensions than the virus particle and having a specificity which is that of the group member. The virus particles themselves may react more specifically than this, since strains of one virus may be serologically divergent, having varying degrees of antigenic overlap.

Cultivation. Growth of most myxoviruses occurs in the amniotic cavity of fertile hens' eggs; in most instances it occurs also, at least after adaptation, in the allantoic cavity. The viruses grow in cultures of chick or mammalian tissues.

Pathogenicity. Produce either inapparent infections or overt ones due to inflammation involving particularly the respiratory tract. Where there is general infection and viscera are involved (e.g.

mumps) symptoms may be mainly referable to attack on particular organs.

Ecology. Usually transmitted by means of secretions of respiratory tract of infected hosts. Arthropods are not known to be concerned in transmission.

Differences between the two subgroups have been tabulated by Waterson (1962), who includes measles, distemper and rinderpest in the second subgroup. All the relevant data are not yet available for every myxovirus and his table particularly contrasts influenzæ-A and Newcastle disease.

	Group I	Group II
Particle size	80–120 mμ	150–250 mμ
Diameter of ribonucleoprotein coil	9 mμ	18 mμ
Filaments	Common	Unusual
Inactivation by hydroxylamine	+	−
Hæmolysis	−	+
Site of formation of soluble antigen	Nucleus	Cytoplasm
Eosinophilic cytoplasmic inclusions	−	+
Formation of incomplete virus	+	−
Multiplicity reactivation (von Magnus)	+	−

(adapted from Waterson, 1962).

Subgroup I: True Influenza Viruses (A, B and C)

These viruses generally, after adaptation, produce transmissible pneumonia in mice and hamsters. Viruses not so adapted will often produce in mice a non-transmissible pneumonia when inoculated intranasally in very large doses. Similarly, encephalitis may at times be produced in rodents, after adaptation; this also may or may not be transmissible in series.

INFLUENZA A VIRUSES

This includes several viruses; that affecting man, *Myxovirus influenzæ-A hominis*, again subdivided into viruses A, A1, A2; swine influenza; one form of horse influenza; fowl-plague—formerly treated as a distinct member of the group; and duck influenza. Since it is possible that an influenza virus affecting one species may pass over to and become epidemic amongst members of another species, some of these distinctions may come to be considered artificial. Members of the Influenza-A group share a common, soluble CF antigen.

INFLUENZA A OF MAN

Synonym: Grippe.
Reviews: Francis (1959). Buzzell & Hanig (1958) (Hæmagglutination).
Causative agent: *Myxovirus influenza-A hominis.*

Morphology and development. As described for the group and first subgroup. Roughly spherical particles, mostly 80 to 120 mμ in diameter; filaments of about this diameter and up to several microns in length may also be present, especially when preparations are made from strains recently isolated from man; also shorter rods and ovoid bodies (Dawson & Elford, 1949).

Chemical composition. The virus contains protein and RNA; traces of DNA are probably impurities. Reports that the RNA alone can transmit infection are not yet generally accepted (Colter & Ellem, 1961). Lipid and carbohydrate are also present (Taylor *et al.*, 1943). Some host protein may be incorporated in the virus. Incomplete forms occur under certain conditions; these may be deficient in RNA (Ada & Perry, 1955). The relative proportions of bases in the nucleic acid have been determined by Ada & Perry (1956) and Sokol & Schramek (1962). Maassab (1963) has lately reported the recovery of infective RNA from cells infected with A2 virus, not from concentrated virus and not from a number of egg-adapted A-viruses.

Physico-chemical characters. Usually inactivated in 30 minutes at 56° C; 90 minutes' heating necessary for some strains. Relatively sensitive to inactivation by U.V. radiation. Density 1·19 to 1·25 in different media (Barry, 1960). Virus retains activity when carried down on the precipitate on treatment with protamine, alum, or calcium phosphate, or with 25 to 35 per cent. methanol at −5°. Maximum stability between pH 7 and 8. Formaldehyde destroys activity (1 : 5000 is adequate against fairly pure preparations); so do soaps, detergents and oxidizing agents such as iodine. Inactivation by various chemicals is described by Dunham & Macneal (1943). The virus will survive for years at −70° C or after lyophilization. Infected tissues retain activity for months in 50 per cent.

glycerol-saline at about 0° C. Activity was demonstrated in dried dust for 14 days (Edward, 1941).

Hæmagglutination. Virus is adsorbed to and agglutinates red blood cells of various species (Hirst, 1941). A2 (Asian) strains agglutinate cells of a wider range of species than do earlier strains (Wang & Liu, 1958). Recently isolated viruses (O phase) agglutinate human and guinea pig better than fowl cells; after adaptation to growth in allantoic cavity (D phase) fowl cells are equally affected (Burnet & Bull, 1943). Naturally occurring strains elute readily at 37° C, having destroyed receptors on the red cell surface or rendered them incapable of reacting with more of the same sort of virus. Mucoproteins occurring in egg white, in many mammalian sera and elsewhere, react with the virus, inhibiting hæmagglutination and being themselves destroyed by an enzyme-like action. The most important of the inhibitors in sera are the α or Francis inhibitor (Francis, 1947), especially active against heated viruses and the β or Chu inhibitor which is effective only against viruses which have not been adapted to mice (Chu, 1951). Hæmagglutination by A2 viruses is inhibited by heated normal sera of several species (Takátsy & Barb, 1959) and by normal horse serum (Cohen & Belyavin, 1959). Hæmadsorption may be useful in diagnosis.

Antigenic properties. All strains share a common "soluble antigen" which is demonstrated by the complement-fixation test and is distinct from that of other group members. Its particles are 10 to 20 mμ in diameter. In addition, a strain specific (V) CF antigen is described (Lief and Henle, 1959). Hæmagglutination-inhibition and neutralization tests and complement-fixation tests with virus particles show that numerous serological races exist, having varying degrees of antigenic overlap, sometimes hardly any; but strains from one outbreak are usually similar. There tends, however, to be a progressive change in antigenic make-up from year to year. Human A viruses are classified (World Health Org., 1959) as A (1933–46), A1 (1947–56) and A2 or Asian (1957–?). There is variation also in affinity for specific antibodies: Q-strains are non-avid, reacting poorly with homologous antisera, in contrast to avid or P-phase strains (Van der Veen & Mulder, 1950).

Interference. Interference in eggs and tissue-culture is shown not only between this and other myxoviruses but also with viruses of unrelated groups including some arboviruses and poxviruses. At least the heterologous interference is mediated by interferon (Isaacs & Lindenmann, 1957).

Cultivation. Occurs in the amniotic cavity of fertile hens' eggs. Viruses recently isolated from human sources grow best amniotically (O phase). After adaptation (D phase) growth is equally good in the allantoic cavity (Burnet & Bull, 1943). The virus also grows in cultures of embryonic chick and various mammalian tissues, but multiplication and cytopathogenicity are very different with different strains. Neurotropic variants are apt to show better CPE. Plaque-formation has been described (Ledinko, 1955). Monkey kidney and human embryonic tissues can be used for primary isolations. Recombination in culture between strains having various "marker" characters has been studied by Burnet & Lind (1951) and reviewed by Kilbourne (1963).

Pathogenicity. Causes influenza and sometimes pneumonia in man: encephalitis and other complications are rare. Natural infection of ferrets and pigs may also occur.

Experimentally ferrets are readily infected (Smith *et al.*, 1933), symptoms are mainly due to inflammation of the nasal passages; after adaptation, pneumonia also may be caused. The virus can be adapted to cause pneumonia in mice, hamsters and other mammals, particularly rodents. In guinea pigs and rats infection is usually inapparent.

Pathological lesions. Viræmia is rarely demonstrable in man and mice. The characteristic lesion in lungs of infected man, ferret and mouse is necrosis of epithelium of finer bronchi (Straub, 1937) and in cells of alveolar walls (Hers *et al.*, 1962). Fatal pneumonia in man is usually caused by secondary bacterial infections; in recent years staphylococci have been the commonest. Virus pneumonia alone can probably cause some deaths. Winternitz *et al.* (1920) described the pathology of fatal cases of the 1918–19 pandemic. Strains neurotropic for mice have been obtained in the laboratory (Stuart-Harris, 1939). Lethal for infected chick embryos in which it produces necrosis in developing lungs after amniotic inoculation. Apart from the effects of virus multiplication, virus particles have a toxic action demonstrable in the mouse lung (Sugg, 1949), in rabbit eyes (Evans & Rickard, 1945) and by a pyrogenic effect in rabbits (Wagner *et al.*, 1949).

Ecology. Transmission is from infected respiratory secretions.

Control. Formolized vaccines have been proved to give some protection over at least some months: incidence in some trials has been about one-third of that in unvaccinated groups. Efficacy of attenuated virus given intranasally has been extensively tested especially in the U.S.S.R. (Smorodintsev *et al.*, 1961).

INFLUENZA A VIRUSES OF OTHER SPECIES

So far as they have been examined, properties of Influenza A viruses affecting species other than man resemble those of the human virus. Differences are noted below.

Swine Influenza

Synonym: *Myxovirus influenza-A suis.*

Antigenic properties. American strains are all closely related to each other by hæmagglutinin-inhibition tests, but European strains are no closer to them than to human strains (Gompels, 1938). No evidence of antigenic changes with time, comparable with those of human influenza. Antihæmagglutinins are present in many human sera, particularly from older people. The significance of the common antigen has been the subject of many studies. It is widely believed that the pandemic of 1918–19 in man was caused by a virus related to swine influenza and that this virus may have first infected pigs at that time (Laidlaw, 1935, Shope, 1935).

Distribution. North America, especially the Middle West. Formerly Europe, including the British Isles. The disease was, however, doubtfully present outside North America for many years: some reported isolations are attributable to laboratory "pick-ups". More recent isolations from Europe are probably genuine.

Pathogenicity. Causes influenza and pneumonia in domestic pigs, particularly when associated with *Hæmophilus influenzæ suis* (Shope, 1931). Causes pneumonia in ferrets and mice without the necessity for adaptation; also in lambs (Barb *et al.*, 1962).

Ecology. Transmission is from infected respiratory secretions. Also (Shope, 1941), by ingestion of earthworms containing virus-infected swine lung worms: this causes no disease until the virus is activated by one or other of various stimuli. This finding was confirmed by Kammer *et al.* (1962). Peterson *et al.* (1961), however, found no evidence of virus survival in earthworms.

Control. Formolized vaccines have been shown to give rise to some immunity but are of doubtful practical use.

Horse Influenza

Synonym: *Myxovirus influenzæ-A equi.*
One of several viruses causing so-called Horse Influenza. Others, not closely related, are dealt with on pp. 226 and 305.

Morphology. Mean diameter of particles 100 mμ.

Hæmagglutination. Agglutinates horse, pig, calf, rhesus, fowl, guinea pig and human red blood cells (Tumová *et al.*, 1959).

Antigenic characters. Shares the CF antigen of the Influenza-A group, but separate in the HAI test.

Cultivation succeeds in fertile eggs and in tissue cultures of bovine kidney, chick embryo kidney and fibroblasts, rhesus kidney and human embryo kidney (Andrewes & Worthington, 1959).

Distribution. Czechoslovakia and elsewhere in Central Europe. Serological evidence suggests that it may occur in Scandinavia and Holland. The agent has recently appeared in the United States (Weekly Reports, 1963).

Pathogenicity. Causes respiratory illness in horses (Tumová *et al.*, 1959). Has been adapted to produce pneumonia in mice inoculated intranasally and encephalitis after intracerebral injection of suckling mice. Causes inapparent infection of ferrets (Andrewes & Worthington, 1959).

FOWL PLAGUE

The term "fowl-pest" is often used to include fowl plague and Newcastle disease. It seems better to abandon the name *Myxovirus pestis-galli* in favour of *M. influenzæ-A* avian strain; the relation to Influenza A was not known when the earlier name was bestowed.

Morphology and development. Virus particles are roughly spherical, mostly 80–100 mμ in diameter: associated filaments average 80 mμ in diameter and are up to 6 μ in length (Dawson & Elford, 1949; Flewett & Challice, 1951). By electron-microscopy (Waterson *et al.*, 1961) the virus is seen to resemble Influenza-A virus. The helical filaments of the nucleoprotein (S- or G-antigen) are broken up into short rods by some treatments (Schäfer & Zillig, 1954). The helices or double helices have a diameter of 9 mμ; a periodicity of 6–7·5 mμ is observable along their structure. The membrane surrounding the core comprises the hæmagglutinin which under ether treatment appears as star-shaped rosettes 35 mμ across with radially arranged spikes. Incomplete virus may be present and in greater variety of form but with little or no contained nucleoprotein.

The nucleoprotein is formed in the nucleus of the infected cell and hæmagglutinin, perhaps later, in the cytoplasm (Breitenfeld & Schäfer, 1957; Franklin, 1958).

Physico-chemical characters. Heating at 55° C for 1 hour or to 60° C for 10 minutes inactivates (Moses *et al.*, 1948).

Hæmagglutination of fowl, rhesus, horse, ox, pig, monkey and probably other cells.

Antigenic properties. Shares the CF antigen of the Influenza-A virus group. Immunologically distinct from other myxoviruses, but minor crossing with *M. influenzæ-A equi* is recorded in the HAI test. Some serological differences between strains occur. In particular virus N isolated in Bavaria (Dinter & Bakos, 1950) differs widely from classical strains by HAI. A strain from Scotland is also very different. A virus isolated from terns (*Sterna hirundo*) in South Africa is antigenically related to the Scottish one (Becker, 1963).

Cultivation. Grows readily in developing hens' eggs and in cultures of fowl and various mammalian tissues including those of rabbit, ox and rhesus monkey, and embryonic human tissues and HeLa cells; a CPE is produced. Attenuation of some strains of virus for fowls is reported to follow cultivation in chick, pigeon or human cells (Hallauer & Kronauer, 1959).

Distribution was formerly world-wide but of recent years the disease has been replaced almost everywhere as a disease of major economic importance by Newcastle disease. It is still prevalent in North Africa and sporadically in a few European countries, perhaps also Burma and Chile.

Pathogenicity. Symptoms in fowls are variable and include dyspnœa, œdema of head and neck, cyanosis and diarrhœa, often with evidence of CNS involvement. The incubation period is from 3 to 7 days. Mortality varies from 40–100 per cent. (Rice, 1930). Pathological lesions are not characteristic but generalized linear and punctiform hæmorrhages are common. Nuclear changes, sometimes described as inclusion bodies, occur in cells of various tissues. Birds of many families are susceptible, including gallinaceous birds, passerines, pigeons, ducks and geese. Experimentally, infection has been transmitted to mice, ferrets and other mammals, mainly by intracerebral inoculation (Findlay & Mackenzie, 1937).

Ecology. Method of transmission is obscure. Experimentally it may be venereal (Todd, 1928).

Control. Virus inactivated by formaldehyde and by phenol has been successful as a vaccine in the hands of some workers. Virus can be attenuated in several ways and used for immunization (Moses *et al.*, 1948).

Duck Influenza

Synonym: *Myxovirus influenzæ-A anatis.*

Morphology. Resembles the human virus. Spheres 80–100 mμ in diameter occur; also filaments (Fraňo *et al.*, 1958).

Hæmagglutination. Agglutinates red blood cells of fowl, rhesus, guinea pig, horse, ox, pig and frog (Blaskovič *et al.*, 1959).

Antigenic characters. Shares the common A CF antigen. By HAI the two British and one Czechoslovakian strains differ but show considerable overlap; they also cross to low titre with the equine virus but not with fowl plague or NDV (H. G. Pereira, personal communication, 1963).

Cultivation of the British virus is possible in tissue cultures of chick-embryo, duckling, ox, rhesus, and embryonic human kidney: CPE produced.

Distribution. Only described from Czechoslavakia and Britain.

Pathogenicity. The Czechoslovak strain caused an outbreak of sinusitis, usually fatal in 3–4 days (Koppel *et al.*, 1956); it was infectious at a dilution of 10^{-5}. One British strain was also isolated from ducklings with sinusitis but its relation to the disease remained unproved (Andrewes & Worthington, 1959).

Plague of Blackbirds

A fatal epizootic amongst blackbirds and other *Turdidae* was described by Maggiore and Valenti (1904) in Italy. A filterable agent was obtained, able to infect other species of birds, but not fowls. A virus related to fowl-plague seems probable, though the authors thought the virus different from fowl-plague.

INFLUENZA B

Original description: Francis (1940), Magill (1940).

Causative agent: *Myxovirus influenzæ-B.*

Morphology and physical properties. As studied in preparations of infected allantoic fluids of fertile hens' eggs: roughly spherical particles mostly 90–110 mμ in diameter; filaments of about this diameter and up to 4 μ long may also be present, but they are not so readily found as with *M. influenzæ-A*. The fine structure of the virus determined by electron-microscopy, resembles that of Influenza A (Waterson, 1962).

Hæmagglutination. Virus is adsorbed to and agglutinates various mammalian and avian red blood cells. No O and D phases demonstrable as with *M. influenzæ-A*, but behaviour as to adsorption and elution very similar. Virus heated to 56° C has its hæmagglutinin very easily inhibited by mucoproteins in many normal mammalian sera (Francis, 1947).

Antigenic properties. A soluble antigen is shared by all strains. By the hæmagglutination-inhibition test there is some antigenic diversity amongst strains but the change from year to year proceeds more slowly than with *M. influenzæ-A*.

Cultivation. Growth occurs in amniotic and allantoic cavities of hens' eggs, 13-day eggs being best for primary isolation. Cultures of monkey kidney may also be used for primary isolation, CPE being produced (Mogabgab *et al.*, 1955). Laboratory-adapted strains are reported as growing, with CPE, in cultures of human embryo, chick embryo, ferret, mouse, calf and pig kidney (Haas & Wulff, 1957), but not in a number of other human cell cultures (Green *et al.*, 1957).

Pathogenicity. Causes influenza and sometimes pneumonia in man. Multiplies in respiratory tract of ferrets but only irregularly produces fever or symptoms. Some strains have been adapted to produce pneumonia in mice and other rodents, but with others this has not been achieved.

In man, Influenza B behaves more like an endemic disease than does Influenza A; small outbreaks are reported in most years but they are rarely very extensive.

Control. Formolized vaccines have been used as for Influenza A, but their success has been harder to evaluate as the incidence of the disease is rarely high. On the basis of serological tests it seems that the virus may be a better antigen than that of Influenza A.

INFLUENZA C

Causative agent: *Myxovirus influenzæ-C*.

Review: Taylor (1951).

A probable cause of influenza-like infections in man (Francis *et al.*, 1950) but much less important in that respect than *M. influenzæ-A* or *M. influenzæ-B*. Less extensively studied than *M. influenzæ-A*, from which it is not known to differ except in the properties described.

Morphology. As studied in amniotic fluids of infected hens' eggs; spheres, mostly 80 to 100 mμ in diameter (Taylor, 1951). Filamentous forms also occur. The fine structure resembles that of Influenza A and B (Waterson *et al.*, 1963).

Hæmagglutination. Agglutinates fowl and some mammalian red cells like other members of the group, but tests are better carried out at 4° C, since elution is rapid at $\pm 20°$ C, although it is often incomplete. Agglutination of guinea pig red blood cells varies between strains. Unlike other group members, its hæmagglutination is feebly inhibited by egg white and other mucoprotein inhibitors, but normal rat serum inhibits. When tests are made with human O cells it appears that the same receptors are involved as with other myxoviruses (White, 1953); but if fowl cells are used, those treated with the receptor-destroying enzyme of *V. choleræ* are still agglutinable (Hirst, 1950); possibly an additional receptor is concerned.

Antigenic properties. Distinct from *M. influenzæ-A* and *B*. No serological races have been described.

Interference. Interferes in eggs with Influenza B and NDV and in mice with W.E.E.

Cultivation. In amniotic cavity of hens' eggs; growth in allantoic cavity doubtful. Some strains multiply in monkey kidney tissue cultures (Mogabgab, 1962).

Pathogenicity. Though antibody rises to the virus have been detected in people with mild respiratory infections, it is only in a few instances that Influenza-C virus has been definitely implicated as a cause of disease. It probably causes inapparent more often than overt infection, since antibodies are present in most adult sera, at least in Britain and the United States. Ready antibody formation suggests that it infects ferrets and hamsters, but it is not known to cause disease in them or in mice. Attempted serial passage in mice unsuccessful; 2 or 3 passages achieved in adult hamsters (Morozenko, 1957).

NEWCASTLE DISEASE

Synonyms: Raniket disease. Avian pneumo-encephalitis. Atypischen Geflügelpest.

In Britain the term fowl-pest is used to include this disease and fowl-plague. The Latin name *Myxovirus multiforme* (Andrewes *et al.*, 1955) is based on the multiformity both of the clinical picture in fowls and of the virus particles.

Original description. Doyle (1927).

Morphology and development. Spherical particles 100–200 mμ in diameter (Dawson & Elford, 1949), or even up to 600 mμ the apparent size varying according to the method of preparation. An inner core is made up of a coiled filament about 17 mμ in diameter with a central hole in it 4 mμ across; a periodicity of 5 mμ in the structure of the filament is produced by tight coiling of a helix, possibly double (Horne & Waterson, 1960, Rott & Schäfer, 1961). Outside the core is a membrane with radially disposed projections incorporating the hæmagglutinin. This hæmagglutinin is found in some preparations in the form of rosettes about 30 mμ across possibly formed by rolling up of pieces of membrane (Rott *et al.*, 1961, Sokol *et al.*, 1961). Filaments of much larger diameter, similar to those of Influenza virus A, are normally absent from allantoic fluids. There is doubt as to the relationship between filaments seen at cell surfaces to the virus on the one hand and cell microvilli on the other (Bang, 1953, Borysko & Bang, 1953). Spheres may change into long irregular pleomorphic forms, some of them sperm-shaped, when active virus is exposed to hypertonic salt solutions (Bang, 1947).

Chemical composition. Contains protein, lipid and RNA (Cunha *et al.*, 1947; Franklin *et al.*, 1957). The helices forming the core have an estimated RNA content of 5·7 per cent (Horne & Waterson, 1960).

Physico-chemical characters. 1 in 5000 formaldehyde inactivates in 1 hour. Further data on resistance to various concentrations of alcohol, merthiolate, formaldehyde, lysol, permanganate are recorded (Cunningham, 1948). Inactivated by heating to 60° C for 30 minutes or to 55° C for 45 minutes. The virus is tough and may persist in hen-houses even after attempted disinfection.

Hæmagglutination. All strains are adsorbed to and agglutinate fowl red blood cells; some strains agglutinate a variety of avian and mammalian red cells. Agglutination tests are best read at 4° C. Elution may be rapid but is often incomplete. The virus particle itself may act as a hæmagglutinin but within infected cells a smaller hæmagglutinating component is present also (Granoff *et al.*, 1950). Human red blood cells treated with some strains of virus are agglutinated by some infectious mononucleosis sera (Burnet & Anderson, 1946). High concentrations of virus will lyse fowl red cells (Kilham, 1949).

Antigenic properties. Immunologically distinct from other members of the group, apart from a possible relationship in the hæmagglutination-inhibition test with mumps virus. Sera of persons convalescent from mumps may show HAI but confusion may be caused by the presence on non-specific inhibitors; these may be present in the sera of various mammals. Immunological differences amongst strains from different sources have been described (Upton *et al.*, 1953).

Interference between NDV and other myxoviruses is demonstrable in fertile eggs; NDV may interfere with poliomyelitis and other enteroviruses in tissue cultures (Chanock, 1955).

Cultivation. Most strains grow readily in all tissues of developing chick embryos and in chick tissue culture, in which they produce cytopathic effects. Cultivation is also reported in cultures of bovine and monkey kidney, human embryonic tissues, HeLa cells and other human lines (Chaproniere & Pereira, 1955; Hallauer, 1958). In some lines the CPE is only visible microscopically (Bankowski & Hyde, 1947). Cultures may remain latently infected for long periods. A plaque technique is described (Bowen, 1958). The properties of a cytotoxic factor developed in culture were described by Mason & Kaufman (1961). Virus cultivated in calf-kidney and some other tissues loses virulence for chicks and may prove useful as an immunizing agent (Gelenezci & Bordt, 1960; Russeff, 1962). Eosinophilic cytoplasmic inclusions and multi-nucleated cells occur in cultures (Oh, 1961).

Distribution. Occurs all over the world in the respiratory and intestinal tracts, blood and tissues of fowls and many other avian species.

Pathogenicity. Causes a fatal disease in fowls, turkeys and other species of birds. Symptoms may be primarily respiratory, or nervous, leading to spasms and paralysis; both may occur—hence the name pneumo-encephalitis. Closed eyes, nasal discharge and watery diarrhœa may be seen. Milder strains cause low mortality but may affect egg production. Incubation period 2–11 days. Conjunctivitis has been caused in poultry workers and laboratory workers; lymphadenitis and some generalised symptoms may occur but recovery is rapid.

Experimentally the virus will, through its toxic effects, cause non-transmissible encephalitis in hamsters and mice (Wenner *et al.*, 1950). Meningo-encephalitis has also been produced in intracerebrally inoculated rhesus monkeys and pigs; and virus even survives for some time in brains of reptiles and dogfish. It may undergo incomplete development in a mouse tumour (Adams & Prince, 1956) but has been adapted to grow progressively (Moore & Diamond, 1956).

Strains of various origin and history behave very differently in chicks, infected eggs and tissue culture; in birds multiplication may occur mainly in turbinates (Burnstein & Bang, 1958) or in spleen and intestine (Kohn, 1959).

Pathological lesions are described by Jungherr *et al.* (1946). Hæmorrhages are seen, though less frequently than in fowl plague: in European strains they are common in the intestine. There may be sinusitis and inflammation of air sacs.

Ecology. Transmission may be through drinking-water; or airborne possibly by inhalation of dust from fæcally contaminated litter; but airborne infection from respiratory secretions is more important, the respiratory tract being many times more effective a portal of entry than the intestinal (Kohn, 1955). The mechanism of transmission was studied by Andrewes & Allison (1961); airborne infection was found to be effective only over short distances. Geese have been suspected of acting as latently infected carriers (Heller, 1957).

Control. Wholesale slaughter of infected stocks is often necessary. Vaccine inactivated by formaldehyde, irradiation or β-propiolactone has been used to protect, but more use is made of virus strains attenuated in one or other way. They may be given into the conjunctiva or wing web or administered in drinking-water, as spray or dust. Even though well attenuated, they may activate other infections, especially chronic respiratory disease.

MUMPS

Synonyms: Epidemic parotitis. Oreillons. *Myxovirus parotitidis.*
Reviews: Cantell (1962).
 Enders & Habel (1956).
 Spooner (1953).

Morphology and development. Virus particles have a soft structure, being contained with a membrane, the whole being readily deformed so that different observers have given widely differing figures (90–600 mμ) for its diameter. 140 mμ is probably a mean figure. The virus core consists of a doubly coiled helix with a periodicity of 5 mμ along the axis, a diameter of 17 mμ and a central hole 4–5 mμ across. Outside the core is a membrane 15–20 mμ thick, its surface covered by small projections (Horne & Waterson, 1960; Horne *et al.*, 1960). Filamentous forms are not reported. Studies with fluorescent antibodies show evidence of presence of antigen in cytoplasm only (Watson, 1952; Traver *et al.*, 1960).

Chemical composition. The helices of the core are thought to be composed of ribonucleoprotein with 10 per cent. ribonucleic acid (Schäfer & Rott, 1959). There is probably lipid in the outer coat.

Physico-chemical characters. Maximum stability at pH 6·5–8·5. Inactivated in 20 minutes at 55° C; at lower temperatures the rate of inactivation varies from strain to strain. Treatment with 0·2 per cent. formalin or by U.V. irradiation inactivates without destroying hæmagglutinin or antigenicity.

Hæmagglutination. Agglutinates red blood cells of fowls, man and other species (Levens & Enders, 1945). Strains of different origin differ in the range of species whose red blood cells are agglutinated and agglutination of different kinds of RBC's is variously affected by inhibitors. The virus is less actively adsorbed to and eluted from RBC's than is influenza. Hæmadsorption is often a more sensitive index of virus activity than hæmagglutination. Virus in high concentration also lyses red blood cells (Morgan *et al.*, 1948).

Antigenic properties. Antigenically homogeneous. As with influenza two complement-fixing antigens can be demonstrated, a smaller, soluble (S) antigen and another (V) associated with the virus particles. In man antibodies to S develop sooner than to V but fade away sooner. A mixed antigen suffices (Burnet & Bull, 1943) for diagnostic tests. Workers disagree as to whether the CF or HAI test is more practically useful. Some feel that non-specific inhibitors make results of HAI tests difficult to interpret. Crossing may occur in both CF and HAI tests with the viruses of Newcastle disease and parainfluenza 1, 2, 3 and 4. The cross-reactions are as a rule only to low titre and they may be "one-way"; human sera are apt to show them better than those of immunized animals (Wenner *et al.*, 1950; Chanock, 1955; DeMeio & Walker, 1957; Gardner, 1957).

An antigen for skin testing has been made by inactivating infected allantoic fluid by heat or otherwise: a positive reaction strongly indicates that the subject is immune (Enders *et al.*, 1946).

Interference. Mumps is reported to interfere in mice with PVM (pneumonia virus of mice) and with WEE in the mouse brain; heated Influenza B interferes with mumps in eggs. Cantell (1959) has studied auto-interference leading to diminished yield when chick embryos are infected with undiluted inocula; it is not certain whether the von Magnus type of incomplete virus is responsible.

Cultivation. Amniotic or yolk-sac inoculation can be used for primary isolations (Habel, 1945). Growth is slower than with influenza. It is best to use 7–8 day old eggs, incubated at 33°–36° C for 4–5 days after inoculation. With "wild" virus, growth may not occur in every egg inoculated but adaptation soon occurs. The allantoic route can then be used and high titres of virus may be obtained with some strains (e.g. Enders) though not with all. In large doses the virus will act on tissue cultures of monkey kidney and HeLa and other human cells, producing giant cells due to a cytolytic property (Henle *et al.*, 1954); this may be analogous to its hæmolytic effect. Cytoplasmic inclusions are also formed in cultures. Serial passage is not necessarily achieved though this is possible with recently isolated strains of virus (HeLa cells and monkey kidney). Growth in mouse embryo cultures is also reported (Kilham & Murphy, 1952) and in Maitland-type cultures of chick amnion (Watson & Cheever, 1955).

A plaque technique may be combined with hæmadsorption for measuring virus activity (Hotchin *et al.*, 1960). Persistent infection of cell-cultures may be demonstrated, as with Newcastle disease (*v*. p. 118).

Pathogenicity. Causes, in man, parotitis, sometimes meningoencephalitis, orchitis, oöphoritis, pancreatitis and other complications. The incubation period is usually 18–21 days. Experimentally it produces similar disease in rhesus monkeys and other primates and has been adapted to multiply in suckling hamster brains. Suckling mice can also be infected intracerebrally, more readily after previous adaptation to hamsters or after cultivation in mouse embryo tissue culture (Kilham & Murphy, 1952). So can suckling rats (Pospišil & Brychtová, 1951). In ferrets inoculated intranasally bronchiolitis and pneumonitis were produced but not more than 3 passages in series could be achieved (Gordon *et al.*, 1956). Serial passage by the intranasal route was also reported in adult hamsters (Burr & Nagler, 1953). Intra-ocular infection of guinea pigs leads to virus multiplication and production of corneal opacity (Bolin *et al.*, 1952). A virus "toxin" is possibly involved here; so, too, in the experiments of Ogasawara *et al.* (1959) where large doses given intranasally to young mice caused pulmonary consolidation not serially transmissible.

Virus was demonstrable in infected monkeys only in the salivary glands and CNS. The attack in their salivary glands is on the acinar cells (Johnson & Goodpasture, 1936).

Ecology. Transmission is from salivary secretions; patients are infectious from 6 days before clinical onset till 9 days after. Virus has been found in the urine regularly during the first 5 days and as late as the 15th day (Utz & Szwed, 1962). It may also be excreted in the milk. It may be present in saliva of persons with symptomless infections (Henle *et al.*, 1948).

Control. A formalin-killed vaccine has been used for immunization with varying success (Hallauer, 1958; Henle *et al.*, 1951a). Attenuated live virus has been given by spray (Henle *et al.*, 1951b); more recently it has been given intradermally to some thousands of children in the U.S.S.R.: a tenfold reduction in incidence is claimed (Smorodintsev *et al.*, 1958; Kliachko *et al.*, 1959).

PARA-INFLUENZA VIRUSES

The para-influenza viruses (Andrewes *et al.*, 1959) have the characters of the myxovirus group but some properties set them apart from the typical influenza viruses A and B, while tending to group them with the viruses of mumps and Newcastle disease (Waterson, 1962).

Morphology. They are larger than true influenza viruses: their nucleoprotein antigen has a diameter of 17 mμ (against 9 mμ). They are more easily disrupted and not inactivated by hydroxylamine. Virus multiplication so far as known is wholly within the cytoplasm and definite cytoplasmic inclusion bodies can be demonstrated. Filamentous forms are not recorded (though present perhaps in

NDV); true recombination and formation of incomplete virus do not seem to occur.

Physico-chemical characters. The viruses are ether sensitive.

Hæmagglutination may not be readily demonstrable until after adaptation to growth in the laboratory. Virus is, however, readily demonstrated by hæmadsorption, the clumping of guinea pig RBC's on infected cells in tissue culture (Vogel & Shelokov, 1957). The viruses are also hæmolytic. Receptors on sensitive RBC's are removed by receptor-destroying enzyme.

Antigenic properties. Para-influenza viruses 1, 2 and 3, mumps and NDV, while antigenically distinct from each other, all show some cross-reaction either in the neutralisation or CF test with at least one other member of the group. Thus with certain sera one can show cross-reactions between mumps and NDV, mumps and para-influenzas 1, 2 and 3 and between para-influenzas 1 and 2 (*cf.* Cook *et al.*, 1959).

Cultivation of newly isolated strains in fertile eggs is usually harder than for influenza; it has not yet been certainly reported for para-influenza 4.

Ecology. Para-influenzas 1, 2 and 3 are particularly infections of small children. Their natural history is discussed by Chanock, *et al.* (1961a).

Para-influenza 1

Synonyms: Sendai. Hæmadsorption virus 2 (HA2). New-born pneumonitis virus. Hæmagglutinating virus of Japan (HVJ). Influenza D.

It was proposed in 1959 (Andrewes *et al.*) that both Sendai and HA2 viruses should be included under para-influenza 1, on the grounds of the close serological relationship of the two agents. Zhdanov (1960) has since argued in favour of their separation.

Reviews: Huebner *et al.* (1958).

Morphology. Diameter variously estimated as 133–250 mμ. Resembles influenza in having a double helical core of nucleoprotein

17 mμ in diameter with regularly arranged subunits; and outside this an outer membrane which again has subunits, this time arranged radially as surface projections (Horne & Waterson, 1960). These projections are 13–15 mμ long and 10–20 mμ wide (Hosaka et al., 1961). There may be an appearance of tails, as in NDV in preparations suspended in saline (Nishikawa, 1954). Preparations stained by fluorescent antibody suggest to Traver et al. (1960) that all viral development occurs in the cytoplasm. Others (Lotte & Kirillova, 1962) have detected specific antigen also in the nucleus.

Chemical composition. An RNA virus.

Physico-chemical characters. Specific gravity 1·12 to 1·13. Stable at −60° C.

Hæmagglutination is readily shown after passage in eggs or tissue culture but on first isolation the hæmadsorption test is more sensitive. Hæmagglutination for human O and guinea pig cells is best done at room temperature (Dick et al., 1961). Cells of numerous other species (but not horse) are also agglutinated (Fukumi et al., 1954). There is adsorption to and enzymatic elution from sensitive cells. The virus will also cause hæmolysis of fowl and other RBC's; this can be avoided by using formalin-treated cells. The hæmagglutinin is apparently more labile—at 47° to 55° C—than that of influenza, and also trypsin-sensitive.

Antigenic properties. Various serological tests are applicable as with other myxoviruses. For demonstrating antihæmagglutinins, Dick & Mogabgab (1961) advise mixing serum and virus, holding for 30 minutes at room temperature, then adding human O RBC's. In CF tests Sendai and HA2 strains cross-react, the former having more group specificity. Bukrinskaya et al. (1962) have described differences found by the CF test between "HA2" and "Sendai" strains of different origins. In hæmagglutinin inhibition and neutralization tests, the relationship is less evident (Cook et al., 1959). Cross-relations with other myxoviruses have been described (p. 123); they are more evident in human sera than in those of immunized animals. Antibodies in fact are present in most adult sera. Reinfections may occur during childhood. Antibodies are also present in sera of guinea pigs of some stocks.

Interference of common cold (rhino-) viruses with Sendai virus in culture was reported by Hitchcock & Tyrrell (1960). Influenza B also interferes with its growth.

Cultivation. *In fertile eggs.* Some but not all newly isolated strains will grow in fertile eggs; Sendai strains grow better. The amniotic route is most sensitive; on passage, growth occurs after inoculation into allantoic cavity and yolk-sac. Embryos are usually not killed. Growth in the allantoic cavity is best at 35·5° C (Fukai & Suzuki, 1955).

In tissue culture HA2 strains grow in tissues of man, monkey, chick embryo and swine. Sendai strains multiply in kidney cells from numerous other species. Cytopathic effects may be absent and the virus is then detected by hæmadsorption. Syncytial formation in cultures of HeLa cells is attributed to cell-coalescence (Marston, 1958); this may be caused by a cell-wall-destroying enzyme (Zhdanov & Bukrinskaya, 1962).

Distribution. The Sendai strain occurs as a latent infection of laboratory mice in Japan, China and the U.S.S.R. This fact makes it difficult to interpret the claims that this virus has been isolated from disease in man, in swine and from hamsters, since in most instances, mice have been used to recover the virus. The HA2 strain undoubtedly occurs as an infection of man, usually in childhood.

Pathogenicity. The Sendai strain causes latent infection in laboratory mice (Chu *et al.*, 1956), being activated so that it causes fatal pneumonia after mouse-to-mouse passage. For reasons mentioned above, some workers are sceptical of claims that the Sendai virus has caused pneumonitis in new-born children (Kuroya *et al.*, 1953), or influenza-like outbreaks in adults (Gerngross, 1957; Zhdanov *et al.*, 1957). Ability to cause pneumonia in pigs (Sasahara, 1955) seems to be well established.

The HA2 strain, on the other hand, has been isolated only from man, originally by Chanock *et al.* (1958), from children suffering from acute laryngo-tracheitis. The virus has only infrequently been isolated from adults but seems likely to be a common cause of childhood infections.

Experimentally. Adults have been experimentally infected with HA2 and, after an incubation of 5 or 6 days, have developed upper respiratory symptoms, sometimes with fever, sometimes resembling common colds (Reichelderfer *et al.*, 1958; Tyrrell *et al.*, 1959).

Strains of Sendai virus vary in pathogenicity for mice. The virus will kill mice when inoculated IC but serial passage by this route has not succeeded. It will produce inapparent infection of ferrets, monkeys and pigs and will produce fatal pneumonitis in rats (Kuroya *et al.*, 1953) and Chinese hamsters (Chun & Chu, 1956). It may cause symptoms in ferrets (Jensen *et al.*, 1955).

The HA2 strain is less pathogenic for mice, producing symptomless infections in them; also (Petersen, 1959) in ferrets, hamsters and rhesus monkeys.

Pathological lesions. Lung lesions in mice caused by the Sendai strain are similar to those produced by influenza. Virus can be recovered in small quantities from various viscera after fatal infections.

Ecology. As already mentioned Sendai strains are latent amongst some laboratory mice. Attempts to induce chronic latent infections in clean stocks of laboratory mice have failed, though Sawicki (1962) found that virus would persist for a few weeks in a masked form.

The term para-influenza 1 appears to include a number of viruses closely related to each other, rather more distantly to the other para-influenza viruses. There are human strains and murine strains; their relationships and pathogenic potentialities are not yet wholly clear.

Control. Jensen *et al.* (1962) report that formolized egg-adapted virus will form a potent immunizing vaccine for man.

Para-influenza 2

Synonyms: Croup-associated (CA) virus. Virus of acute laryngo-tracheo-bronchitis.
General account: Chanock (1956). Beale *et al.* (1958).

Morphology. The size was estimated by Chanock as 90–135 mμ.

Physico-chemical characters. Stable at −70° C. Inactivated in 30 minutes at 58° C.

Hæmagglutination is reported for RBC's of new-born chicks; it is not so good for human O cells. The optimum pH is 8. Virus elutes from the cells when they are warmed to 37° C; the cells then disperse, only to reagglutinate on being returned to 4° C; any enzymatic action is very weak.

Antigenic properties. Neutralizing antibodies are easily detected in tissue culture; a micro-method for CF has also been successfully applied (Beale *et al.*, 1958). Antibodies develop in the course of infections in children: they occur in 90 per cent. of adult human sera—also in some "normal" cynomolgus sera (Chanock, 1956). Cross-reactions with mumps are described (p. 120). The virus is closely related to simian myxovirus SV5 (p. 130).

Cultivation. The virus grows poorly in eggs inoculated amniotically, not reaching a high enough titre for agglutinin to be demonstrable unless after adaptation (De Meio, 1963). It grows well in tissue cultures of HeLa cells, human embryonic lung and amnion, dog kidney, monkey kidney, the last being best for primary isolation (Mogabgab *et al.*, 1961). CPE may be slight at first, but becomes better on passage, appearing in 3 or 4 days. Characteristic effects are formation of syncytia and, in human amnion, appearances recalling a sponge or Swiss cheese. Cytoplasmic inclusions also appear, being less acidophilic and developing more slowly than those of related viruses (Brandt, 1961). Plaques can be produced on monolayers of *Cercopithecus* kidney (Tyrrell *et al.*, 1962).

Pathogenicity. Associated particularly with acute laryngotracheitis (croup) in children aged 6 months to 3 years; tracheotomy has had to be considered in many such cases (Beale *et al.*, 1958). There is evidence that it may occasionally cause minor upper respiratory infections in adults. Mild illnesses resembling common colds have been produced in adult volunteers (Taylor Robinson & Bynoe, 1963). No pathological effects have been produced by inoculation into adult or suckling mice.

Para-influenza 3

Synonyms: Hæmadsorption virus 1.
General account: Chanock *et al.* (1958).

Morphology. A little smaller than para-influenza 1 (diameter 190–250 mμ). As with it there seems to be a helix, 15 mμ across, arranged round a hollow core and with a "herring-bone" pattern visible (Waterson *et al.*, 1961; Stefanov, 1961). A membrane containing the hæmagglutinin units encloses this. Bovine strains are similar (Reczko & Bögel, 1962).

Physico-chemical characters. Survives 30 minutes between pH 4·5 and 9·5. Almost wholly inactivated in 20–30 minutes at 50° C. Survives well at −25° C but only a few days at room temperature (Denny, 1960).

Hæmagglutination of human O, guinea pig and some fowl RBC's is seen after adaptation. The hæmadsorption test is more sensitive for newly isolated virus, the pattern being more diffuse than with some myxoviruses (Bukrinskaia, 1960). The virus also hæmolyses sensitive red cells; bovine strains hæmagglutinate and hæmolyse better at 37° than at 0° C (Hermodsson *et al.*, 1961).

Antigenic properties. Strains of human and bovine origin can be differentiated by neutralization, agglutinin-inhibition and CF tests by the aid of immune guinea pig sera (Ketler *et al.*, 1961; Abinanti *et al.*, 1961). Cross-relations with other myxoviruses have been described (p. 123); they are particularly evident with human sera. Serological evidence supports the idea that this virus is responsible for respiratory disease in children. The CF test is useful for diagnosis.

Interference. Interferes with the growth of poliomyelitis in culture (Chang *et al.*, 1906).

Cultivation. Grows when inoculated into developing eggs amniotically, not allantoically; hæmagglutinins are produced in the fluids. Monkey kidney tissue cultures are best for primary isolation but the virus can be adapted to grow in HeLa and other human cell-lines and (Maassab & Loh, 1960) in chick kidney, producing CPE. Bovine strains, at least, grow in calf kidney cultures. Syncytia and cytoplasmic inclusions are produced in HeLa and KB. cells, less readily in monkey kidney (Deibel & Hotchin, 1961). A substance "syncytin" has been suggested as concerned in syncytium formation (Chany & Cook, 1960). Plaques may be demonstrated on monolayers of a line of human cells (FC) (Deibel, 1959).

Distribution. Human strains have been recognized in the United States, Britain, France and the U.S.S.R. Bovine strains have been recovered from normal as well as infected cattle in the United States and Scandinavia.

Pathogenicity. The virus has been frequently isolated from small children with pharyngitis, bronchiolitis and pneumonia, especially in nursery schools; much less frequently from unaffected children. These facts, supported by serological evidence, suggest that it is the cause of many of these infections (Chanock *et al.*, 1958). It seems to be uncommon as a cause of natural respiratory infections in adults, though on inoculation into volunteers it has apparently produced some common colds (Tyrrell *et al.*, 1959).

It seems to be non-pathogenic for suckling mice or rabbits but to produce inapparent infection on IN inoculation into young hamsters (McKinney *et al.*, 1959; Craighead *et al.*, 1960).

Bovine strains have been recovered particularly from cattle with shipping fever; the facts suggest that a virus which is normally harmless, may produce disease in cattle under conditions of stress. Experimental inoculation into calves has been followed by fever, conjunctivitis and muco-purulent rhinitis (Bakos & Dinter, 1960).

Control. A formalinized vaccine has been used to vaccinate calves: when it was combined with an adjuvant good antibodies were produced, and there was protection against infection (McLelland *et al.*, 1961; Hamparian *et al.*, 1961).

Para-influenza 4

Description: Johnson *et al.*, 1960 (name proposed tentatively).

Morphology. 192–248 mμ in diameter.

Physico-chemical characters. Ether sensitive. Labile at room temperature or 37° C.

Hæmagglutination. Agglutinates guinea-pig RBC's at 4° and room temperature, not at 37° C. Receptors destroyed by RDE. Hæmadsorption demonstrable with guinea pig or rhesus RBC's, poorly with human O, not at all with chick or rat cells.

Antigenic properties. Antibody rises occurred in sera of infected persons. Adult human sera indicate a cross-relation between this virus and mumps.

Cultivation. *In eggs*—doubtful.

In tissue culture—goes to a titre of 10^6/ml, with CPE, after passage in monkey kidney. No growth in HeLa and other cell-lines nor in rabbit kidney.

Pathogenicity. Isolated from 1 student and 30 small children with minor respiratory illness. Relation to human disease not yet established.

Not pathogenic for laboratory animals, but inoculated guinea pigs developed very good antibodies.

SIMIAN MYXOVIRUSES

Synonyms: SV5 (SA virus, of Schultz & Habel (1959) and DA virus of Hsiung (1959) are identical). Simian para-influenza.

Description: Emery & Yorke (1960).

Morphology. 90–150 mμ by gradocol filtration.

Physico-chemical characters. Ether sensitive.

Hæmagglutination of chick RBC's at $0°$ C. The hæmadsorption test will also reveal the virus in infected tissue cultures.

Antigenic properties. Neutralization, hæmagglutinin inhibition and CF tests are applicable; there is some cross-reaction with para-influenza 2 and perhaps 3 by complement fixation (Chanock *et al.*, 1961b). There is probably a second simian myxovirus, referred to as SV41 and distinct from SV5. These may both come to be classified as simian strains of para-influenza 2.

Cultivation. *In fertile eggs*. Multiplies in amniotic and allantoic cavities (Chanock *et al.*, 1961). Growth is reported in monkey and bovine tissue cultures, not those of pig, dog, cat or rat.

Pathogenicity. Apparently very frequently present in cultures of "normal" rhesus or cynomolgus monkeys, but not known to be naturally pathogenic. The DA strain is reported to be a human pathogen (Hsiung, 1959); this claim has been disputed.

Survived 3 but not 7 IC passages in suckling mice; did not survive 4 IN passages in mice (Andrewes & Worthington, 1959). The SA virus of Schultz & Habel (1959) is believed to be identical with this but it does not seem certain that their original virus, which produced encephalitis in hamsters and other species and multiplied in eggs, was the same as that subsequently studied in tissue-culture. The work is therefore difficult to interpret.

Control. Workers using monkey tissue cultures for isolating viruses have been forced to include antisera to this virus in their media, lest this virus turns up and confuses the issue.

REFERENCES

Abinanti, F. R., Chanock, R. M., Cook, M. K., Wong, D., & Warfield, M. (1961) *Proc. Soc. exp. Biol.* (*N.Y.*), **106**, 466.
Ada, G. L., & Perry, B. (1955) *Nature* (*Lond.*), **175**, 854.
Ada, G. L., & Perry, B (1956) *J. gen. Microbiol.*, **19**, 40.
Adams, R. W., & Prince, A. M. (1956) *J. exp. Med.*, **106**, 617.
Andrewes, C. H., & Allison, A. C. (1961) *J. Hyg.* (*Lond.*), **59**, 285.
Andrewes, C. H., Bang, F. B., & Burnet, F. M. (1955) *Virology*, **1**, 176.
Andrewes, C. H., Bang, F. B., Chanock, R. M., & Zhdanov, V. M. (1959) *Virology*, **8**, 129.
Andrewes, C. H., & Horstmann, D. M. (1949) *J. gen. Microbiol.*, **3**, 290.
Andrewes, C. H., & Worthington, G. (1959) *Bull. Wld. Hlth. Org.*, **20**, 435.
Bakos, K., & Dinter, Z. (1960) *Zbl. Bakt. I. Abt. Orig.*, **180**, 1.
Bang, F. B. (1947) *Proc. Soc. exp. Biol.* (*N.Y.*), **64**, 135.
Bang, F. B. (1953) *Bull. Johns Hopk. Hosp.*, **92**, 291 and 309.
Bankowski, R. A., & Hyde, J. (1957) *Amer. J. vet. Res.*, **18**, 743.
Barb, K., Farkas, E., Romváry, J., & Takátsy, G. (1952) *Acta virol.* (Eng. Ed.), **6**, 207.
Barry, R. D. (1960) *Aust. J. exp. Biol. med. Sci.*, **38**, 499.
Beale, A. J., McLeod, D. L., Stackiw, W., & Rhodes, A. J. (1938) *Brit. med. J.*, **1**, 302.
Becker, W. B. (1963) *Virology*, **20**, 318.
Blaskovic, D., Rathova, L., & Borscky, L. (1959) *Acta virol.* (Eng. Ed.), **3**, 17.
Bolin, V. S., Anderson, J. A., & Leymaster, G. R. (1952) *Proc. Soc. exp. Biol.* (*N.Y.*), **79**, 7.
Borysko, E., & Bang, F. B. (1953) *Bull. Johns Hopk. Hosp.*, **92**, 25.
Bower, R. K. (1958) *J. Bact.*, **75**, 496.
Breitenfeld, P. M., & Schäfer, W. (1957) *Virology*, **4**, 328.
Bukrinskaya, A. G. (1962) *Probl. Virol.* (Eng. Ed.), **4**, 146.
Bukrinskaya, A. G., Ho, Y-D., & Gorbunova, A. S. (1962) *Acta virol.* (Eng. Ed.), **6**, 352.
Burnet, F. M., & Anderson, S. G. (1946) *Brit. J. exp. Path.*, **27**, 236.
Burnet, F. M., & Bull, D. R. (1943) *Aust. J. exp. Biol. med. Sci.*, **21**, 55.
Burnet, F. M., & Lind, P. E. (1951) *J. gen. Microbiol*, **5**, 59 and 67.
Burnstein, T., & Bang, F. B. (1958) *Bull. Johns Hopk. Hosp.*, **102**, 127 and 135.
Burr, M. M., & Nagler, F. R. (1953) *Proc. Soc. exp. Biol.* (*N.Y.*), **83**, 714.
Buzzell, A., & Hanig, M. (1958) *Advanc. Virus Res.*, **5**, 289.
Chanock, R. M. (1955) *Proc. Soc. exp. Biol.* (*N.Y.*), **89**, 379.

Chanock, R. M. (1956) *J. exp. Med.*, **104**, 555.

Chanock, R. M., Bell, J. A., & Parrott, R. H. (1961a)   *Perspectives in Virology*, **2**, 126. Minneapolis, Burgess.

Chanock, R. M., Johnson, K. M., Cook, M. K., Wong, D. C., & Vargosko, A. (1961b) *Amer. Rev. resp. Dis.*, **83**:2, 125.

Chanock, R. M., Parrott, R. H., Cook, M. K., Andrews, B. E., Bell, J. A., Reichelderfer, T., Zapikian, A. Z., Mastrota, F. M., & Huebner, R. J. (1958) *New Engl. J. Med.*, **258**, 207.

Chang, C., Daniel, P., & Lepine, P. (1960) *C. R. Acad. Sci. (Paris)*, **250**, 229.

Chany, C., & Cook, M. K. (1960) *Ann. Inst. Pasteur*, **98**, 920.

Chaproniere, D. M., & Pereira, H. G. (1955) *Brit. J. exp. Path.*, **36**, 607.

Chu, C. M. (1951) *J. gen. Microbiol.*, **5**, 739.

Chun, H., & Chu, C. M. (1956) *Acta microbiol. sinica*, **4**, 47.

Cohen, A., & Belyavin, G. (1959) *Virology*, **7**, 59

Colter, J. S., & Ellem, K. O. (1961) *Ann. Rev. Microbiol.*, **15**, 219.

Cook, M. K., Andrews, B. E., Fox, H. H., Turner, H. C., James, W. D., & Chanock, R. M. (1959) *Amer. J. Hyg.*, **69**, 250.

Craighead, J. E., Cook, M. K., & Chanock, R. M. (1960) *Proc. Soc. exp. Biol. (N.Y.)*, **104**, 301.

Cunha, R., Weil, M. L., Beard, D., Taylor, A. R., Sharp, D. G., & Beard, J. W. (1947) *J. Immunol.*, **55**, 69.

Cunningham, C. H. (1948) *Ann. J. vet. Res.*, **9**, 195.

Dawson, I. M., & Elford, W. J. (1949) *J. gen. Microbiol.*, **3**, 298.

Deibel, R. (1959) *Virology*, **8**, 262.

Deibel, R., & Hotchin, J. E. (1961) *Virology*, **14**, 66.

De Meio, J. L. (1963) *J. Bact.*, **85**, 943.

De Meio, J. L., & Walker, J. S. (1957) *J. Immunol.*, **78**, 465.

Denny, F. W. (1960) *Fed. Proc.*, **19**, 409.

Dick, E. C., Mogabgab, W. J., & Holmes, B. (1961) *Amer. J. Hyg.*, **73**, 263.

Dick, E. C., & Mogabgab, W. J. (1961) *Amer. J. Hyg.*, **73**, 273.

Dinter, Z., & Bakos, K. (1950) *Münch. tierärztl. Wschr.*, **6**, 101.

Doyle, T. M. (1927) *J. comp. Path.*, **40**, 144.

Dunham, C. G., & Macneal, W. J. (1943) *J. Lab. clin. Med.*, **28**, 947.

Edward, D. G. ff. (1941) *Lancet*, **2**, 664.

Emery, J. B., & Yorke, C. J. (1960) *Virology*, **11**, 313.

Enders, J. F., & Habel, K. (1956) in *Diagnostic Procedures for Virus and Rickettsial Diseases*. 2nd ed. p. 281. New York: Amer. publ. Hlth. Ass.

Enders, J. F., Kane, L. W., Maris, E. P., & Stokes, J. (1946) *J. exp. Med.*, **84**, 341.

Evans, C. A., & Rickard, E. R. (1945) *Proc. Soc. exp. Biol. (N.Y.)*, **58**, 73.

Findlay, G. M., & Mackenzie, R. D. (1937) *Brit. J. exp. Path.*, **18**, 258.

Flewett, T. H., & Challice, C. E. (1957) *J. gen. Microbiol.*, **5**, 279.

Francis, T. (1940) *Science*, **92**, 405.

Francis, T. (1947) *J. exp. Med.*, **85**, 1.

Francis, T. (1959) in *Viral and Rickettsial Infections of Man*. 3rd Ed. p. 633. Ed. Rivers and Horsfall. London: Pitman Medical.

Francis, T., Quilligan, J. J., & Minuse, E. (1950) *Science*, **112**, 495.

Franklin, R. M. (1958) *Virology*, **6**, 525.

Franklin, R. M., Rubin, H., & Davis, C. A. (1957) *Virology*, **3**, 96.

Fraňo, J. Bystrický, V., & Vrtîak, J. (1958) *Vet. Čes.*, **7**, 411.

Fukai, K., & Suzuki, T. (1955) *Med. J. Osaka Univ.*, **6**, 1.

Fukumi, H., Nishikawa, F., & Kitayama, T. (1954) *Jap. J. med. Sci., Biol.*, **7**, 345.

Gardner, P. S. (1957) *Brit. med. J.*, **1**, 1143.

Gelenczei, E., & Bordt, D. (1960) *Amer. J. vet. Res.*, **21**, 987.

Gerngross, O. G. (1957) *Probl. Virol. (Eng. Ed.)*, **2**, 71.

Gompels, A. E. H. (1953) *J. gen. Microbiol.*, **9**, 140.

Gordon, I., Pavri, K., & Cohen, S. M. (1956) *J. Immunol.*, **76**, 328.

Gottschalk, A. (1959) in *The Viruses* Vol. 3. p. 51. Ed. Burnet and Stanley. New York: Academic Press.

Granoff, A., Liu, O. C., & Henle, W. (1950) *Proc. Soc. exp. Biol.* (*N.Y.*), **75**, 684.

Green, I. J., Lieberman, M., & Mogabgab, W. J. (1957) *J. Immunol.*, **78**, 233.

Haas, R., & Wulff, H. (1957) *Z. Hyg. Infekt.-Kr.*, **143**, 568.

Habel, K. (1945) *Publ. Hlth. Rep.* (*Washington*), **60**, 201.

Habel, K. (1951) *Amer. J. Hyg.*, **54**, 295.

Hallauer, C. (1958) *Arch. ges. Virusforsch.*, **8**, 397.

Hallauer, C., & Kronauer, G. (1959) *Arch. ges. Virusforsch.*, **9**, 232.

Hamparian, V. V., Washko, F. V., Ketler, A., & Hilleman, M. R. (1961) *J. Immunol.*, **87**, 139.

Heller, O. (1957) *Mh. Vet.-Med.*, **12**, 218.

Henle, G., Baske, W. J., Burgoon, J. S., Burgoon, C. F., Hunt, C. F., Hunt, C. R., & Henle, W. (1951a) *J. Immunol.*, **66**, 561.

Henle, G., Deinhardt, F., & Girardi, A. (1954) *Proc. Soc. exp. Biol.* (*N.Y.*), **87**, 386.

Henle, G., Henle, W., Wendell, K. K., & Rosenberg, P. (1948) *J. exp. Med.*, **88**, 223.

Henle, G., Stokes, J., Burgoon, J. S., Baske, W., Burgoon, C. F., & Henle, W. (1957b) *J. Immunol.*, **66**, 579.

Hermodsson, S., Dinter, Z., & Bakos, K. (1961) *Acta. path. microbiol. scand.*, **51**, 75.

Hers, J. F. P., Mulder, J., Masurel, N., & v. d. Kuip, L. (1962) *J. Path. Bact.*, **83**, 207.

Hirst, G. K. (1941) *Science*, **94**, 22.

Hirst, G. K. (1950) *J. exp. Med.*, **91**, 177.

Hitchcock, G., & Tyrrell, D. A. J. (1960) *Lancet*, **1**, 237.

Horne, R. W., & Waterson, A. P. (1960) *J. molec. Biol.*, **2**, 75.

Horne, R. W., Waterson, A. P., Wilding, P., & Farnham, A. E. (1960) *Virology*, **11**, 79.

Hosaka, Y., Nishi, Y., & Fukai, K. (1961) *Biken's J.*, **4**, 243.

Hotchin, J. E., Deibel, R., & Benson, L. M. (1960) *Virology*, **10**, 275.

Hoyle, L., Horne, R. W., & Waterson, A. P. (1961) *Virology*, **13**, 448.

Hsiung, G-D. (1959) *Virology*, **9**, 717.

Huebner, R. J., Rowe, W. P., & Chanock, R. M. (1958) *Ann. Rev. Microbiol.*, **12**, 49.

Isaacs, A., & Lindenmann, J. (1957) *Proc. roy. Soc. B.*, **147**, 258.

Jensen, K. E., Minuse, E., & Ackermann, W. W. (1955) *J. Immunol.*, **75**, 71.

Jensen, K. E., Peeler, B. E., & Dulworth, W. G. (1962) *J. Immunol.*, **89**, 216.

Johnson, C. D., & Goodpasture, E. W. (1936) *Amer. J. Path.*, **12**, 495.

Johnson, K. M., Chanock, R. M., Cook, M. K., & Huebner, R. J. (1960) *Amer. J. Hyg.*, **71**, 81.

Jungherr, E. L., Tyzzer, E. E., Brandly, C. A., & Moses, H. E. (1956) *Amer. J. vet. Res.*, **7**, 250.

Kammer, H., & Hanson, R. P. (1962) *J. infect. Dis.*, **110**, 99.

Kates, M., Allison, A. C., Tyrrell, D. A. J., & James, A. T. (1961) *Biochim. biophys. Acta.* (*Amst.*), **52**, 455.

Ketler, A., Hamparian, V. V., & Hilleman, M. R. (1961) *J. Immunol.*, **87**, 126.

Kilbourne, E. D. (1963) *Progr. med. Virol.*, **5**, 81.

Kilham, L. (1949) *Proc. Soc. exp. Biol.* (*N.Y.*), **71**, 63.

Kilham, L., & Murphy, H. W. (1952) *Proc. Soc. exp. Biol.* (*N.Y.*), **80**, 495.

Kliachko, N. S., Gusarskaia, I. L., Maslennikova, L. K., Sena, N. L., & Tsirlina, S. S. (1959) *Probl. Virol.*, **3,** 25.
Kohn, A. (1955) *Amer. J. vet. Res.* **16,** 450.
Kohn, A. (1959) *Amer. J. Hyg.*, **69,** 167.
Koppel, Z., Vrtiak, J., Vasil, M., & Spierz, S. (1956) *Veterinarstvi*, **6,** 267.
Kuroya, M., Ishida, N., & Shiratori, T. (1953) *Yokohama med. Bull.*, **4,** 217.
Laidlaw, P. P. (1935) *Lancet*, **1,** 1118.
Ledinko, N. (1955) *Nature (Lond.)*, **175,** 999.
Levens, J. H., & Enders, J. F. (1945) *Science*, **102,** 117.
Lief, F. S., & Henle, W. (1958) *Bull. Wld. Hlth. Org.*, **20,** 411.
Lotte, V. D., & Kirillova, F. M. (1962) *Probl. Virol.* (Eng. Ed.), **6,** 711.
Maassab, H. F. (1963) *J. Immunol.*, **90,** 265.
Maassab, H. F., & Loh, P. C. (1960) *Proc. Soc. exp. Biol. (N.Y.)*, **109,** 897.
McKinney, R. W., England, B. L., & Froeda, S. (1959) *Amer. J. Hyg.*, **70,** 280.
McLelland, L., Hampil, B., Hamparian, V. V., Potash, L., Ketler, A., & Hilleman, M. R. (1961) *J. Immunol.*, **87,** 134.
Magill, T. P. (1940) *Proc. Soc. exp. Biol. (N.Y.)*, **45,** 162.
Maggiora, A., & Valenti, G. L. (1903) *Zbl. Bakt. I. Abt. Orig.*, **34,** 326.
Marston, R. Q. (1958) *Proc. Soc. exp. Biol. (N.Y.)*, **98,** 853.
Mason, E. J., & Kaufmann, N. (1961) *Brit. J. exp. Path.*, **42,** 118.
Mogabgab, W. J. (1962) *J. Bact.*, **83,** 209.
Mogabgab, W. J., Dick, E. C., & Holmes, B. (1961) *Amer. J. Hyg.*, **74,** 304.
Mogabgab, W. J., Green, I. J., Dierkhising, O. C., & Philips, I. A. (1955) *Proc. Soc. exp. Biol. (N.Y.)*, **89,** 654.
Moore, A. E., & Diamond, L. C. (1956) *J. Immunol.*, **77,** 81.
Morgan, H. R., Enders, J. F., & Wagley, P. F. (1948) *J. exp. Med.*, **88,** 503.
Morozenko, M. A. (1957) *Probl. Virol.* (Eng. Ed.), **2,** 369.
Moses, H. E., Brandly, C. A., Jones, E. E., & Jungherr, E. L. (1948) *Amer. J. vet. Res.*, **9,** 314.
Nishikawa, F., & Fukumi, H. (1954) *Jap. J. med. Sci. Biol.*, **7,** 513.
Ogasawara, K., Sugai, K., & Iijima, S. (1959) *Virology*, **9,** 714.
Oh., J. O. (1961) *Brit. J. exp. Path.*, **42,** 424.
Petersen, K. B. (1959) *Acta path. microbiol. scand.*, **45,** 213.
Peterson, W. D., Davenport, F. M., & Francis, T. (1961) *J. exp. Med.*, **114,** 1023.
Pospisil, L., & Brychtova, J. (1956) *Zbl. Bakt. I. Abt. Orig.*, **165,** 1.
Reichelderfer, T. E., Chanock, R. M., Craighead, J. C., Huebner, R. J., Turner, H. C., James, W., & Ward, T. G. (1958) *Science*, **128,** 779.
Reczko, E., & Bögel, K. (1962) *Arch. ges. Virusforsch.*, **12,** 404.
Rice, J. P. (1930) *Med. Res. Coun. System of Bacteriology*, **7,** 219. (H.M.S.O.)
Rott, R., Frank, H., & Schäfer, W. (1961) *Z. Naturforsch.*, **16b,** 625.
Rott, R., & Schäfer, W. (1961) *Virology*, **14,** 298.
Russeff, C. (1962) *Zbl. Bakt. I. Abt. Orig.*, **184,** 403.
Sasahara, J. (1955) *Exp. Rep.* 3, *Nat. Inst. anim. Hlth., Tokio*, p. 13.
Sawicki, L. (1962) *Acta virol.* (Eng. Ed.), **6,** 347.
Schäfer, W., & Rott, R. (1959) *Z. Naturforsch.*, **14b,** 629.
Schäfer, W., & Zillig, W. (1952) *Z. Naturforsch.*, **9b,** 779.
Schultz, E. W., & Habel, K. (1959) *J. Immunol.*, **82,** 274.
Shope, R. E. (1931) *J. exp. Med.*, **54,** 373.
Shope, R. E. (1935) *Harvey lectures.*
Shope, R. E. (1941) *J. exp. Med.*, **74,** 41 and 49.
Smith, W., Andrews, C. H., & Laidlaw, P. P. (1933) *Lancet*, **2,** 66.
Smorodintseff, A. A., Chalkina, O. M., Burov, S. A., & Ilyin, N. A. (1961) *J. Hyg. Epidemiol. Microbiol. Immunol (Moscow)*, **5,** 60.

Sokol, F., Blaškovič, D., & Križanová, O. (1961) Acta. virol. (Eng. Ed.), 5, 153.
Sokol, F., & Schramek, S. (1962) Acta virol. (Eng. Ed.), 6, 373.
Spooner, E. T. C. (1953) Brit. med. Bull., 9, 212.
Stefanov, S. B. (1961) Acta. virol. (Eng. Ed.), 5, 128.
Straub, M. (1937) J. Path. Bact., 45, 75.
Stuart-Harris, C. H. (1939) Lancet, 1, 497.
Sugg, J. Y. (1949) J. Bact., 57, 399.
Takátsy, G., & Barb, K. (1959) Nature (Lond.), 183, 52.
Taylor, A. R., Sharp, D. G., Beard, D., Beard, J. W., Dingle, J. H., & Feller, A. C. (1943) J. Immunol., 47, 261.
Taylor, R. M. (1951) Arch. ges. Virusforsch., 4, 485.
Taylor Robinson, D., & Bynoe, M. L. (1963) in the Press.
Todd, C. (1928) Brit. J. exp. Path., 9, 19.
Traver, M. I., Northrop, R. L., & Walker, D. L. (1960) Proc. Soc. exp. Biol. (N.Y.), 104, 268.
Tyrrell, D. A. J., Petersen, K. B., Sutton, R. N. P., & Pereira, M. S. (1959) Brit. med. J., 2, 909.
Tytell, A. A., Torop, H. A., & McCarthy, F. G. (1962) Proc. Soc. exp. Biol. (N.Y.), 108, 723.
Tumova, B., & Fiserova-Sovinova, O. (1959) Bull. Wld. Hlth. Org., 20, 445.
Upton, E., Hanson, R. P., & Brandly, C. A. (1953) Proc. Soc. exp. Biol. (N.Y.), 84, 691.
Utz., J. P., & Szwed, C. F. (1962) Proc. Soc. exp. Biol. (N.Y.), 110, 841.
van der Veen, J., & Mulder, J. (1950) Studies on the antigenic composition of human influenza A virus strains. Thesis, Leiden.
Vogel, J. E., & Shelokov, A. (1957) Science, 126, 358.
Wagner, R. R., Bennett, I. L., & LeQuire, V. S. (1949) J. exp. Med., 90, 321.
Wang, S. P., & Liu, T. Y. (1958) J. infect. Dis., 103, 178.
Waterson, A. P. (1962), Nature (Lond.), 193, 1163.
Waterson, A. P., Hurrell, J. M. W., & Jensen, K. E. (1963) Arch. ges. Virusforsch., 12, 487.
Waterson, A. P., Rott, R., & Schäfer, W. (1961) Z. Naturforsch., 16b, 154.
Watson, B. K., & Cheever, F. S. (1955) J. Immunol., 75, 161.
Watson, B. K. (1952) Proc. Soc. exp. Biol. (N.Y.), 79, 222.
Weekly morbidity & mortality report, U.S. Public Health Service (1963), 12, 157.
Wenner, A. A., Monley, A., & Todd, R. N. (1950) J. Immunol., 64, 305.
White, J. (1953) Brit. J. exp. Path., 34, 668.
Winternitz, M. C., Watson, I. M., & McNamara, F. P. (1920) The pathology of influenza. Yale Univ. Press.
World Health Org. (1959) Technical report series, No. 170.
Zhdanov, V. M. (1960) Virology, 10, 146.
Zhdanov, V. M., & Bukrinskaya, A. G. (1962) Acta virol. (Eng. Ed.), 6, 105.
Zhdanov, V. M., Ritova, V. V., & Golygina, L. A. (1957) Acta virol. (Eng. Ed.), 1, 216.

5

Viruses probably belonging to the Myxovirus group

There follows an account of 6 viruses which on morphological and other grounds seem to be closely related to the myxoviruses.

The Measles-Distemper-Rinderpest Triad
Review: Warren (1960). Carlström (1962).

There is evidence that these three viruses share some antigenic material in common. There are also a number of points of similarity in the pathological effects they produce. Further, they appear, morphologically, to resemble each other and also the para-influenza viruses. From these and other facts it seems that they are closely related to myxoviruses.

The evidence as regards antigenic relations is as follows:

Measles and Distemper

People with a history of measles are particularly apt to have distemper-neutralizing antibodies in their sera (Carlström, 1957). Measles virus produces some immunity to distemper in ferrets (Adams & Imagawa, 1957). Dogs injected with measles develop poor antibodies to distemper but nevertheless show resistance on challenge (Warren *et al.*, 1960; Gillespie & Karzon, 1960). Dogs recovered from distemper show antibodies to measles.

Measles and Rinderpest

Sera of rinderpest-immune cattle have some neutralizing power against measles (Imagawa *et al.*, 1960). Antibodies to rinderpest may develop in the course of measles.

Distemper and Rinderpest

Rinderpest has immunizing power against distemper in dogs and ferrets (Goret *et al.*, 1960; Polding *et al.*, 1959). Rinderpest sera have neutralizing properties against distemper (Imagawa *et al.*, 1960). Distemper virus will give some immunity against rinderpest to cattle (Gilbert *et al.*, 1960). There are nevertheless anomalous results. Not all immune sera cross against the heterologous viruses. Some authors fail to find evidence of cross-reactions. Possibly the shared antigen is deficient in certain circumstances: there are suggestions that less crossing occurs with egg-adapted viruses.

MEASLES

Synonyms: Morbilli. Masern. Rougeole. The MINIA monkey virus of Ruckle (1958) is identical.

Reviews: Babbott & Gordon (1954—for older literature). McCarthy (1959). Black, Reissig & Melnick (1959). Conference (1962).

Morphology and development. Diameter estimated at 140 mμ by filtration. The radiation-sensitive core has half that diameter (Benyesh *et al.*, 1958). The virus resembles para-influenza viruses in that the central core contains helices; these are 16 mμ in diameter with subunits having a 4·5 mμ periodicity. There are radially disposed projections on an outer membrane (Waterson *et al.*, 1961).

Inclusion bodies contain filaments and regularly arranged particles, thought not to represent mature virus (Kallman *et al.*, 1959).

Studies with fluorescent antibody indicate that virus is present in cytoplasm, with some appearing late, perhaps secondarily, in the nucleus (Enders, 1957).

Chemical composition. Most probably an RNA virus (Toyoshima *et al.*, 1960). Tests with nucleic acid inhibitors support this conclusion (Lam & Atherton, 1963).

Physico-chemical characters. Not completely inactivated in 30 minutes at 56° C (Girardi *et al.*, 1958). Survived several days at 36·5° C, over two weeks at 22° C or 4° C and for many months at −15° to −79° C. Withstands lyophilization. Stable between pH 5·5 and 9 for 3 hours at 0° C; inactivated below pH 4·5 (Black, 1959). Formalin 1 : 4000 inactivated in 4 days at 37° C. Ether sensitive.

Hæmagglutination. Concentrated virus agglutinates baboon cells at 4°, 20° and 37° C. Hæmolysis and hæmadsorption have also been demonstrated. No spontaneous elution of hæmagglutinin (Periés & Chany, 1960). Rhesus cells are agglutinated best at 37° C (Rosen, 1961; De Meio & Gower, 1961). Agglutination may be due to whole virus or to a smaller particle. Cells treated with influenza virus or receptor-destroying enzyme are still susceptible. The hæmagglutinin is inactivated by formaldehyde, unlike that of typical myxoviruses (Periés & Chany, 1961).

Antigenic properties. Strains are apparently uniform antigenically. Neutralization of virus is readily shown in tissue culture; and CF antigen is formed in tissue cultures, though in low titre. Hæmagglutinin inhibition is also useful. Neutralizing antibody can be readily measured by plaque-counting techniques in *patas* kidney monolayers (Hsiung *et al.*, 1958). Antibodies may also be produced by immunizing rodents or chicks. For antigenic relations to distemper and rinderpest *cf.* p. 136.

Cultivation. *In fertile hens' eggs.* The virus was adapted to growth in the chick amnion after prior cultivation in tissue cultures of human amnion (Milovanovic *et al.*, 1957). Earlier work reporting successful cultivation on the chick CAM (Rake & Shaffer, 1939) is hard to assess since workers at that time only had the untrustworthy method of inoculation into monkeys as a guide.

In tissue culture. Enders & Peebles (1954) cultivated measles virus in human and monkey tissue cultures. The virus has since been propagated in a number of continuous cell lines of human origin, malignant or otherwise. Human amnion has proved particularly useful. Bovine (Schwarz & Zirbel, 1959) and dog kidney cultures have been used with success; and Wright (1957) reported production of intranuclear inclusions in hamster, mouse and guinea pig cultures. The egg-adapted virus can be grown in chick embryo tissue cultures (Katz *et al.*, 1958). Primate kidney cultures seem best for primary isolation but higher titres may subsequently be attained in other tissues.

Changes produced in culture consist of formation of syncytia and of vacuoles in the cytoplasm of the syncytia, formation of nuclear and cytoplasmic inclusions and finally cell degeneration. The effects are different in various types of cell, and at times another type of change, with production of spindle-cells, is seen; this may be produced by a variant virus. Cell changes take a number of days to develop, perhaps 16 before adaptation and 5 afterwards. Plaques form in 5–10 days in monolayers of *patas* kidney cells (Hsiung *et al.*, 1958).

Pathogenicity. *In man.* In man the fever, coryza and, soon after, the rash and Koplik spots, are familiar. The incubation period is about 14 days. In virgin communities, almost 100 per cent. of infections occur, affecting all ages; but in towns children are chiefly attacked. Mortality is far from negligible especially where, as in parts of West Africa, there is also protein deficiency. Broncho-pneumonia and encephalitis are responsible for many of these deaths. Otitis media and other complications are also troublesome. There is evidence, from the rare cases which die early, of giant cell formation and other changes in lymphoid tissues generally, virus being present in blood and various organs (Sherman & Ruckle, 1958). A fatal giant cell pneumonia is thought to be generally due to measles.

Experimentally. Rhesus, cynomolgus and other monkeys may be susceptible and show rash, lymphopenia and fever; but many contract an undetected infection in captivity and are thereafter immune. It is probably from such inapparently infected monkeys that an agent (MINIA) (Ruckle, 1958) indistinguishable from measles, has been isolated in cultures. The acquired resistance of many monkeys means that they are most unreliable experimental animals for measles.

Production of viraemia in puppies is reported by Sergiev *et al.* (1959).

Tissue culture virus has been adapted to growth in suckling mice (IC) (Imagawa & Adams, 1958) and suckling hamsters (Burnstein *et al.*, 1958).

Pathological lesions. The characteristic giant cells were reported as occurring in tonsils and pharynx early in the disease by Warthin (1931). The intranuclear inclusions were first described by Torres & Teixeira (1932); these are acidophilic, often band-like, and differ from typical Cowdry Type A inclusions in that they may be multiple and there is no margination of basophilic chromatin with disappearance of nucleolus. Cytoplasmic inclusions also occur and these rather than the intranuclear ones are likely to contain the virus. Taniguchi *et al.* (1954) described intranuclear inclusions in bronchial epithelium of infected monkeys.

Ecology. The virus is transmitted from the respiratory tract especially at times before or near the onset of the rash; the conjunctiva may be an important portal of entry. There have been extensive studies of the epidemiology in relation to the 2-year cycle seen in many urban communities. Virus has been recovered from urine (Gresser & Katz, 1960).

Control. Human gamma globulin has been extensively used. If given early and in large amounts it will prevent the disease: given later or in smaller quantity it will give an attenuated disease leaving immunity behind it. Pooled adult sera act similarly but are less potent (Gunn, 1938).

Vaccines. A series of 48 papers on various aspects of immunization against measles has been published (Conference, 1962). Formalinized vaccines made from virus grown in tissue culture have their advocates, but most attention has been paid to living virus attenuated by growth in chick embryo or in other ways. Such vaccines are undoubtedly effective but they do not immunize without causing in many children fever and rash, albeit much milder than the symptoms seen in the natural disease. It is possible that virus may be over-attenuated so that it loses immunogenicity (Enders *et al.*, 1962). Avianized distemper virus is suggested by Adams *et al.* (1959) as a possibly effective antigen.

DOG DISTEMPER

Synonyms: Hard-pad. Maladie de jeune age. Hundestaupe.

Classical Account: Laidlaw & Dunkin (1926). Dunkin & Laidlaw (1926a and b).

Morphology. Diameter 115–160 mμ (Palm & Black, 1961). An earlier estimate of 70–105 mμ (Bindrich & Gralheer, 1954) is less in agreement with microscopical work. Negatively stained preparations examined by electron-microscopy resemble those of measles and rinderpest; helices were 15–17 mμ in diameter (Cruickshank *et al.*, 1962). Filamentous forms of virus are described.

Physico-chemical characters. Inactivated by heating 1 hour at 55° or 30 minutes at 60°. Celiker & Gillespie (1959) found that egg-cultivated virus was more easily killed; they describe resistance to various physical and chemical agents. Bussell and Karzon (1962) determined the half-life of tissue culture virus at various temperatures. It survives for months at −10° C and indefinitely at −76° C or when lyophilized. Dried virus is fairly stable at room temperature, but not above 32° (Piercy, 1961). It is ether-sensitive, inactivated by

0·1 per cent. formaldehyde in a few hours; also by 1 per cent. lysol. Virus inactivated by formalin or the photodynamic action of methylene blue retains antigenicity.

Hæmagglutination. Haig (1956) reports "irregular partial hæmagglutination" of chick and guinea pig RBC's.

Antigenic properties. Neutralizing antibodies can be demonstrated in the various systems available (ferrets, dogs, eggs, mice, tissue culture). A complement-fixing antigen is present especially in the spleen of affected animals and in membranes of infected eggs. Specific precipitates are formed in agar by the Ouchterlouny technique (Mansi, 1957). Relations with measles and rinderpest are discussed on p. 136.

Interference. There is no interference with canine hepatitis virus.

Cultivation. *In fertile eggs.* Virus has been adapted to growth on the CAM by Haig (1948) and Cabasso & Cox (1949). Lesions appear on the membranes after a number of passages. The virus is attenuated for ferrets and dogs and can be used for immunization.

In tissue culture. The virus has been grown in ferret and dog kidney and other tissues, but not all strains grow well. The egg-adapted strain grows also in chick embryo tissue cultures (Cabasso, Kiser & Stebbins, 1959) and will also give small plaques on chick embryo fibroblast monolayers under an agar overlay (Bussell & Karzon, 1962).

Cytopathic effects produced in cultures include formation of giant cells and cytoplasmic, but not nuclear inclusions (Rockborn, 1958; Hopper, 1959).

Pathogenicity. The disease particularly attacks young dogs, causing in typical cases, after 4 or 5 days' incubation, diphasic fever, discharge from eyes and nose, sometimes skin eruption; and, during the secondary fever, vomiting, diarrhœa and often pneumonia (Dunkin & Laidlaw, 1926b). Mortality is variable, on the average about 50 per cent. Nervous symptoms, particularly fits or muscular jerkings, may occur and persist for long periods. Distemper occurs naturally in wolves, foxes, raccoons and mink and may in them simulate rabies.

The disease described as "hard-pad" (McIntyre et al., 1948) is

now regarded as a form of distemper: there is tenderness, then
keratinization of the skin of the feet, usually followed by nervous
involvement and commonly death. Either no virus is recoverable or
that of typical distemper (Koprowski *et al.*, 1950). Distemper is
transmissible to all *Canidæ*, *Mustelidæ*, particularly ferrets: of *Viver-
ridæ* only the Binturong and of *Procyonidæ* only raccoons appear
susceptible (Goss, 1948). So-called cat distemper is an unrelated
disease (p. 345). In ferrets dog distemper is usually fatal (Dunkin &
Laidlaw, 1926a). The incubation period in this animal is about 10
days and characteristic features are vesicle formation around the
mouth, discharge and later crusting of eyes and nose. Neurotropic
strains of virus have been described. The virus has been adapted to
multiplication in suckling mice (Morse *et al.*, 1953; Gutierrez &
Gordon, 1955) and suckling hamsters (Cabasso *et al.*, 1955).

Pathological lesions. In fatal cases in dogs bronchopneumonia was
the rule, but is rarely seen now. There may be gastro-intestinal
inflammation often with necrosis of mucosa. Histologically there
occur cytoplasmic and intranuclear inclusions: the latter may be
hard to find, but they are not uncommon in the bladder (De Monbreun, 1937).

Ecology. The disease is contagious and so readily airborne that
Dunkin & Laidlaw (1926b) could not safely house normal dogs in
the same building as infected ones. Virus is excreted also in urine
and fæces. Carriers of infection have not been reported.

Control. Several methods of vaccination have been described.
(i) Formalinized virus may be given and followed by live virus to
give lasting immunity (Laidlaw & Dunkin, 1928). (ii) Side-to-side
immunization entails the giving of living virus and antisera simultaneously, but separately. (iii) Subsequently virus attenuated for
dogs by continual ferret-passage ("distemperoid" virus of Green,
1939) or by cultivation in eggs (Cabasso *et al.*, 1951) has given the
best results. Now tissue culture propagated virus seems superior.
Hyperimmune sera have also been used for passively protecting
dogs for a short period.

RINDERPEST

Synonym: Cattle-plague.
Reviews: Francis (1946).
    Shope *et al.* (1946).

Morphology. Resembles measles but is more pleomorphic. Average diameter 120–300 mμ. The internal helical component was 17·5 mμ in diameter and there was an enclosing membrane. Filaments like those of Influenza A were seen (Plowright *et al.*, 1962). Breen and de Boer (1963) describe small (40–60 mμ) and large (150–300 mμ) particles, both kinds being present in sacs in cytoplasm.

Physico-chemical characters. Soon loses activity when dried under natural conditions in the field. Survives indefinitely after freeze-drying, though best kept in the cold. The half-life at 56° is measured in minutes. Optimal pH for survival 7·0. Virus in lymphnodes and spleen preserved well at −17° C to −20° C—blood not so well (Lin-Peng, 1957). Ether-sensitive. Strong alkalis are the best disinfectants.

Properties of virus summarized by Scott (1959a).

The iso-electric point was at pH 6·2 (Topacio, 1933).

Hæmagglutination was unsuccessfully sought by Huygelen (1960).

Antigenic properties. Can be studied by complement fixation or by neutralization tests in animals or in tissue culture. For CF tests, an antigen from the fluids of infected eggs proved best (Cooper, 1946). It is generally considered that the virus is antigenically uniform though some unconfirmed reports suggest that there are strain differences. Double-diffusion in agar reveals two antigens in infected tissue, one heat-stable, the other labile (Stone, 1960). This test is useful for detecting antigen in lymph-nodes in acute cases (White, 1962). Antigenic relations with dog distemper and measles have been reviewed (p. 136).

Interference with Rift Valley fever virus is reported, and attenuated strains of rinderpest interfere with virulent ones.

Cultivation. *In fertile eggs.* Some but not all strains have proved adaptable to growth in eggs—either the CAM or yolk. Growth in the yolk-sac was best after preliminary adaptation to the CAM (Shope *et al.*, 1946). Virus passed in yolk-sacs was attenuated for cattle after 20 or more passages (Jenkins & Shope, 1946). The virus was not regularly lethal for chick embryos.

In tissue culture. Virus has been cultivated in kidney or testis of calf, sheep, goat, pig and hamster (Plowright & Ferris, 1959). Cytopathic effects are seen, except with lapinized and caprinized strains (Plowright & Ferris, 1962). Syncytia form in the cultures; also cytoplasmic and nuclear inclusions, the latter said to be smaller than those of measles. Growth in rat tissues is also reported.

Distribution. Rinderpest is a serious plague in many parts of Asia and Africa, though South Africa is now free. Until the last century Europe was affected also. On one occasion it was introduced into Brazil.

Pathogenicity. *In cattle.* Strains vary in virulence and breeds of cattle in susceptibility. In acute rinderpest, there is high fever; constipation is followed by severe diarrhœa. Nasal discharge and mucosal erosions occur and animals may be overcome and die in 2 to 6 days. With milder strains in resistant cattle the disease may be overlooked and may be inadvertently spread.

Water buffaloes (Carabao) may be badly affected; so may sheep and goats, though rarely, and the disease may also infect antelopes, swine, especially European breeds, and camels.

Experimentally the infection has been adapted to goats (Edwards, 1930); it becomes virulent for them but attenuated for cattle (caprinized virus). Rinderpest has also been adapted to rabbits (lapinized virus), producing as a rule an inapparent infection or, at the most, fever (Nakamura *et al.*, 1938; Baker, 1946). However, after many passages, it may produce a fatal disease in rabbits (Scott, 1959b). Infection has also been produced in guinea pigs (Baker *et al.*, 1946) and in susliks (*Citellus*).

Pathological lesions. Virus in the blood is contained in leucocytes. The main lesions consist of inflammation and ulceration affecting the alimentary canal from mouth to rectum. There may be false membranes in stomach and intestines. A secondary patchy pneumonia may occur.

The occurrence of syncytia, nuclear and cytoplasmic inclusions in tissue culture has been mentioned. They have not always been recognized in lesions of affected cattle, though both syncytia and cytoplasmic inclusions were reported by Thiéry (1956) and syncytia by Provost & Villemot (1961).

Ecology. Transmission is by direct contact. Virus is present in nasal discharges, urine and fæces. Carriers may transmit infection. Infected premises are a source of danger for at most a short period.

Control. Slaughter may be necessary when there is introduction into unaffected areas.

Hyperimmune sera have been successfully used to give transient protection.

Vaccination. Side to side inoculation of serum and virus has been used; so have vaccines made by inactivating virus with formalin, phenol and glycerol or chloroform. These are being superseded by living virus attenuated in one or other of three ways—by passage in goats, rabbits or eggs. Virus attenuated in tissue culture is also under investigation (Plowright & Ferris, 1959, 1956; De Boer, 1962). There is an extensive literature on the results of tests of various vaccines. It seems that different degrees of attenuation may be desirable according to the susceptibility of the breed of cattle. Thus avianized virus may be best for very susceptible European breeds and caprinized virus may be best for more resistant Asiatic cattle (Brotherston, 1955–6, 1958). With some but not all vaccines it appears that some febrile reaction must be produced if good immunity is to result; also that some attenuated strains may revert to virulence on passage through cattle.

AFRICAN SWINE FEVER

Synonym: Wart-hog disease.
Review: Maurer *et al.* (1958a). Anon (1960).

Morphology. Resembles measles (A. P. Waterson, personal communication, 1962).

Physico-chemical characters. Inactivated in 30′ at 55°, 10′ at 60°—less heat-resistant than swine fever. Survives for years when dried at room temperature or frozen on skin or muscle. One per cent. formaldehyde inactivates in 6 days.

Hæmagglutination is not reported but hæmadsorption of pig RBC's is seen in cultures in pig marrow or "buffy coat" (Malmquist & Hay, 1960).

Antigenic properties. Quite distinct in cross-immunity tests from swine fever. Immunity even to the homologous strain seems to be transient. No satisfactory serological work is reported. The virus may be antigenically unstable or there may be several serotypes.

Cultivation. Grows in yolk-sac of developing eggs, killing embryos in 6 or 7 days (McIntosh, 1952). It has been grown in cultures of pig bone marrow and buffy coat and shows hæmadsorption in 24 hours, later CPE (Malmquist & Hay, 1960).

Distribution. In East, South and West Africa. Reached Portugal and Spain in 1957 but may have been stamped out there.

Pathogenicity. Very fatal amongst domestic pigs. The incubation period is 7–9 days in the field, 2 to 5 days experimentally. Symptoms include high fever, cough and diarrhœa and resemble those of classical swine fever. There is leucopenia. Surviving pigs may have viræmia for months (De Tray, 1957). The disease probably naturally infects wart-hogs (*Phacochærus*) and probably bush-pigs (*Potamochærus*) and these too may be carriers.

Experimentally, an inapparent infection has been produced in rabbits (Velko, 1956); there was no attenuation for swine after 26 rabbit passages.

Pathologically the lesions resemble those of classical swine fever but are more severe with many hæmorrhages and with severe karyorrhexis of lymphocytes (de Kock *et al.*, 1940; Maurer *et al.*, 1958b). Post mortems reveal fluid in body cavities, hæmorrhagic lymph nodes, engorgement and œdema of the gall-bladder.

Ecology. Domestic pigs in Africa may contract infection from wart-hogs. Thereafter infection is by contact and through fomites. Infected premises remain dangerous for long periods.

Control. Specific prophylaxis has not yet been achieved.

RESPIRATORY SYNCYTIAL (RS) VIRUS

Synonym: Chimpanzee coryza agent (CCA).

Morphology. 120–130 mµ in diameter. There is a core of coiled filaments within an outer membrane as with para-influenza viruses (Waterson & Hobson, 1962).

Studies with fluorescent antibody show presence of virus in cytoplasm of infected cells (Bennett & Hamre, 1962).

Chemical composition. Probably an RNA virus.

Physico-chemical characters. Survives quick freezing to $-70°$ but some workers report that isolations are many fewer from frozen than from fresh material. Inactivated in 1 hour at 56° (half-life 2·8′) or in 170 hours at 37° (half-life 7·2 hours) (Jordan, 1962). Ether-sensitive.

Hæmagglutination is not reported; nor hæmadsorption. Despite this, other characters suggest that this is a myxovirus.

Antigenic characters. The neutralization and CF tests may be used for diagnosis. Some workers find the latter less sensitive. Not all strains of virus are serologically alike (R. M. Chanock and D. Taylor-Robinson, personal communications). There is a CF antigen smaller than the virus particle.

Cultivation. Multiplication in eggs is not reported.
The virus grows in cultures derived from human cancer cells (KB, HeLa, Hep. 2, also Chang liver cells), less readily in monkey kidney cultures. Syncytia are produced—hence the name—readily in Hep. 2, less readily in some other cell lines (Jordan, 1962). CPE seen after 5–7 days; but maximal virus titres are found much earlier (Beem et al., 1960; Bennett & Hamre, 1962). Virus is mostly closely associated with the cells. Plaques are formed on Hep. 2 monolayers (Kisch & Johnson, 1963).

Distribution. Recorded from North America and Europe but probably world-wide.

Pathogenicity. Causes minor respiratory infection with rhinitis and cough. In children, especially infants, the lower respiratory tract may be involved in some 50 per cent. of cases and bronchitis, bronchiolitis or bronchopneumonia, sometimes fatal, may occur (Beem et al., 1960; Chanock et al., 1961; McLelland et al., 1961). Antibody, present in a large number of persons over 4, does not always prevent reinfection. Such reinfections may take the form of a common cold (Johnson et al., 1961). Afebrile colds have been produced after an incubation period of about 5 days by deliberate infection of adult volunteers (Kravetz et al., 1961).
The virus has also caused outbreaks of colds amongst captive chimpanzees, from which, indeed, the virus was originally isolated (Morris, Blount & Savage, 1956). Coates & Chanock (1962) recovered virus after inoculating ferrets, mink and marmosets. Serial

passage in ferrets was possible. There were no symptoms but nasal lesions with giant cells and inclusion bodies were found 3 to 6 days after inoculation.

Ecology. Infections with this virus are prevalent over rather brief periods during the winter months, virus apparently disappearing in between. Virus has occasionally been recovered from washings from apparently normal persons during outbreaks.

Control. No experiments with vaccines are reported.

PEROMYSCUS VIRUS

Morris *et al.* (1963) described a new hæmadsorbing virus, probably a myxovirus, isolated from white-footed mice (*Peromyscus leucopus*). It grew well in eggs inoculated by various routes and in cultures of monkey tissues; it was lethal to suckling rodents of several species when inoculated I.C.

REFERENCES

Adams, J. M., Imagawa, D. T., Wright, S. W., & Tarjan, G. (1959) *Virology*, **7**, 351.
Adams, J. M., & Imagawa, D. T. (1957) *Proc. Soc. exp. Biol. (N.Y.)*, **96**, 240.
Anon. (1960) *Bull. Off. int. Épiz.*, **53**, 1352.
Babbott, F. L., & Gordon, J. E. (1954) *Amer. J. med. Sci.*, **228**, 334.
Baker, J. A. (1946) *Amer. J. vet. Res.*, **7**, 179.
Baker, J. A., Terrence, J., & Greig, A. S. (1946) *Amer. J. vet. Res.*, **7**, 189.
Beem, M., Wright, F. H., Hamre, D., Egerer, R., & Oehme, M. (1960) *New Engl. J. Med.*, **263**, 523.
Bennett, C. R., & Hamre, D. (1962) *J. infect. Dis.*, **110**, 8.
Benyesh, M., Pollard, E. C., Opton. E. M., Black, F. L., Bellamy, W. D., & Melnick, J. L. (1958) *Virology*, **5**, 256.
Bindrich, H., & Gralheer, K. (1954) *Arch. exp. vet. Med.*, **8**, 204.
Black, F. L. (1959) *Virology*, **7**, 184.
Black, F. L., Reissig, M., & Melnick, J. L. (1959) *Advanc. Virus Res.*, **6**, 205.
Breese, S. S., & de Boer, C. (1963) *Virology*, **19**, 340.
Brotherston, J. G. (1955–56) *Vet. Rev. Annot.*, **2**, 95.
Brotherston, J. G. (1958) *Vet. Rev. Annot.*, **3**, 45 and **4**, 49.
Burnstein, T., Frankel, J. W., & Jensen, J. H. (1958) *Fed. Proc.*, **17**, 507.
Bussell, R. H., & Karzon, D. T. (1962) *Virology*, **18**, 589.
Cabasso, V. J., Burkhart, R. L., & Leaming, J. D. (1951) *Vet. Med.*, **46**, 167.
Cabasso, V. J., & Cox, H. R. (1949) *Proc. Soc. exp. Biol. (N.Y.)*, **71**, 246.
Cabasso, V. J., Douglas, J. M., Stebbins, M. R., & Cox, H. R. (1955) *Proc. Soc. exp. Biol. (N.Y.)*, **88**, 199.
Cabasso, V. J., Kiser, K., & Stebbins, M. R. (1959) *Proc. Soc. exp. Biol. (N.Y.)*, **100**, 551.
Carlström, G. (1957) *Lancet*, **2**, 344.
Carlström, G. (1962) *Amer. J. Dis. Child.*, **103**, 287.
Celiker, A., & Gillespie, J. H. (1954) *Cornell Vet.*, **44**, 276.

Chanock, R. M., Kim, H. W., Vargosko, A. J., Deleva, A., Johnson, K. M., Cumming, C., & Parrott, R. H. (1961) *J. Amer. med. Ass.*, **176**, 647.
Conference (1962) *Amer. J. Dis. Child.*, **103**, 219.
Coates, H. V., & Chanock, R. M. (1961) *Amer. J. Hyg.*, **76**, 302.
Cooper, H. K. (1946) *Amer. J. vet. Res.*, **7**, 228.
Cruickshank, J. G., Waterson, A. P., Kanarek, A. D., Berry, D. M. (1962) *Rev. vet. Sci.*, **3**, 485.
De Boer, C. (1962) *J. Immunol.*, **89**, 170.
de Kock, G., Robinson, E. M., & Keppel, J. J. G. (1940) *Onderstepoort J. vet. Sci.*, **14**, 31.
De Meio, J. L., & Gower, T. A. (1961) *Virology*, **13**, 367.
De Monbreun, W. A. (1937) *Amer. J. Path.*, **13**, 187.
de Tray, D. E. (1957) *Amer. J. vet. Res.*, **18**, 811.
Dunkin, G. W., & Laidlaw, P. P. (1926a) *J. comp. Path.*, **39**, 201.
Dunkin, G. W., & Laidlaw, P. P. (1926b) *J. comp. Path.*, **39**, 213.
Edwards, J. T. (1930) *Bull. agric. Res. Inst. Pusa, No.* 199.
Enders, J. F. (1957) *J. nat. Cancer Inst.*, **19**, 735.
Enders, J. F., Katz., S. L., & Holloway, A. (1962) *Amer. J. Dis. Child.*, **103**, 335.
Enders, J. F., & Peebles, T. C. (1954) *Proc. Soc. exp. Biol. (N.Y.)*, **86**, 277.
Francis, J. (1946) *Vet. Rec.*, **58**, 501.
Gilbert, Y., Molnet, P., & Goueffon, Y. (1960) *C.R. Acad. Sci.*, **250**, 2953.
Gillespie, J. H., & Karzon, J. T. (1960) *Proc. Soc. exp. Biol. (N.Y.)*, **105**, 547.
Girardi, A. J., Warren, J., Goldman, C., & Jeffries, B. (1958) *Proc. Soc. exp. Biol. (N.Y.)*, **98**, 18.
Goret, P., Pilet, C., Girard, M., & Camara, T. (1960) *Ann. Inst. Pasteur*, **98**, 610.
Goss, L. J. (1948) *Amer. J. vet. Res.*, **9**, 65.
Green, R. G. (1939) *J. Amer. vet. med. ass.*, **95**, 465.
Gresser, I., & Katz, S. L. (1960) *New Engl. J. Med.*, **263**, 452.
Gunn, W. (1938) *Lancet*, **1**, 795.
Gutierrez, J. C., & Gorham, J. R. (1955) *Amer. J. vet. Res.*, **16**, 325.
Haig, D. A. (1948) *Onderstepoort J. vet. Sci.*, **23**, 149.
Haig, D. A. (1956) *Onderstepoort J. vet. Res.*, **27**, 19.
Hopper, P. K. (1959) *J. comp. Path.*, **69**, 78.
Hsiung, G. D., Mannini, A., & Melnick, J. L. (1958) *Proc. Soc. exp. Biol. (N.Y.)*, **98**, 68.
Huygelen, C. (1960) *Bull. epizoot. Dis. Afr.*, **8**, 121.
Imagawa, D. T., & Adams, J. M. (1958) *Proc. Soc. exp. Biol. (N.Y.)*, **98**, 567.
Imagawa, D. T., Goret, P., & Adams, J. M. (1960) *Proc. nat. Acad. Sci. (Wash.)*, **46**, 1119.
Jenkins, C. L., & Sharpe, R. E. (1946) *Amer. J. Vet. Res.*, **7**, 174.
Johnson, K. M., Chanock, R. M., Rifkind, D., Kravetz., H. M., & Knight, V. (1961) *J. Amer. med. Ass.*, **176**, 663.
Jordan, W. S. (1962) *J. Immunol.*, **88**, 581.
Kallman, F., Adams, J. M., Williams, R. C., & Imagawa, D. T. (1959) *J. biophys. biochem. Cytol.*, **6**, 379.
Katz, S. L., Milovanovic, M. V., & Enders, J. F. (1958) *Proc. Soc. exp. Biol. (N.Y.)*, **97**, 23.
Kisch A. L., Johnson K. M. (1963) *Proc. Soc. exp. Biol. (N.Y.)*, **112**, 583.
Koprowski, H., Jervis, G. A., James, T. R., Burkhart, R. D., & Poppensiek, G. C. (1950) *Amer. J. Hyg.*, **51**, 63.
Kravetz, H. M., Knight, V., Chanock, R. M., Morris, J. A., Johnson, K. M., Rifkind, D., & Utz, J. P. (1961) *J. Amer. med. Ass.*, **176**, 657.
Laidlaw, P. P., & Dunkin, G. W. (1926) *J. comp. Path.*, **39**, 222.
Laidlaw, P. P., & Dunkin, G. W. (1928), *J. comp. Path.*, **41**, 1.

II

Lam, K. S. K., & Atherton, J. G. (1963) *Nature (Lond.)*, **197,** 820.
Lin-Peng, C. (1957) *Acta vet. Zootechn. sinica*, **2,** 73.
McCarthy, K. (1959) *Brit. med. Bull.*, **15,** 201.
McIntosh, B. M. (1952) *J. S. Afr. vet. med. Ass.*, **23,** 217.
MacIntyre, A. B., Trevan, D. J., & Montgomerie, R. F. (1949) *Vet. Rec.*, 60, 635.
McLelland, L., Hilleman, M. R., Hamparian, V. V., Ketler, A., Reilly, C. M., Cornfield, D., & Stokes, J. (1961) *New Engl. J. Med.*, **264,** 1169.
Malmquist, W. A., & Hay, D. (1960) *Amer. J. vet. Res.*, **21,** 104.
Mansi, W. (1957) *J. comp. Path.*, **67,** 297.
Maurer, F. D., Griesemer, R. A., & Jones, T. C. (1958a) in Dunne, *Diseases of Swine*, Iowa State College Press.
Maurer, F. D., Griesemer, R. A., & Jones, T. C. (1958b) *Amer. J. vet. Res.*, **19,** 517.
Milovanovich, M. V., Enders, J. F., & Mitus, A. (1957) *Proc. Soc. exp. Biol. (N.Y.)*, **95,** 120.
Morris, J. A., Blount, R. E., & Savage, R. E. (1956) *Proc. Soc. exp. Biol. (N.Y.)*, **92,** 544.
Morris, J. A., Bozeman, F. M., Aulisio, C. G., & Shirai, A. (1963) *Proc. Soc. exp. Biol (N.Y.)*, **113,** 296.
Morse, H. G., Chow, T. L., & Brandly, C. A. (1951) *Proc. Soc. exp. Biol. (N.Y.)*, **84,** 10.
Nakamura, J., Wagatsuma, S., & Fukusho, K. (1938) *J. Jap. Soc. vet. Sci.*, **17,** 25.
Palm, C. R., and Black, F. L. (1961) *Proc. Soc. exp. Biol. (N.Y.)*, **107,** 588.
Periés, J. R., & Chany, C. (1960) *C.R. Acad. Sci. (Paris)*,**251,** 820.
Periés, J. R , & Chany, C. (1961) *C.R. Acad. Sci. (Paris)*, **252,** 2956·
Piercy, S. E. (1961) *Vet. Rec.*, **73,** 898.
Plowright, W., & Ferris, R. D. (1959) *J. comp. Path.*, **69,** 152.
Plowright, W., & Ferris, R. D. (1962) *Rev. vet. Sci.*, **3,** 172.
Plowright, W., Cruickshank, J. G., & Waterson, A. P. (1962) *Virology*, **17,** 118.
Polding, J. B., & Simpson, R. W. (1959) *Vet. Rec.*, **69,** 582.
Provost, A., & Villemot, J. M. (1961) *Ann. Inst. Pasteur*, **101,** 276.
Rake, G., & Shaffer, M. F. (1939) *Nature (Lond.)*, **144,** 672.
Rockborn, G. (1958) *Arch. ges. Virusforsch.*, **8,** 485.
Rosen, L. (1961) *Virology*, **13,** 139.
Ruckle, G. (1958) *Arch. ges. Virusforsch.*, **8,** 139.
Schwartz, A. T. F., & Zirbel, L. W. (1959) *Proc. Soc. exp. Biol. (N.Y.)*, **102,** 711.
Scott, G. R. (1959a) *Bull. epizoot. Dis. Afr.*, **7,** 173.
Scott, G. R. (1959b) *J. comp. Path.*, **69,** 149.
Sergiev, P. G., Rizantseva, N. F., & Smirnova, E. V. (1959) *Probl. Virol.* (Eng. Ed.), **4,** 50.
Sherman, F. E., & Ruckle, G. (1958) *Arch. Path. (Chicago)*, **65,** 587.
Shope, R. E., & colleagues (1946) *Amer. J. vet. Res.*, **23,** 133.
Stone, S. S. (1960) *Virology*, **11,** 638.
Taniguchi, T., Kamahora, J., Kato, S., & Hagiwara, K. (1954) *Med. J. Osaka Univ.*, **5,** 367.
Thiery, G. (1956) *Rev. Élev.*, **9,** 117.
Topacio, T. (1933) *Philippine J. Sci.*, **57,** 427.
Torres, G. M., & Texeira, J. de C. (1932) *C.R. Soc. Biol. (Paris)*, **109,** 138.
Toyoshima, H., Hata, S., Takahashi, M., Miki, T., & Okuno, Y. (1960) *Biken's J.*, **3,** 241.
Velho, E. L. (1956) *Bull. Off. int. Épiz.*, **46,** 335.

Warren, J. (1960) *Advanc. Virus Res.*, **7**, 27.
Warren, J. Nadel, M. K., Slater, E., & Millian, S. J. (1960) *Amer. J. vet. Res.*, **21**, 111.
Warthin, A. S. (1931) *Arch. Path. (Chicago)*, **11**, 864.
Waterson, A. P., Cruickshank, J. G., Lawrence, G. D., & Kanarek, A. A. (1961) *Virology*, **15**, 379.
Waterson, A. P., & Hobson, D. (1962) *Brit. med. J.*, **2**, 1166.
White, G. (1962) *Vet. Rec.*, **74**, 1477.
Wright, J. (1957) *Lancet*, **1**, 669.

6

Rabies

Synonyms: Hydrophobia. Lyssa. Wut. Tollwut. Rage.
Reviews:　Johnson (1959).
　　　　　　 Tierkel (1959).

Morphology and development. Evidence from filtration
(Galloway & Elford, 1936) and other workers suggests that the
diameter is 100–150 mμ. The specific antigen can be located by the
aid of fluorescent antibody in the Negri bodies and other particulate
material in the cytoplasm of nerve cells (Goldwasser & Kissling,
1959) and salivary glands (Goldwasser *et al.*, 1958).
　Almeida *et al.* (1962) describe virus bodies resembling those of
myxoviruses. The nucleoprotein core, however, consisted of an
apparently flattened helix. Rods 110–112 mμ wide were seen in
nerve cells by Matsumoto (1962).

Chemical composition. According to Sokolov and Vanag
(1962) the Negri bodies consist of a DNA matrix containing RNA
granules.

Physico-chemical characters. The virus is inactivated in
1 hour at 54–56° C but is more stable when dried. Repeated freezing
and thawing destroys it. Reports on its ether resistance are conflicting. In unpublished experiments the author (1961) found that
fixed virus dropped 100-fold in titre overnight when exposed to
20 per cent, ether at 4°. Remlinger & Bailly (1932) report variation
in its sensitivity; they, however, were using the crude method of
immersing whole infected brains in pure ether. The virus survives
lyophilization and persists for months in pieces of nervous tissue in
50 per cent. glycerol.

Antigenic properties. Neutralizing and CF antibodies are
readily demonstrated. In tests in agar gel, fixed virus tested against
specific sera shows two lines of precipitate (Villemot & Provost,
1959). Differences between strains in neutralizability by sera or in

antigenic potency have been widely reported but cannot be related to definite divergencies in antigenic structure.

The soluble CF antigen has been studied by van den Ende *et al.* (1957). It is stable between pH 6 and 10 and still reactive though less antigenic after heating to 56° C or treating with 0·35 per cent. formaldehyde. Antigens of several sizes may be present (Mead, 1962).

Interference with poliomyelitis Type II is reported by Kanazawa & Ohtomi (1958): and with Western encephalitis virus in tissue culture, the latter effect being mediated by interferon (Kaplan *et al.*, 1960).

Cultivation. *In fertile eggs.* Some strains of virus multiply when inoculated on the CAM (Kligler & Bernkopf, 1938); also in the allantoic cavity or yolk-sacs of 7-day embryos (Koprowski & Cox, 1948). Inoculated embryos are smaller than normal but the chicks usually hatch and die later. The virus is, however, fatal when inoculated in 1-day embryos (Yoshino *et al.*, 1956). The Flury strain adapted to eggs has been used for immunization, the high egg pass (HEP) strain being more attenuated than the LEP (low egg pass) (Koprowski & Cox, 1948). Virus has also been grown in duck eggs and used for immunization (see below) (Peck *et al.*, 1956).

In tissue culture. Rabies multiplies in tissue cultures of chick and mouse embryo (Webster & Clow, 1937), in embryo rabbit brain and in hamster kidney but gross changes (CPE) have not usually been observed. However, antigen has been detected in cytoplasm of infected hamster kidney by the fluorescent antibody technique (Kaplan *et al.*, 1960); and slow degeneration of cells has been seen in tissue cultures of a mouse ependymoma (Atanasiu & Laurent, 1957). Fernandes (1962) cultivated fixed virus in diploid human and canine cell lines and observed CPE.

Street virus is apparently cultivated with much greater difficulty than fixed.

Distribution. Occurs all over the world but has been excluded from Britain and Australia by quarantine.

Pathogenicity. The incubation period in dogs is from 10 days to 6 months or even more, usually 20–60 days. In man it is usually from 15 days to 5 months but may be as long as a year. Infected dogs show great excitement (furious rabies) with great salivation,

changed behaviour, especially biting; this is followed by depression
and paralysis (dumb rabies) and, soon after, by death. At times,
only dumb rabies is seen. The same two stages are seen in man:
the characteristic feature of the excited stage is hydrophobia and
death may occur at this stage. Paralytic rabies is the only form seen
after vampire-bat bites. In cattle and horses the symptoms vary
greatly and diagnosis may be difficult. The disease may be chronic
and inapparent in bats and probably also in skunks and other
Mustelidæ, also at times in rats (Svet-Moldavskaya, 1958). In other
species the infection is usually fatal. Species naturally affected include
cats, foxes, jackals, wolves, mongooses, skunks—in fact almost all
terrestrial carnivores. Not only vampires but insectivorous and
fruit-eating bats (including those of the old world) may be infected.
Herbivora are infected by bites of carnivora or bats.

Street virus is freely excreted in the saliva of dogs and other
species including man; but fixed virus is not.

Experimentally, almost every readily available mammal has proved
susceptible; also chicks. On intracerebral passage through rabbits
the naturally occurring "street" virus soon becomes exalted for that
species, producing a paralytic disease with an incubation period of
only 4 to 6 days; simultaneously it becomes attenuated for man and
produces no disease in him when given subcutaneously. This is
"fixed" virus. It may be adapted to mice by IC inoculation and
may be infective for them when diluted 10^{-7}, causing a paralytic
disease. Large doses given IN to mice and guinea pigs will kill them.
Egg-adapted virus is pathogenic for rodents and other species when
given IC but not IM; the HEP strain loses even that power for most
species (Koprowski *et al.*, 1954).

Pathological lesions in the brain are those of encephalitis with
neuronal degeneration especially in the mid-brain and medulla.
Cellular infiltration is often slight. The diagnostic Negri bodies are
particularly abundant in nerve-cells in Ammon's horn of the hippocampus; they consist of cytoplasmic eosinophilic bodies 2–10 μ
across, often multiple, with an inner structure of basophilic granules.
They probably represent an cellular reaction to presence of virus and
characterize infection with street virus. With most strains of fixed
virus they are absent; smaller cytoplasmic bodies in nerve-cells may,
however, occur.

Cell-degeneration and infiltration occur in infected salivary
glands.

All the evidence suggests that virus reaches the central nervous
system by travelling along nerves. Viræmia, at least in infected mice,

is brief (Borodina, 1959). In bats, virus may localize in the brown interscapular fat (Sulkin *et al.*, 1957).

Ecology is excellently reviewed by Johnson (1959). Infection is transmitted by bites of infected species, particularly dogs, cats, wolves, foxes, mongooses and skunks, the saliva of which is infective. This may infect through a superficial wound without a bite. In towns, dogs and cats are of chief importance; in other parts wolves (Iran), foxes (Central Europe, North America), vampire bats (Caribbean and South America), mongooses (South Africa), skunks (North America). Rodents, e.g. ground-squirrels in Nigeria, may also act as vectors (McMillan & Boulger, 1960). Insectivorous bats in America have recently been found infected; the disease in them may be fatal or they may carry the virus for long periods (*cf.* Enright, 1951). Johnson (1959) thinks that bat rabies is an "aberrant cycle", the natural basic reservoir being more probably in weasels, skunks or other mustelids.

Control. Six months' quarantine of imported dogs and cats suffices to keep Britain free from rabies. Immunization of dogs and cats with live attenuated Flury strain is effective; a single dose gives immunity for 3 years (Tierkel *et al.*, 1953). The phenol-killed or Semple vaccine used in the past is less effective. The LEP strain is not sufficiently attenuated for immunizing cattle for which the HEP strain has been extensively and successfully used (Carneirov *et al.*, 1955).

For the treatment of human beings bitten or suspected of having been bitten, various modifications have been used of Pasteur's method of massive repeated injections of fixed virus. Virus attenuated by drying, with phenol and other substances or by simple dilution has been used, but according to Greenwood (1946) there is no statistical evidence that one method is better than another. Some have disputed (Webster, 1939) that post-infection treatment is of proved value, but this scepticism is not general. The Semple phenolized vaccine is chiefly used now but the Flury strain is under trial (Fox *et al.*, 1957). Virus grown in duck embryos and inactivated with β-propiolactone has also been effective in producing antibodies in man (Powell & Culbertson, 1959). Use of this or Flury vaccine should avoid the neuro-paralytic accidents which may follow injection into man of vaccines containing much nerve tissue. Recent work is bringing immune serum into favour, particularly in combination with vaccine. There is some evidence of its value (Baltazard & Bahmanyar, 1955).

REFERENCES

Almeida, J. D. (1962) *Virology*, **18,** 147.

Atanasiu, P., & Laurent, C. (1957) *C.R. Acad. Sci. (Paris)*, **245,** 2562.

Baltazard, M., & Bahmanyar, M. (1955) *Bull. Wld. Hlth. Org.*, **13,** 747.

Borodina, T. A. (1959) *Probl. Virol.*, **4,** 96.

Carneiro, V., Black, C., & Koprowski, H. (1955) *J. Amer. vet. med. Ass.*, **127,** 366.

Enright, J. B. (1951) *Ann. Rev. Microbiol.*, **10,** 369.

Fernandes, M. V. (1962) *Abstracts VIIIth Int. Congr. Microbiol.*, 99.

Fox, J. P., Koprowski, H., Conwell, W. P., Black, J., & Gelfand, H. M. (1951) *Bull. Wld. Hlth. Org.*, **17,** 869.

Galloway, I. A., & Elford, W. J. (1936) *J. Hyg. (Lond.)*, **36,** 532.

Goldwasser, R. A., & Kissling, R. E. (1958) *Proc. Soc. exp. Biol. (N.Y.)*, **98,** 219.

Goldwasser, R. A., Kissling, R. E., Carski, T. R., & Host, T. S. (1959) *Bull. Wld. Hlth. Org.*, **20,** 579.

Greenwood, M. (1946) *Bull. Hlth. Org. L. o. N.*, **12,** 301.

Johnson, H. N. (1959) in *Viral and Rickettsial Infections of Man*. Ed. Rivers and Horsfall. 3rd. Ed. London: Pitman Medical.

Kanazawa, K., & Ohtomi, Y. (1958) *Virology*, **6,** 570.

Kaplan, M. M., Wecker, E., Forsch, J., & Koprowski, H. (1960) *Nature, (Lond.)*, **186,** 821.

Kligler, I. J., & Bernkopf, H. (1938) *Proc. Soc. exp. Biol. (N.Y.)*, **39,** 212.

Koprowski, H., Black, J., & Nelsen, D. J. (1954) *J. Immunol.*, **72,** 94.

Koprowski, H., & Cox, H. R. (1948) *J. Immunol.*, **60,** 533.

McMillan, B., & Boulger, L. R. (1960) *Ann. trop. Med. Parasit.*, **54,** 165.

Matsumoto, S. (1962) *Virology*, **17,** 198.

Mead, T. H. (1967) *J. gen. Microbiol.*, **27,** 397 and 415.

Peck, F. B., Powell, H. M., & Culbertson, C. G. (1956) *J. Amer. med. Ass.*, **162,** 1373.

Powell, H. M., & Culbertson, C. G. (1959) *Sth-west. Vet.*, **12,** 281.

Remlinger, P., & Bailly, J. (1935) *Bull. Inst. Pasteur*, **33,** 609.

Sokolov, N. N., & Vanag, K. A. (1962) *Acta virol.* (Eng. Ed.), **6,** 452.

Sulkin, S. E., Krutzsch, P. H., Allen, R., & Wallis, C. (1957) *J. exp. Med.*, **110,** 369.

Svet-Moldavskaya, I. A. (1958) *Acta Virol.* (Eng. Ed.), **2,** 228.

Tierkel, E. S. (1959) *Advanc. vet. Sci.*, **5,** 183.

Tierkel, E. S., Kissling, R. E., Edison, M., & Habel, K. (1953) *Proc. 90th ann. Meeting Amer. vet. Med. Ass.*, p. 443.

van den Ende, M., Polson, A., & Turner, G. S. (1957) *J. Hyg. (Lond.)*, **55,** 361.

Villemot, J. M., & Provost, A. (1959) *Ann. Inst. Pasteur*, **96,** 712.

Webster, L. T. (1939) *Amer. J. Hyg.*, **30,** 113.

Wester, L. T., & Chow, A. D. (1937) *J. exp. Med.*, **66,** 125.

Yoshino, K., Kuma, N., Kondo, A., & Kitaoka, M. (1956) *Jap. J. med. Sci. Biol.*, **9,** 259.

7

Avian Leucosis-Sarcoma Complex

There exists a group of neoplastic conditions primarily affecting domestic fowls and not clearly separable. These are avian sarcomata, myeloblastosis, erythroblastosis, lymphoid leucosis, osteopetrosis, visceral lymphomatosis, neuro-lymphomatosis and finally a latent virus recently detected in cultures of "normal" chicken embryos (Rubin, 1961). Evidence is accumulating (Burmester, 1957) in favour of a unitarian hypothesis (Biester & Devries, 1944) which holds that these are manifestations of a single disease. It seems likely, however, that neuro-lymphomatosis may be a condition separate from the rest. The agents causing the other conditions are probably RNA viruses, very similar in size and morphology and closely related antigenically. Those most studied in the laboratory, such as the Rous sarcoma and some of the leucosis viruses, have probably become partly fixed in their properties and may now be very different from what they were in their original "wild" state. Though now such viruses breed true, as a rule, they do not invariably do so and injection of a leucosis virus may produce a local tumour or osteopetrosis. Some viruses in this group, however, may exist in a latent state in fowls, so that interpretation of experiments has to be very cautious. The virus of visceral lymphomatosis is transmitted through the egg; probably Rubin's (1961) latent virus also: and some strains of the former are certainly infectious amongst young chicks. The established sarcoma and leucosis strains are commonly considered not infectious, apart from a recent report by Burmester *et al.* (1960). Though viruses of the group are mainly reported as occurring amongst domestic fowls, some of the fowl sarcomata have been transmitted to ducks, turkeys and other species and adapted to grow preferentially in them.

We may, therefore, provisionally imagine an ubiquitous virus or group of viruses, transmitted through the egg or by contact, not infrequently changing, perhaps by mutation, into a form producing sarcomata or leucoses; this event would be a blind alley from the virus' viewpoint as such neoplasms are normally fatal and non-contagious.

AVIAN SARCOMATA

Synonyms: These include the Rous sarcoma (chicken tumour
No. 1), (Rous, 1911), the Fujinami and other fowl
tumours; also tumour MH2 (Murray-Begg endothelioma).

Review: Shrigley (1915). Harris (1953).
Andervont (1959). Rubin (1962).

Morphology and development. Virus particles have a diameter
of about 75 mμ (Bernhard *et al.*, 1956) or rather less (Gaylord, 1955).
They contain an electron-dense nucleoid 35–40 mμ across, surrounded by two membranes. They are found extracellularly or at
the surface of cells or within vacuoles; these last may, indeed, be
invaginations of the cell surface. Morphologically identical particles
occur in other fowl tumours, in fowl leucosis (*cf.* p. 162) and even
in the spleen of normal chick embryos (Benedetti & Bernhard,
1957). The significance of these last is discussed on p. 166. Similar
particles, reported, however, to be rather larger—110 mμ across—
have been found in the Murray-Begg endothelioma (Rouiller *et al.*,
1956). The bodies may be detected in as few as 1 in 50 tumour cells
(Epstein, 1956): they are more abundant in young, rapidly growing
tumours produced by injecting very potent filtrates (Haguenau
et al., 1958). Rubin's (1955) work suggests that virus particles are
liberated quite slowly, possibly one per 100 cells every hour, but
later work suggests that particles can at times be released much more
freely. The tumour cells are certainly in some sort of equilibrium
with virus, not necessarily being destroyed; the virus is in fact a
"moderate" one.

Chemical composition. All the available evidence indicates
that this is an RNA virus (Noyes, 1960). Bather (1957, 1958) found
about 1·42 per cent. of RNA in fairly pure preparations, the purine
and pyrimidine bases being in the same ratios as in normal fowl
tissues. Crawford (1960) also found much RNA and hardly any
DNA in "purified" preparations. Hæmin, catalase and acid phos-
phatase are also associated with virus particles but may be merely
adsorbed. Forssman antigen is also intimately associated with the
virus.

Physico-chemical characters. Inactivated in 30 minutes at
54°. The rate of inactivation at various temperatures between 37°

and 60° was determined by Dougherty (1961). Stable at −76° C for 1–2 years in the presence of citrate. Survives for many years when dried from the frozen state. Readily oxidized: cysteine hydrochloride and HCN help to preserve it. Can be adsorbed to kaolin and alum, or purified by the aid of fluorocarbon or chromatographic techniques. Sensitive to 20 per cent. ether and to desoxycholic acid. Its stability in various buffers is described by Bryan (1955). The specific gravity of the virus has been variously estimated as 1·13, 1·3 and varying between 1·16 and 1·19 (Crawford, 1960).

The virus is ten times more resistant to UV radiation than a typical myxovirus (Newcastle disease) (Rubin & Temin, 1959). The target sensitive to radiation has about the same diameter (45 mμ) (McCree, 1960) as has NDV.

No hæmagglutinins are described.

Antigenic properties. Fowls with slow-growing tumours develop neutralizing antibodies: these may also be produced by immunizing other species—geese, rabbits, goats. Viruses producing histologically distinct tumours may be closely related antigenically, yet not identical (Andrewes, 1933): or they may be antigenically remote (Carr & Campbell, 1959). One strain of Rous sarcoma has changed during propagation so that it is antigenically far removed from other strains (Simons & Dougherty, 1961). One can also demonstrate complement-fixation and agglutination of elementary bodies. Many normal fowls develop during their growth some antibodies against the Rous virus: and such antibodies occur particularly often in flocks with high losses from lymphomatosis (Kenzy & Neuzil, 1953). The known serological relations with other viruses in the group (*cf.* p. 162) doubtless explain these facts. Birds of a flock held in strict isolation had much poorer antibodies (Duran-Reynals *et al.*, 1953).

Antisera against normal fowl proteins will neutralize the virus. There are contradictory reports in the literature as to whether such antisera made in mammals do or do not require complement for their demonstration. There is in any case much evidence that host protein is very closely associated with the virus particle. So also, from the results of experiments on immunological tolerance, is Forssmann antigen (Harris and Simons, 1958).

Rubin (1956) has produced evidence that the anti-fowl sera may act on susceptible cells, not on the virus.

Interference. A number of viruses of several families have been propagated in Rous sarcomata. In some instances they have proved oncolytic (Nankervis *et al.*, 1959). Interferon inhibits virus growth on the CAM (Strandstrom *et al.* 1962) and infected cells produce interferon (Bader, 1962).

Cultivation. *In fertile eggs.* Tumour viruses, especially Rous, have been propagated on the CAM giving rise to foci of ectodermal proliferation (Keogh, 1938; Harris, 1954): such virus behaves as usual when injected into chicks.

In tissue culture. There was dispute for a long time as to whether monocytes or fibroblasts were the susceptible cells. It is now agreed that fibroblasts can be infected and given malignant properties; this may or may not be possible also for other cell-types. Lo *et al.* (1955) described destructive effects on chick fibroblasts followed by some regeneration of cultures with development of multinucleate giant cells; the pH of infected cells rapidly dropped. Recently, workers using monolayers of chick embryo cells have observed foci of cell-proliferation which can be counted for purposes of virus assay (Manaker & Groupé, 1956; Temin & Rubin, 1958; Rubin, 1960). Different clones of virus may produce foci of different cell types, either round or fusiform (Temin, 1960). The Schmidt-Ruppin strain produced CPE in rat, guinea-pig and mouse cells (Bergman & Jonsson, 1962). Current studies of tissue cultures for elucidating cell-virus relations cannot be reviewed here (*cf.* Prince, 1960; Temin & Rubin, 1959).

Pathogenicity. Sarcomata occur sporadically amongst fowls, more in some flocks than in others. Not all are transplantable and still fewer are filterable *ab initio*. Present knowledge is mainly based on studies on the Rous No. 1 and a few other laboratory-propagated tumours.

Experimentally the Rous virus behaves very differently in different circumstances. Bryan's strain of enhanced virulence is active in very high dilutions. At other times the virus' activity is so depressed that transplantable tumours may for several passages fail to yield active filtrates. This is seen more often after inoculation of small doses of virus into older birds. Growths are usually progressive and fatal but they occasionally regress temporarily or permanently. Lesions in viscera or elsewhere may be due to the virus itself or may be true metastases. In very young chicks the virus causes multiple hæmor-rhages and rapid death without evidence of neoplasia; necrosis of endothelial cells is suggested as the cause (Duran-Reynals, 1940). Some viruses, as already indicated, may cause either localized tumour growth or generalized leucosis (Stubbs & Furth, 1935). Two viruses (Rous No. 1 and MH2) produced adeno-carcinomata when inoculated into the kidney of young chicks (Carr, 1959).

Other species of birds may be infected with Rous virus—pheasants, guinea-fowls, turkeys, quails and, less readily, birds more remote zoologically, pigeons and ducks. There is a striking account of adaptation to ducks and readaptation of the duck virus to chicks by Duran-Reynals (1942). The Fujinami sarcoma goes readily in ducks (Fujinami, 1928). There have recently come reports that some strains of Rous virus may infect rats, causing hæmorrhagic cysts (Zilber & Krynkova, 1957; Svet Moldavsky & Skorikova, 1960).

Ahlström and his colleagues have produced progessively growing, metastasizing, transplantable sacromata in new-born rats (Ahlström & Jonsson, 1962), new-born and adult hamsters (Ahlström & Forsby, 1962); also in suckling mice and young guinea pigs. Only temporary growth occurred in young rabbits (Ahlström, Jonsson & Forsby, 1962). Only one strain (Schmidt-Ruppin) of Rous virus was effective. Considerable evidence indicated that tumours were due to multiplication of infected rodent cells.

Pathological lesions. Rapidly growing Rous sarcomata are soft growths containing much mucinous material mixed with blood-pigments; slow-growing ones are firm and white. Metastases are frequent, especially in lungs, liver and heart. Other filterable growths described by Rous and others are an intracanalicular spindle-celled (rifted) sarcoma, fibrosarcomata, osteochondro-sarcomata, endothelioma.

Ecology. As already indicated, the avian sarcomata are probably an uncommon manifestation of the activity of an ubiquitous virus. Evidence that they are contagious would therefore be surprising. Evidence that contact-transmission can occur within a cage concerns the "hotted-up" Bryan strain and is exceptional (Burmester *et al.*, 1960). Ectoparasites could conceivably be concerned.

AVIAN LEUCOSIS

Reviews: Beard *et al.* (1955).
(all types) Beard (1959).
Atanasiu (1957).
Darcel (1960).

A. Lymphoid Leucosis

Synonyms: Fowl lymphomatosis. Visceral leucosis.
The neural and ocular forms are not considered here (*cf.* p. 166).
The RPL 12 strain has been particularly studied.

Morphology and development. Electron-micrography has revealed particles 70 to 117 mμ across (Sharp *et al.*, 1952). Dmochowski *et al.* (1959) describe bodies 72 mμ across with a central 30 mμ nucleoid surrounded by a membrane. Less information is available than for the myeloblastic and erythroblastic leucoses.

Physico-chemical characters. Most early reports do not say with which type of leucosis they were dealing. It is likely that the agents of lymphoid, erythroblastic and myeloblastic leucosis react similarly. Furth (1932) reports that "leucosis" virus can be preserved by desiccation and that blood mixed with glycerol to 50 per cent. remains active for at least 104 days. The virus survives for 14 days at 4° C but not at 37° C.

Antigenic properties. Neutralizing antibodies are passed from an immune hen to newly hatched chicks through the egg-yolk. The virus is closely related antigenically to those of Rous sarcoma and of erythromyeloblastosis.

Interference. A number of arthropod-borne viruses inoculated into a lymphoid tumour led to regressions (Sharpless *et al.*, 1950).

Cultivation. The virus has not been certainly grown in tissue culture.
In several papers published in 1958 and 1959 cultivation of the RPL 12 strain was claimed; it soon appeared that in fact a fowl adenovirus (GAL, *cf.* p. 190) was concerned.

Pathogenicity. This is the commonest form of leucosis and it is increasing. Affected birds become pale and listless and show diarrhœa in the terminal stages. Except for the RPL 12 and a few other strains it has been hard to pass experimentally: those strains, however, infect young chicks which die after 4 to 36 weeks.
Pathological lesions comprise infiltration of various viscera with lymphoblasts and lymphocytes. The spleen is enlarged, the liver enlarged and either diffusely greyish-red, marbled or nodular. There is anæmia, and lymphoblasts may be found in the blood.

Ecology. In contrast to the other forms of leucosis and to fowl tumours, this virus, which is transmitted experimentally with greater difficulty, seems to be naturally contagious (Burmester, 1957). Susceptible chicks exposed to infected ones have a much higher incidence than do controls (Waters & Bywaters, 1949). The virus seems to be transmitted through the egg (Cottral *et al.*, 1954).

B. Avian Erythroblastosis

Synonym: Erythroleucosis.

Morphology and development. Particles in filtered, centrifuged plasma may be present up to 10^8–10^{10}/ml; these have a diameter of about 102 mμ. In sections they occur in cytoplasmic inclusions and then seem to be 55–90 mμ across, having a central nucleoid of 40 mμ and a single or double outer membrane (Bernhard *et al.*, 1958). They seem to be liberated from the cell surface when in a mature form by a process of budding. In salt solutions the particles may appear pleomorphic, perhaps tailed, as does Newcastle disease (Sharp *et al.*, 1955).

Chemical composition. Presumably RNA like myeloblastosis. There is, in contrast to that virus, no associated adenosine triphosphatase nor Forssman antigen.

Physico-chemical characters. The rate of heat-inactivation was studied by Eckert *et al.* (1955). Maximum stability was at ph 7. Ether-sensitive.

Antigenic properties. Antisera made either in fowls or rabbits will neutralize the virus' activity, agglutinate virus-suspensions and specifically fix complement (Bonar *et al.*, 1956). There is cross-reactivity both by neutralization and precipitation tests between the viruses of erythroleucosis and myeloblastosis and also against fowl tumour viruses. Furthermore there is some neutralization by rabbit antisera prepared against normal chick tissues (Kabat & Furth, 1941; Beard & Beard, 1957).

Cultivation. *In fertile eggs.* Passed in series by IV inoculation of 11, 12 or 13-day old embryos. 40 to 70 per cent. of embryos died with lesions as in hatched birds (Atanasiu *et al.*, 1957). Embryos of turkeys, quail, pheasants, guinea-fowl and ducks have also been infected (Pollard & Hall, 1941).

In tissue culture the virus is less readily established than is myeloblastosis. There is evidence that erythroblasts in culture liberate virus by a budding process, while surrounding the central body by a double membrane. Either fibroblasts or marrow could be infected *in vitro* (Lagerhof, 1960; Heine *et al.*, 1960).

Pathogenicity. The symptoms of the disease are those of progressive anæmia and weakness.

In chicks inoculated intravenously with a big dose, the incubation period is about 9 days; death follows after a few days more. Susceptibility does not seem to vary with age. Inoculated guinea-fowls, turkeys and pheasants may show transient anæmia or even leukæmia; some fatal infections in guinea-fowls are reported by Engelbreth-Holm & Meyer (1932).

Freshly isolated strains may give rise on inoculation either to erythro- or to myelo-blastosis. After passage in the laboratory they commonly but not invariably breed true.

Infected birds show profound anæmia and the blood contains large numbers of erythroblasts. The blood changes are described by Furth (1931). Enormous numbers of virus particles are present in the plasma—up to 10^{10}/ml. There is great enlargement of the spleen and the bone marrow is uniformly greyish-red, fat having largely disappeared.

Ecology. Natural chick to chick transmission is not reported.

C. Myeloblastosis

Morphology and development. Virus particles have a diameter of 80–110 mμ with denser cores about 40 mμ across; there is no essential difference in morphology between them and the agents of fowl tumours or other forms of leucosis. Those of myeloblastosis have been hard to find in myeloblasts: they appear to develop within the cytoplasm in viroplasts or "grey bodies" which may arise from mitochondria and later to turn into vesicles within which virus particles may be seen. They may be rapidly liberated from cells, but no "budding" as with erythroblastosis is described. They may be present in larger numbers in macrophages of spleen and bone marrow, possibly as a result of phagocytosis (Bonar *et al.*, 1959).

Chemical composition. Bodies contain 2·3 per cent. of RNA (Allison & Burke, 1962). An adenosine-triphosphatase is regularly associated with this virus in contrast to that of erythroblastosis; its activity can be used as a method of titrating the virus (Mommaerts *et al.*, 1954). Forssman antigen is also associated with virus—see below.

Physico-chemical characters. The density of particles is estimated as 1·29, or 1·059 when hydrated (Sharp *et al.*, 1946). The iso-electric point lies between pH 7 and 8·5. Heating for 10′ at 56° inactivates (Eckert *et al.*, 1955).

Antigenic properties. Antisera have been prepared in rabbits; also, by injecting formalinized virus into fowls. Neutralizing and complement-fixing antibodies develop. The virus is closely related antigenically to those of erythroblastosis and Rous sarcoma, but in precipitation tests, the virus and that of erythroblastosis only partly cross-reacted (Beard *et al.*, 1957). As with other viruses of the group, antisera to normal fowl tissues neutralize and fix complement with virus preparations. In contrast to erythroblastosis virus, myelo-blastosis reacts also with anti-Forssman sera (Eckert *et al.*, 1955).

Cultivation. The virus grows well in tissue cultures of myelo-blasts from the blood of infected birds; here the changes described above under "Morphology" have been followed (Bonar *et al.*, 1959). Cells from normal chick marrow have also been infected (Beaudreau *et al.*, 1960); also osteoblasts and other cells (Baluda & Goetz, 1961).

Pathogenicity. As with erythroblastosis the symptoms are those of anæmia leading to progressive weakness and death. The incuba-tion period after intravenous inoculation is proportional to the dose. The white blood count is higher than with erythroblastosis and may reach over 2,000,000/cu. mm. Circulating cells are largely myelo-blasts. The plasma may also contain up to 10^{12} virus particles/cu. mm. (Eckert *et al.*, 1955). Liver and spleen are enlarged, greyer and more mottled than with erythroblastosis. There may be associated sarcomata.

Myeloblastosis given IV to 5-day turkey poults has produced mainly erythroblastosis (Bland, 1959).

D. Osteopetrosis

Synonyms: Thick leg disease. Marble bone. Diffuse osteo-periostitis.

This is a non-malignant condition in which there is excessive activity of osteoblasts leading to great thickening of the bones. It is apt to appear in a proportion of birds inoculated with the agents of lymphoid or other forms of leucosis but is not commonly trans-missible as such, and there is accordingly no information as to the properties of a specific osteopetrosis virus. Holmes (1963) succeeded in transmitting the disease from fowls to young turkeys, though it does not occur naturally in these.

E. Latent Chick Viruses

Explanation is needed for the development of antibodies to Rous and related viruses in normal birds and for the finding of bodies resembling those viruses in normal chick embryonic and other tissues (Benedetti, 1957).

Rubin (1961) has found that normal chick embryos may contain an agent which, at least on first recovery, produces no cytopathic effects in tissue culture but interferes with the growth of Rous virus. He called it Resistance-inducing factor (RIF). In one flock, one of every six hens had a chronic RIF viræmia (Rubin *et al.*, 1962). It was serologically related to Rous virus and resembled it in its sus-ceptibility to ether, heat and UV radiation. On passage in culture it became capable of affecting cells so that they grew in disorganized fashion. Later it was found that when 11-day embryos were in-oculated, tumours or leucosis were apt to develop after they had hatched (Baluda & Jamieson, 1961) and the virus is probably an avirulent kind of leucosis virus.

A second agent ("Rous-associated virus") is described by Rubin & Vogt (1962) but may not be distinct. It resembles related viruses morphologically and produces erythroblastosis after IV inoculation into chick embryos.

NEUROLYMPHOMATOSIS

Synonyms: Fowl paralysis. Range paralysis. Nervous form of lymphoid leucosis.

As mentioned earlier, this disease is probably distinct ætiologically from other forms of leucosis. It may simulate these in the pathological findings—for excessive accumulations of lymphocytes may be a feature of both and neurolymphoma lesions may at times become malignant. The agents of all these conditions have been so prevalent, often in a latent state, that it is not surprising that transfers from birds with fowl paralysis have set up other forms of leucosis and vice versa.

Evidence of transmission by inoculation is so scanty that one cannot say anything about the properties of the supposed causative virus.

Pathogenicity. In the nervous form of the disease, there is progressive paralysis, usually of a wing or leg. Quite young chicks may be affected, but it begins most commonly in birds 2–8 months old. There is an ocular form (grey eye) in which one sees loss of colour in the iris and irregularities in the shape of the pupil, going on to blindness.

The disease has been recorded in pheasants, turkeys and quails (Andrewes & Glover, 1939; Jungherr, 1938; Wight, 1963).

Lesions in the nerves are first those of inflammation, with œdema and infiltration with lymphocytes, lymphoblasts and plasma-cells. At length the nerves become grossly thickened as a result of this infiltration, but the axons themselves are only secondarily affected. Similar cellular infiltration of the iris and other parts of the eye causes the lesions in the ocular form.

Blakemore (1945) and Asplin (1947) recovered an agent from cases of neurolymphomatosis. This caused focal necroses in heart and liver of inoculated chicks and was susceptible to treatment with sulphonamides. It is not now thought to be causally related to fowl paralysis.

Ecology. Fowl paralysis was first described in 1907, became troublesome, especially in the United States, in 1925, but has since become less common, while visceral lymphomatosis has increased.

It is probably transmitted in the egg and evidence suggests that some cocks may transfer the disease in the sperm (Blakemore, 1934). Certainly it is particularly prevalent in certain families of birds. There are suggestive reports of contact-transmission in the field (Cole & Hutt, 1951; Burmester et al., 1954). There is one report suggesting that a tick (*Argus persicus*) might transmit infection (Brown & Cross, 1941).

REFERENCES

Ahlström, C. G., & Forsby, N. (1962) *J. exp. Med.*, **115**, 839.
Ahlström, C. G., & Jonsson, N. (1962) *Acta path. microbiol. scand.*, **54**, 145.
Ahlström, C. G., Jonsson, N., & Forsby, N. (1962) *Acta path. microbiol. scand.* suppt., **154**, 127.
Allison, A. C., & Burke, D. (1962) *J. gen. Microbiol.*, **27**, 181.
Andervont, H. B. (1959) in *The Viruses* Vol. III. Ed. Burnet and Stanley New York: Academic Press.
Andrewes, C. H. (1933) *J. Path. Bact.*, **37**, 27.
Andrewes, C. H., & Glover, R. E. (1939) *Vet. Rec.*, **51**, 934.
Asplin, F. D. (1947) *J. comp. Path.*, **57**, 116 & 134.
Atanasiu, P. (1957) *Revue Hémat.*, **12**, 404.
Atanasiu, P., Vieuchange, J., & Strunge, B. (1957) *Acta int. Unio contra Cancrum*, **7**, 213.
Bader, J. P. (1962) *Virology*, **16**, 436.
Baluda, M. A., & Goetz, I. E. (1961) *Virology*, **15**, 185.
Baluda, M. A., & Jamieson, P. P. (1961) *Virology*, **14**, 33.
Bather, R. (1957) *Brit. J. Cancer*, **11**, 611.
Bather, R. (1958) *Brit. J. Cancer*, **12**, 256.
Beard, J. W. (1959) in *Perspectives in Virology* I. Ed. Pollard. New York. Wiley & Sons, p. 197.
Beard, J. W., & Beard, D. (1957) *J. nat. Cancer Inst.*, **19** 923.
Beard, J. W., Sharp, D. G., & Eckert, E. A. (1955) *Advanc. Virus Res.*, **3** 149.
Beaudreau, G. S., Becker, C., Bonar, R. A., Wallbank, A. M., Beard, D., & Beard, J. W. (1960) *J. nat. Cancer Inst.* **24**, 395.
Benedetti, E. L. (1957) *Bull. Cancer*, **44**, 473.
Benedetti, E. L., & Bernhard, W. (1957) *J. Ultrastruct. Res.*, **1**, 309.
Bergman, S., & Jonsson, N. (1962) *Acta path. microbiol. scand.* suppl., **154**, 130.
Bernhard, W., Oberling, C., & Vigier, P. (1956) *Bull. Cancer*, **43**, 407.
Bernhard, W., Bonar, A. R., Beard, D. & Beard, J. W. (1958) *Proc. Soc. exp. Biol. (N.Y.)*, **97**, 48.
Biester, H. E., & Devries, L. B. (Eds.) (1944) *Diseases of Poultry*, p. 367. Iowa State College Press.
Blakemore, F. (1934) *4th Rep. Univ. Cambridge Inst. Anim. Path.*, p. 39.
Blakemore, F. (1945) *J. comp. Path.*, **55**, 1.
Bonar, R. A., Parsons, D. F., Beaudreau, G. S., Beeker, C., & Beard, J. W. (1959) *J. nat. Cancer Inst.*, **23**, 199.
Bonar, R. A., Sharp, D. G., Beard, D., & Beard, J. W. (1956) *Proc. Soc. exp. Biol. (N.Y.)*, **92**, 774.
Brown, J. C., & Cross, J. C. (1941) *Science*, **93**, 528.
Bryan, W. R. (1955) *J. nat. Cancer Inst.*, **16**, 285.
Burmester, B. N. (1957) *Texas Rep. Biol. Med.*, **15**, 540.
Burmester, B. N., Fontes, A. K., & Walter, W. G. (1960) *J. nat. Cancer Inst.*, **25**, 307.
Burmester, B. N., & Gentry, R. F. (1954) *Cancer Res.*, **14**, 34.
Carr, J. G. (1959) *Virology*, **8**, 269.
Carr, J. G., & Campbell, J. G. (1958) *Brit. J. Cancer*, **12**, 631.
Cole, R. K., & Hutt, F. B. (1957) *Poult. Sci.*, **30**, 205.
Cottrall, C. E., Burmester, B. R., & Waters, N. F. (1954) *Poult. Sci.*, **33**, 1174.
Crawford, L. V. (1960) *Virology*, **12**, 143.
Darcel, C. le Q. (1960) *Cancer Res.*, **20**, 2.
Dmochowski, L., Gray, C. E., Burmester, B. R., & Gross, M. A. (1959) *Proc. Soc. exp. Biol. (N.Y.)*, **100**, 514.
Dougherty, R. M. (1961) *Virology*, **14**, 371.
Duran-Reynals, F. (1940) *Yale J. Biol. Med.*, **13**, 77.

Duran-Reynals, F. (1942) *Cancer Res.*, **2**, 343.
Duran-Reynals, F., Burmester, B. R., Cottral, G. E., & Bryan, E. (1953) *Cancer Res.*, **13**, 408.
Eckert, E. A., Green, I., Sharp, D. G., Beard, D., & Beard, J. W. (1955) *J. nat. Cancer Inst.*, **16**, 153.
Engelbreth-Holm, J., & Meyer, A. R. (1932) *Acta path. microbiol. scand.*, **9**, 293.
Epstein, M. A. (1956) *Brit. J. Cancer*, **10**, 33.
Fujinami, A. (1928) *Trans. Jap. path. Soc.*, **18**, 616.
Furth, J. (1931) *Arch. Path. (Chicago)*, **12**, 1.
Furth, J., (1932) *J. exp. Med.*, **55**, 495.
Gaylord, W. H. (1955) *Cancer Res.*, **15**, 80.
Haguenau, F., Dalton, A. J., & Moloney, J. B. (1958) *J. nat. Cancer Inst.*, **20**, 633.
Harris, R. J. C. (1953) *Advanc. Cancer Res.*, **1**, 233.
Harris, R. J. C. (1954) *Brit. J. Cancer*, **8**, 731.
Harris, R. J. C. (1958) *Nature (Lond.)*, **181**, 1485.
Heine, U., Beaudreau, G. S., Becker, C., Beard, D., & Beard, J. W. (1961) *J. nat. Cancer Inst.*, **26**, 359.
Holmes, J. R. (1958) *J. comp. Path.*, **68**, 439.
Holmes, J. R. (1963) *J. comp. Path.*, **73**, 136.
Jungherr, E. (1939) *J. Amer. vet. med. Ass.*, **94**, 49.
Kabat, E. A., & Furth, J. (1941) *J. exp. Med.*, **74**, 257.
Kenzy, S. G., & Neuzil, P. V. (1953) *Amer. J. vet. Res.*, **14**, 123.
Keogh, E. V. (1938) *Brit. J. exp. Path.*, **19**, 1.
Lagerhöf, B. (1960) *Acta path. microbiol. scand.*, **49**, 361.
Lo, W. H. Y., Gey, G. O., & Shapras, P. (1955) *Bull. Johns Hopk. Hosp.*, **97**, 248.
McCrea, J. F. (1960) *Ann. N. Y. Acad. Sci.*, **83**, 692.
Manaker, R. A., & Groupé, V. (1956) *Virology*, **2**, 839.
Mommaerts, E. B., Sharp, D. G., Eckert, E. A., Beard, D., & Beard, J. W. (1954) *J. nat. Cancer Inst.*, **14**, 1011.
Munroe, J. S., & Windle, W. F. (1963) *Science*, **140**, 1415.
Noyes, W. F. (1960) *Virology*, **12**, 488.
Pollard, M., & Hall, W. J. (1941) *J. Amer. vet. med. Ass.*, **99**, 218.
Prince, A. M. (1960) *Virology*, **11**, 371.
Rouiller, C., Haguenau, F., Golde, A., & Lacour, F. (1956) *Bull. Cancer*, **43**, 10.
Rous, P. (1911) *J. exp. Med.*, **13**, 397.
Rubin, H. (1955) *Virology*, **1**, 445.
Rubin, H. (1956) *Virology*, **2**, 545.
Rubin, H. (1960) *Virology*, **10**, 29.
Rubin, H. (1961) *Virology*, **13**, 200.
Rubin, H. (1962) *Bact. Rev.*, **26**, 1.
Rubin, H., & Temin, H. M. (1959) *Virology*, **7**, 75.
Rubin, H., & Vogt, P. K. (1962) *Virology*, **17**, 184.
Rubin, H., Fanshier, L., Coinchius, A., & Hughes, W. F. (1962) *Virology*, **17**, 143.
Sharp, D. G., Beard, D., & Beard, J. W. (1955) *Proc. Soc. exp. Biol. (N.Y.)*, **90**, 168.
Sharp, D. G., Eckert, E. A., Beard, D., & Beard, J. W. (1952) *J. Bact.*, **63**, 151.
Sharpless, G. R., Davies, M. C., & Cox, H. R. (1950) *Proc. Soc. exp. Biol. (N.Y.)*, **73**, 270.
Shrigley, E. W. (1957) *Ann. Rev. Microbiol.*, **5**, 241.
Simons, P. J., & Dougherty, R. M. (1961) *Virology*, **15**, 200.
Strandström, H., Sandelin, K., & Oker-Blom, N. (1962) *Virology*, **16**, 384.

Stubbs, E. L., & Furth, J. (1935) *J. exp. Med.*, **61**, 593.
Svet–Moldavsky, G. J., & Skorikova, A. S. (1960) *Acta virol.*, **4**, 47.
Temin, H. M. (1960) *Virology*, **10**, 182.
Temin, H. M., & Rubin, H. (1958) *Virology*, **6**, 669.
Temin, H. M., & Rubin, H. (1959) *Virology*, **8**, 209.
Waters, N. F., & Bywaters, J. H. (1949) *Poult. Sci.*, **28**, 254.
Wight, P. A. L. (1963) *Vet. Rec.*, **75**, 685.
Zilber, L. A. & Krynkova, I. N. (1957) *Probl. Virol.*, **2**, 247.

8

Viruses Associated with Mouse Tumours

All the viruses described in this chapter have been isolated from tumours or leukæmias in rodents. Though they will cause tumours or leukæmias on passage, they are not all necessarily the causative agents of the growths which yielded them. They are probably normally latent viruses, only exceptionally causing neoplasms. They are probably all medium-to-large RNA viruses, inactivated by ether and apparently resemble myxoviruses and fowl tumour viruses morphologically.

MAMMARY CANCER VIRUS OF MICE

Synonyms: Milk factor. Bittner agent.
Reviews: Bittner (1948).
        Dmochowski (1959).
        Andervont (1959).

Morphology and development. Clusters of particles (A-particles) 65–70 mμ across are found close to the nucleus of tumour cells in close relation to the Golgi apparatus. They contain a nucleoid and are surrounded by single or double membranes. They may be arranged round the periphery of small vacuoles. Within the canaliculi of the affected mammary gland are larger bodies (B-particles) about 130 mμ across. These contain one, sometimes more, nucleoids, usually placed eccentrically. Bernhard and his colleagues (1955, 1956) suggest that these larger bodies arise from the smaller ones and may be a later stage of development. There is evidence suggesting that virus may be liberated from the cell surface by a budding process (Moore et al., 1959). Similar appearances are described by Dmochowski et al. (1954). The surface membrane appears, by negative-staining techniques, to be covered with minute projections a little shorter than those seen in myxoviruses (Lyons & Moore, 1962).

Chemical composition. In pellets of partly purified virus Dmochowski *et al.* (1959) found a considerable amount of RNA but no DNA.

Physico-chemical characters. The virus is fairly stable between pH 5 and 10·2. Specific gravity 1·22. It may be preserved by freeze-drying; or for years at −76° C. Inactivated in 30 minutes at 56° C and in 90 hours at 37° C. Withstands petroleum ether and acetone (Barnum *et al.*, 1945). Can be purified with the aid of a fluorocarbon. No conclusive evidence as to resistance to ethyl ether.

Antigenic properties. Neutralizing antibodies can be prepared in rabbits and guinea pigs, not in mice. Viruses derived from 3 strains of mice were antigenically alike (Blair, 1960). Specific precipitins (Imagawa *et al.*, 1948) and complement-fixing antibodies are described. Brown & Bittner (1961), however, consider such tests unreliable and prefer to look for the power of sera to prevent virus from entering cells, as tested for with fluorescent antibody.

Cultivation. *In fertile eggs.* Attempts at cultivation in eggs have given mainly negative results; at any rate claims to have succeeded remain unconfirmed.

In tissue cultures. Activity has been maintained in cultures of embryonic mouse skin in fibroblasts derived from mouse mammæ. Multiplication was not proved but electron-microscopical studies suggested that development was occurring (Lasfargues *et al.*, 1958, 1960). Pikovski (1953) reported multiplication in cultures of chick fibroblasts but this remains unconfirmed.

Habitat. Wild as well as laboratory mice may harbour the virus (Andervont & Dunn, 1956).

Pathogenicity. The virus is commonly latent and only causes mammary cancers when in a genetically susceptible strain of mice and when the appropriate hormonal influences operate (breeding in ♀♀, œstrogen treatment in ♂♂). Mice can be infected, best when very young, *per os* or by parenteral injection by any route. Virus is present in the cancers, but even more abundantly in the lactating mamma: also in liver, spleen and other tissues of cancerous mice; it is not found in urine or fæces. Production of tumours has been largely relied on in titrations of virus; results are irregular, and more cancers may develop after injection of dilute inocula (Bittner, 1945). Presence of an inhibitor may explain some of the anomalies. Tumours develop in inoculated young mice in 6 months to 2 years.

Pathological lesions. The mammary tumours are typical adeno-carcinomata. Their appearance is preceded, according to some workers, by hyperplastic changes in the mammæ.

Ecology. Infection is transmitted when baby mice ingest milk of mothers of a high cancer strain such as C3H. It may then, in susceptible mice, be passed similarly for many generations, whether the mother mice develop cancer or remain latently infected. In more resistant strains of mice or after small initial infecting doses the incidence of tumours falls in succeeding generations and the infection becomes extinguished. Fœtuses are not ordinarily infected *in utero* and if removed by Cæsarean section and suckled on mothers of a low cancer strain, they develop few if any tumours. There are, however, reports (e.g. Bittner, 1952) that males of a high cancer strain may transmit infection to their offspring, often but not necessarily infecting the mother.

MOUSE LEUKÆMIA

We have now to consider a number of viruses producing leukæmia, sometimes lymphosarcoma, in mice. First comes Gross's virus which seems to be the causative agent of a lymphoid leukæmia occurring commonly in certain inbred strains of mice. The other leukæmia viruses have mostly been obtained by injecting filtrates of propagable tumours into mice, especially newborns. These leukæmias do not correspond to any commonly occurring natural disease. It is likely that the viruses are normally wholly latent infections which may be able to reach higher levels of activity when multiplying in a neoplasm, and after propagation become "fixed viruses" with properties differing from those they possessed when latent. They are probably not causally related to the neoplasms from which they come. References will be found in Moloney's review (1960b). The relation of the various viruses to each other has been imperfectly worked out.

Reviews: Dmochowski   (1961).   Gross   (1957a).   Moloney (1960b). Sinkovics (1962).

Spontaneous Lymphoid Leukæmia

Synonyms: AK leukæmia. Gross's leukæmia.
Much of the work published before about 1958 is confused by the fact that material being studied was in fact a mixture of leukæmia and polyoma viruses.

Morphology and development. The particles described by Dmochowski & Grey (1957) and the larger ones of Bernhard & Guérin (1958) may well represent leukæmia virus; they were 80–110 mμ across with a 30–40 mμ nucleoid. Gradocol membrane filtration suggests that the virus' diameter is less than 100 mμ (Gross, 1957a).

Chemical composition. Hays (1961) reports rather unconvincing evidence of transmission by a nucleic acid preparation from leukæmic material—but it contained both DNA and RNA.

Physico-chemical characters. Ether-sensitive. Survives for months at −70° or when lyophilised. Inactivated in 30 minutes at 65°–68° C.

Hæmagglutination. Gross (1959) reports agglutination at 4° C or room temperature with filtrates of leukæmia material, but convincingly only with filtrates previously heated for 30 minutes at 55° C. Polyoma virus also shows hæmagglutination which is improved by heating; the leukæmia hæmagglutinin is said to differ in that it does not elute from the RBC's and is much more active against mouse than against guinea-pig cells.

Antigenic properties. Neutralized by specific antisera made in rabbits. There is a possible antigenic relation to Graffi's virus (*cf.* p. 177) (Moloney, 1960b).

Cultivation. Gross's A-strain has apparently been propagated, but without CPE, in embryo cells of C3H and perhaps other mice: it was released continuously into tissue culture fluid (Gross *et al.*, 1961).

Pathogenicity. The virus has been obtained from inbred mice with a very high incidence of spontaneous leukæmia (especially sublines of AK mice). Filtrates inoculated into new-born mice (especially C3H strain) with a very low leukæmia incidence induced leukæmia, but only after 8–11 months, much longer than is seen after cell-transmission. Moreover the leukæmia thereafter behaved as if the cells were genetically C3H rather than AK (*cf.* numerous papers by Gross). By passage of filtrates through newborn C3H mice Gross obtained his A-line of high virulence which would infect mice up to 14 days old and produce leukæmia after only 3 or 4 months (Gross, 1957b): it would also now cause leukæmia in day-old rats (Gross, 1961). The possibility of repeating Gross's work has depended on using mice genetically the same as his. It appears that multiplication of the virus occurs primarily in the thymus.

Ecology. Gross has maintained that this leukæmia is an example of "vertical transmission" of infection from one generation to another through the ovum. Such transmission has been achieved for one or two generations in C3H mice but not indefinitely (Gross, 1955).

Control. Development of this form of leukæmia either naturally or in inoculated mice can be prevented or diminished by thymectomy (Levinthal *et al.*, 1959; Miller, 1962).

Mouse Leukæmia (Friend's strain)

Friend's leukæmia strain is one of several which have come to light in the course of serial passage of cancerous material in mice, but which are unknown as a natural disease of mice.

Review: Friend (1959).

Morphology and development. Size about 87 mμ. Particles are surrounded by double membranes. By negative staining methods electron-microscopy reveals what seem to be regularly-arranged subunits on the surface. The particles are found especially in vacuoles in the cytoplasm of megacaryocytes and in tissue spaces. They may seem apparently budding from the surface of leukæmic cells (de Harven & Friend, 1960).

Physico-chemical characters. Inactivated in 30 minutes at 50° C. Survives well at −76° or after lyophilization. Ether-sensitive. Inactivated by 1 : 200 formaldehyde.

Antigenic properties. Neutralizing antibodies are readily produced both in rabbits and mice; there was no evidence of crossing with Gross's or Schwartz's leukæmia virus nor with polyoma. CF antibodies have not been reported; tests for precipitins in agar-gel gave equivocal results. Related antigenically to Moloney's leukæmia virus (*v.* p. 177) (Moloney, 1960b).

Cultivation. Virus persists in cultures of mouse embryo but continued multiplication has not been proved.

Pathogenicity. Experimentally, the virus when first described would readily infect adult mice but only DBA/2 and Swiss mice. (It is unusual for an agent with such limited specificity to infect particularly a strain which, like the Swiss, is not inbred.)

Injected mice show enlargement of liver and spleen within a few days; yet the disease may run a course of 2 or 3 months. The spleens soon become palpable through the abdominal wall. Mice die either within a few weeks from hæmorrhage, sometimes from a ruptured spleen, or, after several months, from leukæmia. Infection has been produced with spleen suspensions diluted 10^{-3} or 10^{-1}. The malignant cells lack the autonomy once believed to be ordinarily a character of malignancy; for transfer is always through infection of host cells by the virus, not through cell-transplantation (Furth, 1959). Young rats were infected by Mirand & Grace (1962b).

Pathological lesions. According to Metcalf *et al.* (1959) the disease is a leukæmia of reticulum-cell type, combined with erythroblastosis. The blood contains primitive cells up to 300,000/cu mm often showing mitosis. The liver, spleen and bone marrow are massively infiltrated with similar immature cells. There is sometimes ascites.

Ecology. Mirand & Grace (1962a) found that inoculated mothers would pass infection on to their offspring (? how) and that young so infected showed the reticular-cell disease but anæmia rather than erythroblastosis.

Control. Formalinized vaccines made from leukæmia spleens produced definite immunity in mice both against filtrates and cell-suspensions used for challenge.

Infections possibly related to the above have been described by Taylor & Macdowell (1949) and Pope (1961).

Mouse Leukæmia (Moloney strain)

This is another leukæmia arising during propagation of a mouse tumour, in this case the S37 mouse sarcoma.
Original description: Moloney (1960a).

Morphology. Tailed particles are described by Dalton *et al.* (1962).

Physico-chemical characters. Inactivated in 30 minutes at 56° C Stable to 10 per cent. ether (this requires confirmation; related viruses are ether-labile).

Antigenic properties. Cells infected with the virus apparently elaborate a new antigen as does polyoma (*v.* p. 200) (Sachs, 1962).

Cultivation. Leukæmia cells were successfully grown *in vitro*; also virus infected normal mouse embryo and kidney cell cultures. No CPE observed (Ginsburg & Sachs, 1961).

Pathogenicity. The virus will induce lymphoid leukæmia in adult mice of several strains. First changes appear in 8 weeks. Transplants from induced leukæmias lead to lymphocytic neoplasms of varying biological behaviour (Dunn *et al.*, 1961) (*cf.* fowl leukæmias, p. 157). Leukæmias were reported to occur frequently in the offspring of mice which had been inoculated in infancy (Salaman & Harvey, 1961). The virus has recently been found to infect also rats and new-born hamsters (Moloney, 1962). It is apparently transmitted "vertically" to embryos *in utero* but even better through the mother's milk (Law, 1962).

A number of other rodent leukæmia viruses have been studied less fully or only in single laboratories. They are reviewed by Sinkovics (1962); references will be found in that review.

Graffi's Mouse Chloroleukæmia (Graffi, 1957, 1960)

This is a myeloleukæmia obtained by inoculating filtrates of several transplantable tumours in suckling mice of the Agnes Bluhm strain (which perhaps carries the virus). Serial transplantation was at first achieved with difficulty but, later, filtrates were passed in series in several strains of mice, and rats were also infected. Particles of several sizes were revealed by electron-microscopy but it is uncertain which of them represent the virus. The virus was ether-sensitive and inactivated in 30 minutes at 56°–65° C. There may be some antigenic relation to Gross's virus.

Breyere-Moloney Virus

This came from an undifferentiated plasma-cell tumour in BALB mice. The filterable agent recovered caused lymphocytic neoplasms of various tissues in mice and rats. The virus' size was estimated at 100 mμ.

Kaplan's Virus

This was obtained from an X-ray induced lymphosarcoma. It resembles Gross's virus.

Stansky's Virus

This produces lymphosarcomas and reticular-cell growths after 5–8 months' latency.

Schwartz's Virus

Two mouse leukæmias have been described, transmissible respec-tively in Swiss and C3H. The C3H strain generally resembled Gross's virus but produced leukæmia in 12–20 days in 70 per cent. of adult C3H mice. The virtues of brain extracts in producing or accelerating leukæmias claimed by Schwartz and his colleagues have not been confirmed by other workers.

Rauscher's Virus

This virus is similar to Friend's in its general behaviour but is antigenically distinct and goes in more strains of mice and in newborn rats. It is ether-sensitive, and inactivated in 30 minutes at 56° C. Zeigel & Rauscher (1963) describe heads, roughly hexagonal, 120 mμ across, with tails of variable length but up to 0·5 μ long and sometimes double.

LEUKÆMIAS IN OTHER RODENTS

Leukæmias apparently caused by viruses have been described in rats (Svec *et al.*, 1957) and guinea pigs (Jungeblut & Kodza, 1963).

REFERENCES

Andervont, H. B. (1959) in *The Viruses*, vol. III, Ed. Burnet & Stanley. New York: Academic Press.

Andervont, H. B., & Dunn, T. B. (1956) *Acta int. Unio contra Cancrum*, **12**, 530.

Barnum, C. P., Ball, Z. B., Bittner, J. J., & Visscher, A. B. (1945) *Science*, **100**, 575.

Bernhard, W., Bauer, A., Guérin, M., & Oberling, C. (1955) *Bull. Cancer*, **42**, 163.

Bernhard, W., & Guérin, M. (1958) *C.R. Acad. Sci. (Paris)*, **247**, 1802.

Bernhard, W., Guérin, M., & Oberling, C. H. (1956) *Acta int. Unio contra Cancrum*, **12**, 544.

Bittner, J. J. (1945) *Proc. Soc. exp. Biol. (N.Y.)*, **59**, 43.

Bittner, J. J. (1948) *Cancer Res.*, **8**, 625.

Bittner, J. J. (1952) *Cancer Res.*, **12**, 387.

Blair, P. B. (1960) *Proc. Soc. exp. Biol. (N.Y.)*, **103**, 188.

Brown, E. R., & Bittner, J. J. (1961) *Proc. Soc. exp. Biol. (N.Y.)*, **106**, 303.

Dalton, A. J., Haguenau, F., & Moloney, J. B. (1962) *J. Nat. Cancer Inst.*, **29**, 1177.

De Harven, E., & Friend, C. (1960) *J. biophys. biochem. Cytol.*, **7**, 747.

Dmochowski, L. (1953) *Advanc. Cancer. Res.*, **1**, 103.

Dmochowski, L. (1961) *Progr. Med. Virol.*, **3**, 363.

Dmochowski, L., & Grey, C. E. (1959) *Texas Rep. Biol. Med.*, **15**, 704.

Dmochowski, L., Grey, C. E., Pearson, L. D., Ward, D. N., Hurlbert, R. B., Griffin, A. C., & Bresson, A. L. (1959) *Proc. Soc. exp. Biol. (N.Y.)*, **102**, 174.

Dunn, T. B., Moloney, J. B., Green, A. W., & Arnold, B. (1961) *J. nat. Cancer Inst.*, **26**, 189.

Friend, C. (1959) in *Perspectives in Virology*, **1**, 231, New York: John Wiley.

Furth, J. (1959) in *Perspectives in Virology*, **1**, 262, New York: John Wiley.

Ginsburg, H., & Sachs, L. (1961) *Virology*, **13**, 380.

Graffi, A. (1957) *Ann. N.Y. Acad. Sci.*, **68**, 540.

Gross, L. (1955) *Acta hæmat.*, **13**, 13.

Gross, L. (1957a) *Ann. N.Y. Acad. Sci.*, **68**, 501.

Gross, L. (1957b) *Proc. Soc. exp. Biol. (N.Y.)*, **94**, 767.

Gross, L. (1959) *Proc. Soc. exp. Biol. (N.Y.)*, **101**, 113.

Gross, L. (1961) *Proc. Soc. exp. Biol. (N.Y.)*, **106**, 890.

Gross, L., Dreyfuss, Y., & Moore, L. A. (1961) *Proc. Amer. Soc. Cancer Res.*, **3**, 231.

Hays, E. F., Simmons, N. S., & Beck, W. S. (1958) *Nature (Lond.)*, **180**, 1419.

Imagawa, D. T., Green, R. G., & Halvorson, H. O. (1948) *Proc. Soc. exp. Biol. (N.Y.)*, **68**, 162.

Jungeblut, C. W., & Kodza, H. (1963) *Arch. ges. Virusforsch.*, **12**, 537.

Lasfargues, E. Y., Moore, D. H., & Murray, M. R. (1958) *Cancer Res.*, **18**, 1281.

Lasfargues, E. Y., Murray, M. R., & Moore, D. H. (1960) *Nat. Cancer Inst. Monogr.*, no. 4, 151.

Law, L. W. (1962) *Proc. Soc. exp. Biol. (N.Y.)*, **111**, 615.

Levinthal, J. T., Buffett, R. F., & Furth, J. (1959) Proc. Soc. exp. Biol. (N.Y.), 100, 610.
Lyons, M. J., & Moore, D. H. (1962) Nature (Lond.), 194, 1141.
Metcalf, D., Furth, J., & Buffett, R. F. (1959) Cancer Res., 19, 52.
Miller, J. F. A. P. (1962) in Ciba foundation symposium Tumour Viruses of Marine Origin, p. 262. London, Churchill.
Mirand, E. A., & Grace, J. T. (1962a) Virology, 16, 344.
Mirand, E. A., & Grace, J. T. (1962b) Virology, 17, 364.
Moloney, J. B. (1960a) J. nat. Cancer Inst., 24, 933.
Moloney, J. B. (1960b) Fed. Proc., 21, 19.
Moore, D. H., Lasfargues, E. Y., Murray, M., Haagensen, C. D., & Pollard, E. C. (1959) J. biophys. biochem. Cytol., 5, 85.
Pikowski, M. A. (1953) J. nat. Cancer Inst., 13, 1275.
Pope, J. H. (1961) Aust. J. exp. Biol. med. Sci., 39, 521.
Rich, M. A., & Johns, L. W. (1963) Virology, 20, 373.
Sachs, L. (1962) J. nat. Cancer Inst., 29, 759.
Salaman, M. H., & Harvey, J. J. (1961) Nature (Lond.), 191, 509.
Sinkovics, J. G. (1962) Ann. Rev. Microbiol., 16, 75.
Svec, F., Hlavay, E., Thurzo, V., & Kossey, P. (1957) Acta hæmat., 17, 34.
Taylor, M. J., & Macdowell, E. C. (1949) Cancer Res., 9, 144.
Zeigel, R. F., & Rauscher, F. J. (1963) J. nat. Cancer Inst., 30, 207.

PART II

DNA Viruses

9

Adenoviruses

Most work on the properties of adenoviruses has been carried out on those of human origin under which head (see below) they are described in detail. The following properties seem to characterize the group. The particles are icosahedral in shape 70 mμ–90 mμ in diameter and composed of a DNA core with a number of subunits or capsomeres on the surface. These show 5–3–2 axial symmetry with a centre-to-centre spacing of about 7 mμ. There is a difference of interpretation of electron-micrographs: the number of capsomeres is estimated by different workers to be either 162 or 252. The capsomeres may be spherical or prismatic; it is uncertain which. There is no membrane round the capsid. Virus particles multiply in cell-nuclei, in which they may often be demonstrated by electron-microscopy in crystalline array. They are ether-resistant, rather stable also to changes in temperature and pH. Most of them agglutinate RBC's of one species or another. All but avian strains share a common soluble antigen. They produce characteristic cytopathic effects in tissue-cultures.

ADENOVIRUSES OF HUMAN ORIGIN

Synonyms: Adenoidal-conjunctival-pharyngeal (APC) agents. Agents of ARD (acute respiratory disease). RI (respiratory infective) agents. Diseases caused include acute pharyngitis or febrile catarrh, pharyngo-conjunctival fever and epidemic kerato-conjunctivitis.

Reviews: Huebner *et al.* (1954). Huebner, Rowe & Chanock (1958). Pereira (1959). Ginsberg (1962). Pereira *et al.* (1963).

Twenty-eight serotypes have been distinguished.

Morphology and development. The negative staining technique applied to electron-microscopy by Horne *et al.* (1959) has revealed that the virus particles are rigid icosahedra (twenty-sided figures), often appearing hexagonal in profile. Horne and his colleagues report the presence of identical protein subunits (capsomeres) on the surface arranged so that 6 lie along each edge of the 20 triangular faces, making 252 in all. Other workers, however, maintain, as mentioned above, that there are only 162 capsomeres. Within the capsid is a dense nucleoprotein core or nucleoid 30 mμ across in which a filamentous structure is visible (Epstein *et al.*, 1960; Valentine, 1960). The bodies are often arranged in a crystalline structure, forming a cubic lattice with centre-to-centre spacing of 60–65 mμ (Low & Pinnock, 1956). Besides crystals of virus particles, infected nuclei may contain crystalline arrangements of protein particles each 15 mμ across (Morgan *et al.*, 1957; Valentine, 1960). Studies with fluorescent antibody show that specific antigen is formed within nuclei before complete virus is demonstrable. Virus is released slowly from cells but the mechanism of its release is not clear (Pereira *et al.*, 1959). Morgan *et al.* (1956) had evidence suggesting rupture of the nuclear membrane and release of virus into the cytoplasm.

Chemical composition. These are DNA viruses, as shown by staining of the particles in the nucleus by Feulgen's method or with acridine orange. According to Allison & Burke (1962) particles consist of 30 per cent. DNA. A report that infection has been produced with virus extracted with cold phenol (Portocala *et al.*, 1961) is not yet accepted as proof that an infectious DNA has been demonstrated.

Physico-chemical characters. Discrepancies between the virus' size as measured optically and by centrifugation are resolved if one accepts Allison & Burke's (1962) figure of 1·34 gm/cm^3 for the density.

Types 1–3 were inactivated by exposure for 10′–20′ to 50° C but type 4 was more stable. All were rather stable at 36–37° C and when held at pH values between 6 and 9 (Ginsberg, 1956). In some experiments suspensions were not wholly inactivated when held 30′ at pH 1·5 to 2·5. Adenoviruses are ether-resistant; they are more resistant to photodynamic inactivation by toluidine blue than is vaccinia but less so than enteroviruses (Hiatt *et al.*, 1960).

Hæmagglutination. RBC's of a number of species are agglutinated (Rosen, 1958, 1960; Nász *et al.*, 1962), rat cells most commonly.

Human O, rhesus, *Cercopithecus* and mouse RBC's are clumped by some strains. As a rule several isolates belonging to a single type behave alike but some discrepancies are recorded.

Rosen (1960) has pointed out that adenoviruses can be grouped according to their behaviour in the HA test. Types 3, 7, 11, 14, 16, 20, 21, 25, 28 clump rhesus but not rat RBC's. Types 8, 9, 10, 13, 15, 19, 22, 23, 24, 26, 27 clump rat cells but rhesus cells are affected not at all or to lower titre. Types 1, 2, 4, 5, 6 partially agglutinate rat but not rhesus cells while no hæmagglutinins have been demonstrated for Types 12 and 18. These differences show a considerable correlation with differences in other biological properties. The properties of the hæmagglutinins derived from various serotypes differ in a number of ways (Simon, 1962).

Human O cells treated with receptor-destroying enzyme, by influenza virus or by a factor present in some adenovirus cultures are less readily agglutinated (Kasel *et al.*, 1960). It has also been shown that the group-specific adenovirus antigen adsorbed to tanned sheep RBC's renders these agglutinable by corresponding specific antisera. The antigen concerned is smaller than the virus itself.

Antigenic properties. By neutralization tests with rabbit antisera in tissue culture the 28 types are distinct, cross-reactions being seldom recorded. Type 7 is divisible by this test into two subtypes (7 and 7a). Human sera following adenovirus infections are apt to show heterotypic responses particularly between Types 3, 7 and 14. The kinetics of the neutralization test have been studied by Kjellen (1957).

Complement fixation occurs with a soluble antigen common to all adenoviruses. However, if immune rabbit sera are used in quantitative studies, it is possible to type adenoviruses using the CF test, since homologous titres are higher than heterologous (Pereira, 1956).

Antigenic relations can be brought out also with the gel-diffusion test, the results corresponding generally with those of the CF test. Lines seen may be (i) group-specific, (ii) type-specific, or (iii) of intermediate specificity, grouping some of the types together. Immuno-electrophoresis permits separation of 3 antigens from Type 5 (Pereira *et al.*, 1959). One, trypsin-sensitive, corresponds to the "toxic factor" to be described (p. 186) as responsible for early CPE in tissue-culture. Pereira (1960) presents evidence that 3 antigens A, B and C demonstrable by gel-diffusion are made up thus: A = a group-specific component α + DNA; C = a type-specific component γ + DNA; B is a complex of the two components β and γ.

The hæmagglutinin-inhibition test may also be used: relationships between types thus revealed do not always correspond with those found by other tests.

No interference in culture between a polio- and an adeno-virus could be detected in tissue culture (Binn & Hilleman, 1958).

Cultivation. HeLa cells have been chiefly used in studies of adenoviruses. Some strains, however, require some adaptation before growing well. There is an early cytopathic effect which may be visible within a few hours; this is due to a protein separable from the virus particles; its action is evident also in heat-inactivated virus preparations (Pereira & Kelly, 1957; Pereira, 1958; Everett & Ginsberg, 1958). It is probably identical with the cell-detaching factor of Rowe *et al.* (1958). A late CPE, shown mainly by nuclear alterations, is associated with virus-multiplication. Some adeno-viruses (Types 1, 2, 5, 6) cause cell-clumping and formation of eosinophilic inclusions, followed by nuclear enlargement and degeneration with formation of large irregular inclusions. Types 3, 4 and 7 cause different effects: a central Feulgen-positive nuclear inclusion takes the form of honeycombs or rosettes and may contain angular crystalline bodies (Barski 1956; Boyer *et al.*, 1959). By a number of other biological tests Types 1, 2, 5, 6 and Types 3, 4 and 7 fall into separate subgroups. Intranuclear masses of virus particles are often themselves arranged in crystalline array, especially with Types 3, 4 and 7. Adenovirus infection of cells leads to arrest of mitosis and to lowering of pH (Fisher & Ginsberg, 1957)—in con-trast to the finding in enterovirus-infected cultures, where the pH becomes higher than in controls. The viruses grow in human tissue cultures of several kinds.

Some strains have been adapted to growth in cultures of rabbit kidney (Type 5, *cf.* Kelly & Pereira, 1957). Adaptation to monkey (Hartley *et al.*, 1956) or swine kidney cultures (Guerin & Guerin, 1958) has been easier. CPE produced in some animal tissues may be caused by the toxic factor, serial propagation not being achieved.

Pathogenicity. Infection of man may be inapparent or take the form of one of the minor respiratory infections of childhood. Types 1, 2 and 5 are particularly concerned; also in sporadic infections in adults. These, too, are the types commonly found latent in human adenoids and tonsils (Rowe *et al.*, 1955). Types 3, 4, 7, 14 and 21 in particular cause outbreaks of fever and pharyngitis, especially in service recruits and boarding schools. Occurrence of conjunctivitis in some outbreaks has led to the use of the term "pharyngo-conjunctival fever". Adenoviruses may cause one form of atypical pneumonia, unassociated with development of cold agglutinins. Type 8 is commonly associated with epidemic kerato-conjunctivitis, occurring amongst shipyard workers in the United States (Jawetz, 1959) and Britain but also in outbreaks of swimming-pool conjuntivitis (Fukumi *et al.*, 1958). Other adenoviruses types have been recovered from sporadic cases of follicular conjunctivitis, particularly in Arabia (Bell *et al.*, 1960). Several authors have isolated adenoviruses from children with rashes, described in one instance (Neva & Enders, 1954) as "roseola infantum"; the relation of the viruses to the infection is not established. Huebner (1959) gives the types most commonly associated with various syndromes: types less commonly isolated are in brackets. Acute respiratory disease: 4, 7 (3, 14). Pharyngo-conjunctival fever: 3, 7a (1, 2, 5, 6, 14). Acute febrile conjunctivitis: (1, 2, 3, 5). Follicular conjunctivitis: 3, 7a (1, 2, 5, 6, 14). Epidemic kerato-conjunctivitis: 8 (3, 7a, 9). Virus pneumonia in infants (7a, 1, 3). Pneumonia in adults: 4, 7 (3).

Experimentally. Pathogenic effects on man have been confirmed by experimental inoculation of volunteers, both intranasal (Roden *et al.*, 1956) and ocular (Mitsui *et al.*, 1957). Intramuscular inoculation of live virus has also caused acute respiratory disease (Hilleman *et al.*, 1957).

Laboratory animals are generally insusceptible to human strains. However, Pereira & Kelly (1957) produced latent infections with Type 5 in rabbits, cultivating virus from the spleen till as much as 2 months later. The good antibody response to a single dose of virus in guinea pigs, cotton-rats and hamsters has suggested that virus may multiply in them (Rowe *et al.*, 1955; Ginsberg, 1956).

Types 1, 2, 5 and 6 have produced pneumonia in young pigs deprived of colostrum (Betts *et al.*, 1962). Type 5 causes fatal infections in very young hamsters (Pereira *et al.*, 1963a). Types 12 and 18 have produced tumours in new-born hamsters (Trentin *et al.*, 1962; Huebner *et al.*, 1962).

Pathological lesions. Little information is available, since infections are rarely fatal. However, Chany *et al.* (1958) have described nuclear changes similar to those seen in tissue culture in the lesions of fatal pneumonia in infancy.

Ecology. Infection is probably mainly air-borne from respiratory secretions: but virus is frequently present in stools and may also be recovered from urine (Hanshaw & Weller quoted by Gresser & Katz, 1960). Types above No. 9, except 14 and 21, have been recovered almost wholly from the intestinal tract. Virus latent in tonsils and adenoids is believed to persist after an infection. Respiratory outbreaks in recruits are recorded in winter months, while "swimming-bath conjunctivitis" is a summer disease.

Control. Formalinized vaccines have proved of value in controlling epidemics in recruits. Types 3, 4 and 7 grown in monkey kidney cultures have been used (Hilleman et al., 1955, 1957). Hitchcock et al. (1960) report that vaccination of man may be practicable, using live virus attenuated in pig tissue cultures.

ADENOVIRUSES OF SIMIAN ORIGIN

A number of adenoviruses are included in the SV (Simian Virus) series of Hull and his colleagues (1956, 1957, 1958 and personal communication, 1960). These have been renumbered by Pereira et al. (1963b).

Morphology. M2 (SV39) was studied by electron micrography (Archetti et al., 1961) and found to resemble human adenoviruses closely: it was 70–80 mμ in diameter, hexagonal in outline. Apparently a capsid, with subunits arranged 6 a side on surface triangles and 50–60 Å in diameter, enclosed a partly helical nucleoid. Tyrrell et al. (1960) found that M6 (SV17) resembled human strains in structure: they estimated its diameter at 65 mμ.

Physico-chemical characters. M6 (SV17) was ether-resistant and stable between pH 2·6 and 10·5 (Tyrrell et al., 1960).

Hæmagglutinin. M6 resembles human adenovirus 9 in clumping human, ox, rhesus and sheep RBC's. The hæmagglutinin was inactivated in 10' at 56° but resisted trypsin. Tyrrell et al. (1960) reported on its sensitivity and on that of the receptors on human RBC's to various reagents.

Antigenic properties. Simian strains share the CF antigen with human strains but are distinct, so far as tested, by the neutralization tests.

Pereira *et al.* (1963b) have not distinguished as many separate serotypes as had Hull. They describe one (C1) of chimpanzee origin and 12 isolated from monkey (mainly rhesus or cynomolgus) kidneys or stools. The correspondence between the new numbering and that of Hull is as follows: M1 = SV1, M2 = SV23, M3 = SV32, M4 = SV15, M5 = SV11, M6 = SV17, M7 = SV20, M8 = SV25, M9 = SV27, M10 = SV33, M11 = SV36. A number of other strains described by Hull and other workers are related to some of the above but do not differ sufficiently to be clearly separable.

Cultivation. Simian strains grow better in monkey kidney tissue than in human cells; a chimpanzee strain (Rowe *et al.*, 1958) is said to grow equally well in both. Prier & LeBeau (1958) report that M9 (SV27) has a CPE similar to that of human adenoviruses 3 and 4. So had M6 (S17): this strain also grew, though poorly, in calf kidney cells.

Habitat. One strain has been isolated from tissues of a chimpanzee, others from rhesus and cynomolgus monkeys. Felici *et al.* (1959) recovered 17 adenoviruses from rectal swabs of "Asiatic and African monkeys".

Pathogenicity. M6 is the only one known to be pathogenic. Goffe (quoted by Tyrrell *et al.*, 1960) found it causing rhinitis and conjunctivitis amongst captive patas (*Erythrocebus patas*) monkeys.

ADENOVIRUSES OF BOVINE ORIGIN

At least two serological types have been isolated from fæces of cattle (Klein *et al.*, 1959, 1960). They grow in trypsinized calf cells but not in HeLa cells: the first to be described grew poorly in monkey kidney cultures, the second not at all. Types 1 and 2 agglutinate RBC's from rats: Type 2 is active also against those of mice. They share the adenovirus CF antigen. There is no evidence of pathogenicity for cattle.

A third serotype, reported by A. B. Sabin to H. G. Pereira, causes striking CPE in monkey kidney cultures; and when given IC to rhesus or cynomolgus monkeys causes fatal encephalitis.

ADENOVIRUSES OF MURINE ORIGIN

The virus described by Hartley & Rowe (1960) had a size esti-mated by filtration as 100 mμ. It was ether-sensitive, inactivated in 30' at 56° C. No hæmagglutinin was detected. There was cross-complement fixation with other adenoviruses shown well only when guinea pig sera were used. CF antibodies were present in sera from 3 mouse colonies, none from 9 others. The virus grew, producing CPE, in mouse fibroblasts and kidney cultures, not in those from several other species. Suckling mice, inoculated by various routes, suffered fatal infection, disseminated pathological changes being present particularly in the brown fat, heart and adrenals. Virus was present in urine and contact transmission occurred within a cage.

ADENOVIRUSES OF AVIAN ORIGIN

Synonym: GAL virus (Gallus-adenovirus-like).

This virus, identified as an adenovirus by Burmester *et al.* (1960) was at one time thought to be the cause of lymphomatosis of fowls.

It resembles adenoviruses in so many ways that it may be included despite the lack of demonstrable group antigen.

Morphology. Davies & Englert (1961) report that negative staining reveals 162 surface capsomeres, 5 a side on surface triangles and 95 Å in diameter. Macpherson *et al.* (1961), on the other hand, report 252 surface units, apparently in rows of 6, 50–60 Å wide, 100–110 Å long with an axial hole. The average diameter of the whole virus is 97·5 mμ. Crystalline appearances have been seen in infected nuclei (Atanasiu & Lepine, 1960).

Physico-chemical characters. Ether-stable.

Antigenic properties. Neutralized by specific antisera. The common adenovirus soluble antigen has not been demonstrated.

Cultivation. Grown in tissue cultures of embryonic chick liver, spleen, kidney and other tissues. Plaque formation occurs in mono-layers (Stoker, 1959). There is evidence of growth within the nucleus, virus being released only when the cell membrane disintegrates (Sharpless *et al.*, 1961). The CPE is typical of that for adenoviruses.

Pathogenicity. Inoculated chicks may show some necrosis of liver cells with basophilic nuclear inclusions (Sharpless & Jungherr, 1961).

INFECTIOUS CANINE HEPATITIS

Synonyms: Rubarth's disease. Fox encephalitis. Hepatitis infectiosa canis.

Review: Rubarth (1947)—original description; and identification with fox encephalitis (Green *et al.*, 1930).

The virus was shown to be an adenovirus by Kapsenberg (1959). Reasons for so doing have been marshalled by Carmichael & Barnes (1961).

Morphology. By negative staining resembles other adenoviruses (Davies *et al.*, 1961). Tajima *et al.* (1958) estimate the diameter as 65 mμ. Some strains form intranuclear virus crystals.

Physico-chemical characters. Survives well when frozen or dried: even for several years in 50 per cent. glycerol. Inactivated in 150' at 50° C, in 3–5' at 60° C (Ikegami *et al.*, 1959). Survives for days in 0·5 per cent. phenol but is inactivated in 24 hours by 0·2 per cent. formaldehyde (Surdan *et al.*, 1959). Stable at room temperature between pH 3 and 9. Ether-stable.

Hæmagglutination. According to Fastier (1957) the virus agglutinates fowl RBC's at 4° C and pH 7·5–8: but Espmark & Salenstedt (1961) could not confirm this and found agglutination of rat and human O cells at pH 6·5–7·5, temperature being immaterial.

Antigenic properties. Shares the CF antigen of human strains but is distinct by neutralization (Kapsenberg, 1959). The agar-gel-diffusion method is useful for diagnosis, antigen being present in various dog tissues (Mansi, 1955, 1957). An antiserum to human viruses diffused against dog hepatitis antigen showed 3 lines, while immune dog serum tested against human virus antigen showed none (Heller & Salenstedt, 1960). Similar results are obtained in CF tests. An antigen tested intradermally in dogs gives reactions only in susceptibles (Prier & Kalter, 1954).

Interference. Most authors state that there is no interference between this and dog distemper.

Cultivation. A claim (Miles *et al.*, 1951) that the virus is cultivable in yolk-sacs of hens' eggs has not been confirmed.

The virus grows readily in cultures of dog, ferret, raccoon and pig kidney or testis producing a CPE and, in monolayers, readily counted plaques. Intranuclear inclusions are found *in vitro*; also crystals, possibly of protein rather than of packed virus (Leader *et al.*, 1960).

Distribution. Occurs wherever there are many dogs or foxes.

Pathogenicity. The disease in dogs may be inapparent. Symptoms are commonest in newly weaned puppies: these may show high fever, apathy, œdema, vomiting and diarrhœa. Transient corneal opacity is common. The mortality is 10–25 per cent. The incubation period after contact is 6–9 days but is less (3–6 days) after experimental infection. Adenoviruses may also cause "kennel cough".

In foxes the disease presents as acute encephalitis with convulsions passing into paralysis and coma; death usually occurs within 24 hours. There may be nasal and ocular discharge and diarrhœa.

Experimentally. Dogs and foxes may be infected by any route, including the oral. Other canines, coyotes and wolves, are susceptible: also raccoons. Grey foxes (*Urocyon*) are, however, resistant (Green *et al.*, 1934). Inoculation on to the cornea may lead to opacity and this may be partly due to a toxic action as it is seen also in inoculated kittens and ferrets which are not otherwise susceptible and in which the virus has not been passed in series (Cabasso *et al.*, 1954). Toxic effects may also be shown in suckling mice (Kapsenberg, 1959). Salenstedt (1958) reports that when guinea pigs were inoculated subcutaneously, there were fever, viræmia, viruria and lymphocytosis and "up to 25 per cent. died", often showing perihepatitis: there is no mention of serial transmission.

Pathological lesions. In dogs dying of the disease there are seen subcutaneous œdema, ascites, often blood-stained, hæmorrhages in various viscera, a swollen, pale liver with thickened, often hæmorrhagic, gall-bladder. In the fatal fox disease, the symptoms are seen to have been due to cerebral hæmorrhages—the virus is not truly neurotropic. Lesions, especially in the liver, show numerous nuclear inclusions resembling those of other adenovirus infections. Lucas

(1940), who studied them closely, did not consider them as Type A inclusions of Cowdry.

Ecology. Spread is probably from respiratory tract or via the urine, since recovered animals may excrete virus in the urine for many months. On fur-ranges the infection may be enzootic over long periods.

Control. Formalinized and attenuated live virus vaccines have both been used. Virus attenuated by growth in pig tissue culture has been successfully used in a bivalent vaccine, combined with attenuated distemper virus (Cabasso *et al.*, 1958; Piercy & Sellers, 1960). The ocular route has sometimes been used for immunization, success being judged by the appearance of opacity.

REFERENCES

Allison, A. C., & Burke, D. (1962) *J. gen. Microbiol.*, **27**, 181.
Archetti, I., Boccianelli, D. S., & Toschi, G. (1961) *Virology*, **13**, 149.
Atanasiu, P., & Lepine, P. (1960) *Ann. Inst. Past.*, **98**, 915.
Barski, G. (1956) *Ann. Inst. Past.*, **91**, 614.
Bell, S. D., Rota, T. R., & McComb, S. T. (1960) *Amer. J. trop. Med.*, **9**, 523.
Betts, A. O., Jennings, A. R., Lamont, P. H., & Page, Z. (1962) *Nature (Lond.)*, **193**, 45.
Binn, L. N., & Hilleman, M. R. (1958) *J. infect. Dis.*, **103**, 127.
Boyer, G. S., Denny, F. W., & Ginsberg, H. S. (1959) *J. exp. Med.*, **110**, 827.
Burmester, B. R., Sharpless, G. R., & Fontes, A. K. (1960) *J. nat. Cancer Inst.*, **24**, 1443.
Cabasso, V. J., Stebbins, M. R., & Avampato, J. M. (1958) *Proc. Soc. exp. Biol. (N.Y.)*, **99**, 46.
Cabasso, V. J., Stebbins, M. R., Norton, T. W., & Cox, H. R. (1954) *Proc. Soc. exp. Biol. (N.Y.)*, **85**, 239.
Carmichael, L. E., & Barnes, F. D. (1961) *Proc. Soc. exp. Biol. (N.Y.)*, **107**, 214.
Chany, C., Lepine, P., Lelong, M., Le-Tan-Vinh, Satgé, P., & Virat, J. (1958) *Amer. J. Hyg.*, **67**, 367.
Davies, M. C., & Englert, M. E. (1961) *Virology*, **13**, 143.
Davies, M. C., Englert, M. E., Stebbins, M. R., & Cabasso, V. J. (1961) *Virology*, **15**, 87.
Epstein, M. A., Holt, S. J., & Powell, A. K. (1960) *Brit. J. exp. Path.*, **41**, 559.
Espmark, J. A., & Salenstedt, C. R. (1961) *Arch. ges. Virusforsch.*, **11**, 61.
Everett, S. F., & Ginsberg, H. S. (1958) *Virology*, **6**, 770.
Fastier, L. B. (1957) *J. Immunol.*, **78**, 413.
Felici, A., Gori, G. B., Mancini, G., Castelli, L., & Balducci, D. (1959) *Riv. Ist. Sieroter. ital.*, **34**, 299.
Fisher, T. H., & Ginsberg, H. S. (1957) *Proc. Soc. exp. Biol. (N.Y.)*, **95**, 47.
Fukumi, H., Nishikawa, F., Kurimoto, U., Inoue, H., Usui, J., & Hirayama, T. (1958) *Jap. J. med. Sci. Biol.*, **11**, 467.

Ginsberg, H. S. (1956) *J. Immunol.*, **77**, 271.

Green, M., & Piña, M. (1963) *Virology*, **20**, 199.

Green, M. (1962) *Virology*, **18**, 312.

Green, R. G., Ziegler, N. R., & Carlson, W. C. (1934) *Amer. J. Hyg.*, **19**, 343.

Green, R. G., Ziegler, N. R., Green, B. B., & Dewey, E. T. (1930) *Amer. J. Hyg.*, **12**, 109.

Gresser, I., & Katz, S. L. (1960) *New Engl. J. Med.*, **263**, 452.

Guérin, L. F., & Guérin, M. M. (1958) *Proc. Soc. exp. Biol. (N.Y.)*, **96**, 322.

Hartley, J. W., Huebner, R. J., & Rowe, W. P. (1956) *Proc. Soc. exp. Biol. (N.Y.)*, **92**, 677.

Hartley, J. W., & Rowe, W. P. (1960) *Virology*, **11**, 645.

Heller, L. A., & Salenstedt, C. R. (1960) *Virology*, **11**, 640.

Hiatt, C. W., Kaufman, C., Helprin, J. J., & Baron, S. (1960) *J. Immunol.*, **84**, 480.

Hilleman, M. R., Warfield, M. S., Anderson, S. A., & Werner, J. H. (1957) *J. Amer. med. Ass.*, **163**, 4.

Hilleman, M. R., Werner, J. H., & Stewart, M. T. (1955) *Proc. Soc. exp. Biol. (N.Y.)*, **90**, 555.

Hitchcock, G., Tyrrell, D. A. J., & Bynoe, M. L. (1960) *J. Hyg. (Lond.)*, **58**, 277.

Horne, R. W., Brenner, S., Waterson, A. P., & Wildy, P. (1959) *J. molec. Biol.*, **1**, 89.

Huebner, R. J. (1959) *Publ. Hlth. Rep. (Wash.)*, **74**, 6.

Huebner, R. J., Rowe, W. P., & Lane, W. T. (1962) *Proc. nat. Acad. Sci. (Wash.)*, **48**, 2057.

Huebner, R. J., Rowe, W. P., & Chanock, R. M. (1958) *Ann. Rev. Microbiol.*, **12**, 49.

Huebner, R. J., Rowe, W. P., Ward, T. G., Parrott, R. H., & Bell, J. A. (1954) *New Engl. J. Med.*, **251**, 1077.

Hull, R. N., & Minner, J. R. (1957) *Ann. N.Y. Acad. Sci.*, **67**, 413.

Hull, R. N., Minner, J. R., & Mascoli, C. C. (1958) *Amer. J. Hyg.*, **68**, 31.

Hull, R. N., Minner, J. R., & Smith, J. W. (1956) *Amer. J. Hyg.*, **63**, 204.

Ikegami, T., Konishi, S., & Ochi, Y. (1959) *Jap. J. vet. Sci.*, **21**, 38.

Jawetz, E. (1959) *Brit. med. J.*, **1**, 873.

Kapsenberg, J. G. (1959) *Proc. Soc. exp. Biol. (N.Y.)*, **101**, 611.

Kasel, J. A., Rowe, W. P., & Nemes, J. L. (1961) *J. exp. Med.*, **114**, 717.

Kelly, B., & Pereira, H. G. (1957) *Brit. J. exp. Path.*, **38**, 396.

Kjellén, L. (1957) *Arch. ges. Virusforsch.*, **7**, 307.

Klein, M., Earley, E., & Zellat, J. (1959) *Proc. Soc. exp. Biol. (N.Y.)*, **102**, 1.

Klein, M., Zellat, J., & Michaelson, T. C. (1960) *Proc. Soc. exp. Biol. (N.Y.)*, **105**, 340.

Leader, R. W., Pomerat, C. M., & Lefeber, C. G. (1960) *Virology*, **10**, 268.

Low, B., & Pinnock, P. R. (1956) *J. biophys. biochem. Cytol.*, **2**, 483.

Lucas, A. M. (1940) *Amer. J. Path.*, **16**, 739.

Macpherson, I., Wildy, P., Stoker, M. G. P., & Horne, A. W. (1961) *Virology*, **13**, 146.

Mansi, W. (1955) *J. comp. Path.*, **65**, 291.

Mansi, W. (1957) *J. comp. Path.*, **67**, 297.

Miles, J. A. R., Parry, H. B., Larin, N. M., & Platt, H. (1951) *Nature (Lond.)*, **168**, 699.

Morgan, C., Godman, G. E., Rose, H. M., Howe, C., & Huang, H. S. (1957) *J. biophys. biochem. Cytol.*, **3**, 505.

Morgan, C., Howe, C., Rose, H. M., & Moore, D. H. (1956) *J. biophys. biochem. Cytol.*, **2**, 351.

Nász, I., Leńgyel, A., Dán, P., & Kulcsár, G. (1962) *Acta microbiol. Acad. Sci. hung.*, **9,** 69.
Neva, F. A., & Enders, J. F. (1954) *J. Immunol.*, **72,** 315.
Pereira, H. G. (1956) *J. Path. Bact.*, **72,** 105.
Pereira, H. G. (1958) *Virology*, **6,** 601.
Pereira, H. G. (1959) *Brit. med. Bull.*, **15,** 225.
Pereira, H. G. (1960) *Nature (Lond.)*, **186,** 571.
Pereira, H. G., Allison, A. C., & Niven, J. S. F. (1963) *Nature (Lond.)*, **196,** 244.
Pereira, H. G., Allison, A. C., & Farthing, C. P. (1959) *Nature (Lond.)*, **183,** 895.
Pereira, H. G., Huebner, R. J., Ginsberg, H. S., & van der Veen, J. (1963) *Virology*, **20,** 613.
Pereira, H. G., & Kelly, B. (1957) *Nature (Lond.)*, **180,** 615.
Piercy, S. E., & Sellers, R. F. (1960) *Res. vet. Sci.*, **1,** 84.
Portocalá, R., Boeru, V., Aderca, I., & Samuel, J. (1961) *C.R. Acad. Sci. (Paris)*, **252,** 362.
Prier, J. E., & Kalter, S. S. (1954) *Proc. Soc. exp. Biol. (N.Y.)*, **86,** 177.
Prier, J. E., & Le Beau, R. W. (1958) *J. Lab. clin. Med.*, **51,** 495.
Roden, A. T., Pereira, H. G., & Chaproniere, D. M. (1956) *Lancet*, **2,** 592.
Rosen, L. (1958) *Virology*, **5,** 574.
Rosen, L. (1960) *Amer. J. Hyg.*, **71,** 120.
Rowe, W. P., Hartley, J. W., Roizman, B., & Levy, H. B. (1958) *Proc. Soc. exp. Biol. (N.Y.)*, **108,** 713.
Rowe, W. P., Huebner, R. J., Hartley, J. W., Ward, T. G., & Parrott, R. H. (1955) *Amer. J. Hyg.*, **61,** 197.
Rubarth, S. (1947) *Acta path. microbiol. scand.*, **69,** 222 (supplement).
Salenstedt, C. R. (1958) *Arch. ges. Virusforsch.*, **8,** 600.
Sharpless, G. R., & Jungherr, E. L. (1961) *Amer. J. vet. Res.*, **22,** 986.
Sharpless, G. R., Levine, S., Davies, M. C., & Englert, M. E. (1961) *Virology*, **13,** 315.
Simon, M. (1962) *Acta microbiol. Acad. Sci. hung.*, **9,** 45.
Stoker, M. G. P. (1959) *Virology*, **8,** 250.
Surdan, C., Cure, C., Dumitriu, C., & Wegener, M. (1959) *Acta virol.*, **3,** 115.
Tajima, M., Motohashi, T., & Samejima, T. (1961) *Amer. J. vet. Res.*, **22,** 236.
Trentin, J. J., Yabe, Y., & Taylor, G. (1962) *Science*, **137,** 835.
Tyrrell, D. A. J., Buckland, F. E., Lancaster, M. C., & Valentine, R. C. (1960) *Brit. J. exp. Path.*, **41,** 610.
Valentine, R. C. (1960) *Fourth internat. Congr. Electron Microscopy*, 577.

10

Papovaviruses

The name Papovavirus has been proposed (Melnick, 1962) for a group of viruses related to rabbit papilloma and polyoma. The name covers the two first letters of PApilloma and POlyoma, with VA for vacuolating agent. The group has been further defined by a study group of the virus subcommittee of the International nomenclature committee for bacteria and viruses (Rowe *et al.*, 1964).

Properties of the members are as follows:

Diameter 30–50 mμ probably mean 45 mμ. Form basically icosahedral with 5–3–2 symmetry but filamentous forms occur with several. The number of capsomeres has been variously estimated as 42, 60 and 92, as mentioned below. The viruses contain DNA which is double-stranded; they are ether-stable and most of them withstand heating for 30 minutes to 56°–65°. Most of them are potentially oncogenic. Their development is mainly intranuclear.

This chapter contains descriptions of five definite members of the group and of six others, less studied but probably belonging here also.

RABBIT PAPILLOMA

The virus so-called in the literature is that naturally affecting the skin of cottontail rabbits (Sylvilagus). The oral papillomatosis of domestic rabbits is due to a different virus (*v.* p. 206).

Synonym: Shope papilloma.
Reviews: Shope (1933) (original description).
Bryan & Beard (1940).

Morphology and development. Virus particles are icosahedra, 45 mμ in diameter. The number of capsomeres is not generally agreed. Williams *et al.* (1960), also Breedis *et al.* (1962) conclude that there are 60, but others think that there are 42 or 92. Williams *et al.* (1960) describe elongated forms. Virus apparently begins to multiply in the nucleolus, particles then seen being 33 mμ in diameter; the rest of the nucleus is soon involved and mature virus particles can be found in large quantity. They may be arranged in orderly patterns but are not seen in such regular crystalline arrangements as with adenoviruses (Moore *et al.*, 1959). Some preparations may contain incomplete virus.

Chemical composition. DNA, which is double-stranded, forms 6–8 per cent. of the total weight (Watson & Littlefield, 1960). Knight (1950) identified 18 amino-acids in purified material. Extraction with hot or cold phenol yielded an active material, sensitive to deoxyribonuclease, possibly separating infective DNA (Ito, 1960). Apparently induces arginase formation in infected skin (Rogers, 1959).

Physico-chemical characters. Heat-resistant: inactivated in 30' at 70° not at 67°. Survives well in 50 per cent. glycerol—up to 20 years (Fischer & Green, 1947). Much more resistant to X-radiation than are most viruses (Syverton *et al.*, 1941). Density in aqueous suspension 1·133 (Sharp *et al.*, 1946). Stable between pH 3 and 7. Iso-electric point about pH 5·0 (Sharp *et al.*, 1942) but Breedis *et al.* (1962) found that particles containing different amounts of DNA had densities varying from 1·29 to 1·34. Ether-resistant. Can be purified by means of fluorocarbon or by precipitation with methanol (Fischer, 1949).

Hæmagglutination. Though rabbit RBC's adsorb the virus, they are not agglutinated (Barabadze, 1960).

Antigenic properties. Activity is readily neutralized by sera of recovered rabbits. Warts from domestic rabbits, which may contain no demonstrable infective virus, may nevertheless induce antibodies when inoculated IP. Complement-fixing antigen is readily extracted from cotton-tail warts, much less readily from warts in domestic rabbits; it is more stable to UV irradiation than infectivity but is not mechanically separable from the virus particle (Kidd, 1938). No cross-immunity was demonstrable between this virus and those causing warts in cattle and dogs nor with the rabbit oral papilloma.

The use of fluorescent antibody has revealed that antigen is concentrated in kerato-hyaline and keratinized layers of the skin, not in the deeper proliferating cells (Noyes & Mellors, 1957).

Cultivation is reported in organ-cultures of skin of new-born rabbits: at least proliferation of epidermal cells was observed, though no multiplication of virus was proved (de Maeyer, 1962).

Pathogenicity. Only reported to occur naturally in *Sylvilagus floridanus* (cotton-tail rabbit) in North America. There is, however, one record of a small growth in a jack-rabbit (*Lepus californicus*) (Beard & Rous, 1935). The natural tumours are often tall, thin, black or grey horns. They persist for many months but ultimately regress, rarely (in cotton-tails) becoming malignant.

Experimentally, domestic rabbits (*Oryctolagus*), also several species of *Lepus*, can be infected by rubbing virus into scarified skin. In domestic rabbits growth is "relatively exuberant and fleshy and may be pink or sooty, low or projecting, dry or succulent" (Rous & Beard, 1934). Warts commonly regress but much more often than in cotton-tails, go on to become malignant. From domestic rabbit, unlike cotton-tail, warts, virus is usually recoverable with difficulty, though transplantation through 14 domestic rabbits in series has been reported. There has been much dispute as to whether "masked virus" in tame rabbits is qualitatively or only quantitatively different from that in cotton-tails. Shope has suggested that it may in the former be present as incomplete virus, possibly infective DNA. The papillomata and resulting cancers have been the basis of much important work on the relation between viruses and tumours (Rous & Beard, 1934, 1935; Greene, 1955, etc.). Greene (1953) reported that the virus would infect embryonic rat skin, causing growths serially transplantable in rats.

The proliferative epithelial changes leading to superficial warts in wild and tame rabbits are described by E. W. Hurst (in Shope, 1933); and those of transplanted warts by Rous & Beard (1934). Noyes (1959) and Stone *et al.* (1959) found virus mainly in keratinizing, not in proliferating, layers of epithelium.

Ecology. Natural transmission is probably by direct contact, though mosquitoes and reduviid bugs can transmit the virus experimentally (Dalmat, 1958); and a possible role of nematodes as transmitting agents has been suggested by Rendtorff & Wilcox (1957).

Control. Evans *et al.* (1962) report that vaccination with tissue suspensions may cause some regressions of growths.

INFECTIOUS WARTS
(of man)

Synonyms: Verruca vulgaris. Myrmecia. Papilloma. Common wart. Condyloma.

Various clinical types of warts are described: juvenile (plane), digitate, filiform, plantar, genital, laryngeal. It is uncertain how far all these are due to one virus. Microscopical evidence together with clinical studies suggests that two agents at least may be concerned. Lyell & Miles (1951) separate two types: (i) Myrmecia— with intranuclear and cytoplasmic inclusions; (ii) Verruca vulgaris. Strauss *et al.* (1949) also hold that warts are of two kinds. Experimental data mostly concern Lyell & Miles's first type (with inclusions) and the following facts seem mainly to concern them. There is no evidence concerning the properties of a hypothetical virus causing a second type.

Morphology. Icosahedra 45 mμ in diameter with 42 surface capsomeres; may be packed into crystalline masses within nuclei (Strauss *et al.*, 1949; Melnick, 1962): multiplication seems to be wholly within nuclei. However, Chapman *et al.* (1963) suggest a diameter of 38 mμ and find virus also in the cytoplasm. The figure of 42 capsomeres reported by several workers can only be accepted provisionally. Howatson (1962) describes cylindrical forms of virus.

Chemical composition: DNA.

Physico-chemical characters. Survives heating 30' at 50°; also, for some time, in 50 per cent. glycerol.

Cultivation. A single report of cultivation on the chorioallantoic membrane remains unconfirmed.

Pathogenicity. Warts in man tend to persist for many months but ultimately regress. Genital warts or condylomata acuminata, however, may become malignant. Various names for clinical types, mentioned above, testify to the varied appearances in different sites. Experimental transmission to man has been reported, the incubation period varying between 6 weeks and 8 months. A laryngeal papilloma inoculated on to the skin produced flat cutaneous warts (Ullman,

1923). Isolated reports of transmissions to a baboon and a dog lack confirmation.

Histologically the essential change is of proliferation of the Malpighian layer of the skin, but appearances vary greatly in different types. The eosinophilic intranuclear inclusions have been studied by Bunting *et al.* (1952) and Bloch & Godman (1957): they are of Cowdry's Type B. Masses in cytoplasm are vacuolated.

The type of wart which forms no nuclear inclusions is perhaps the commoner: it is more apt to be chronic and multiple, more difficult to treat; the incubation period after inoculation may be 10–12 months (Lyell & Miles, 1951). Howatson (1962) finds that the mode of development of virus in the skin is like that described for rabbit papilloma: most virus is in keratinized layers.

Ecology. Transmission is by direct contact; in the case of genital warts it is thought to be venereal.

Control. Warts may be cured by X-rays, cautery, nitric acid or other directly destructive means. Their tendency to regress has naturally enhanced the reputation of various remedies not far removed from witch-craft.

POLYOMA

Synonyms: SE (Stewart-Eddy) polyoma. Mouse parotid tumour virus.

Reviews: Eddy (1960)—virology.
                Stewart (1960)—pathology.

Morphology and development. Most estimates of diameter agree upon 45 mμ, though some suggest 30 mμ. The virus is roughly spherical, perhaps icosahedral, with a shell of 42 long hollow capsomeres regularly disposed on its surface (Wildy *et al.*, 1960). Mattern *et al.* (1963) maintain that 92 is the probable number of capsomeres. Horne & Wildy (1961) and Howatson (1962) have figured filamentous forms; Stoker (1962) has suggested how these might have been built up from the subunits which normally form icosahedra. Particles are first found in the nucleus where they may be more or less regularly packed: they are sometimes contained within vacuoles. Later they reach the cytoplasm and here they seem to be larger (Negroni *et al.*, 1959). Release from cell is gradual. In tumour cells antigen stainable by fluorescent antibody (? incomplete virus) may appear in the cytoplasm without evidence of earlier growth in nucleus (Sachs & Fogel, 1960). Neither external membrane nor dense nucleoid could be demonstrated by Bernhard *et al.* (1959).

Chemical composition. Histochemical (Allison & Armstrong, 1960) and biochemical studies (Smith *et al.*, 1960) agree that this is a DNA virus. Isolation of an infectious DNA was reported by Di Mayorca *et al.* (1959), and confirmed by Harris *et al.* (1961).

Physico-chemical characters. Survives many months at 4° C or −70° C and 8 weeks at 37° C. Heating 30′ at 60° did not affect the titre: at 70° it was usually inactivated. It was resistant to ether, 2 per cent. phenol and 50 per cent. ethanol (Brodsky *et al.*, 1959). Winocour (1963) separated full (DNA-containing) particles (specific gravity 1·339) from empty ones (sp. gr. 1·297).

Hæmagglutination. The virus agglutinates cells of many species at 4° over a pH range of 5·4–8·4: guinea pig cells, being most reliable, are chiefly used. There is non-enzymatic elution at 37° C (Eddy *et al.*, 1958). Many animal sera and cell extracts contain non-specific hæmagglutinin inhibitors; these have been removed by heating and in other ways (Deinhardt *et al.*, 1960).

Antigenic properties. Infected mice and hamsters develop anti-hæmagglutinins, neutralizing and CF antibodies. It has not been possible to separate hæmagglutinin or CF antigen from the virus by mechanical means (Rowe *et al.*, 1958). Cells rendered malignant by polyoma virus develop a new non-viral antigen; reaction against this is important in tumour immunity (Habel, 1962).

Interference. The virus interferes with the growth of vesicular stomatitis virus *in vitro* (Deinhardt & Henle, 1960). It is sensitive to interferon (Allison, 1961).

Cultivation. Multiplies in cultures of embryo and other mouse tissues; also in mouse tumours and in other rodent tissues. In infected cultures nuclei are enlarged and chromatin coarsened. The early reports of growth in monkey and chick tissues have not been confirmed. In monolayers, plaque formation occurs; two types of plaques have been described, due to variants with slightly different biological properties (Gotlieb-Stematsky and Leventon, 1960).

Some multiplication occurs in rat tumour tissue *in vitro* (Sachs & Fogel, 1960). There may be a destructive effect on cultivated mouse cells or a stable cell-virus association may be set up: embryonic cells of mouse or hamster may thus be rendered malignant *in vitro* (Vogt & Dulbecco, 1960; Stoker & MacPherson, 1961).

Pathogenicity. Normally a completely inapparent infection affecting some stocks of laboratory mice, also wild mice (*Mus musculus*) from both urban and rural environments. Spontaneous tumours due to the virus are exceedingly rare.

Experimentally, virus quantitatively exalted in tissue culture and inoculated into suckling mice, rats, guinea pigs or hamsters leads to production of tumours of many histological types, parotid tumours being amongst the most frequent in mice and sarcomata in hamsters. Older mice may be infected but no tumours are caused. Apart from tumours, the virus may cause in suckling mice dwarfism, nephritis, anæmia and conjunctivitis (Stewart *et al.*, 1958). Some inoculated baby hamsters also die with acute hæmorrhagic disease (Negroni *et al.*, 1959). The tumours caused by polyoma virus may be transplantable but it may be impossible to recover virus from the transplanted tumours. Inoculated new-born rabbits develop multiple fibromata which regress (Eddy *et al.*, 1959). Fibrosarcomata have also been produced in new-born ferrets (Harris *et al.*, 1961).

Ecology. Transmission of silent infection among mice is probably by the intranasal route. Virus is excreted in fæces and urine and may be present in the litter of the nests.

In laboratories working with the virus, the environment may become heavily contaminated, so that uninoculated mice become infected and there is every chance of an accidental "pick-up" of virus in the course of experiments (Rowe *et al.*, 1961).

K VIRUS

Description: Kilham & Murphy (1953). Fisher & Kilham (1953).

Morphology. Spheres 40–50 mμ across. Mattern *et al.* (1963) put the diameter as 50 mμ and the number of capsomeres as 92, perhaps 72, but Parsons (1963) gives the number as 42.

Chemical composition. Contains 2-stranded DNA (Mattern *et al.*, 1963).

Physico-chemical characters. Resisted heating to 70° C for 3 hours but not 4½; withstood 60° C for 4 hours. Ether-stable. Not readily inactivated by 0·5 per cent. formalin.

Hæmagglutination. Sheep RBC's are agglutinated by tissue-suspensions from suckling mice at room temperature or 37°. Heating at times unmasks the hæmagglutinin (Kilham, 1961).

Cultivation. The virus failed to grow in eggs.

Pathogenicity. Causes fatal pneumonia and sometimes liver lesions after inoculation by various routes into mice less than 10 days old. The incubation period is 6–15 days, varying with the route of inoculation. Virus in high titre is found in all tissues. Nuclear inclusions occurred in endothelium of lung arterioles.

Ecology. Virus was found in urine and fæces up to 4 weeks after inoculation.

VACUOLATING VIRUS

Synonym: SV40. Vacuolating agent.

Description: Sweet & Hilleman (1960).

Morphology. 40 mμ in diameter, with, probably, 42 surface capsomeres.

Chemical composition. DNA, double-stranded. An infectious DNA has been extracted by Boiron *et al.* (1962) and Gerber (1962).

Physico-chemical characters. Stable on storage at −20° C and −70° C. Withstands heating for 1 hour, perhaps longer, at 56° C. Ether-resistant. Inactivation by 1 : 4000 formalin at 37° C is slower than for poliovirus, and some active vacuolating virus has probably been present in some formolized poliovirus and adenovirus vaccines. It is, however, more readily inactivated by the photo-dynamic action of toluidine blue.

Hæmagglutination. No hæmagglutinins detected for guinea pig, chick or human RBC's.

Antigenic properties. Neutralizing antibodies, revealed in tests in tissue culture, were present in sera of 12/18 rhesus sera. They have not been found in "normal" human sera but are present in sera of numerous people who have been given adenovirus or polio vaccines (ostensibly inactivated).

Cultivation. Multiplies in a variety of cells in culture but when first discovered was cytopathic only for grivet (*Cercopithecus æthiops*) kidney cultures (Sweet & Hilleman, 1960), and to a less extent patas kidney and rhesus testis cultures. In the grivet cultures it produces vacuolation of cytoplasm, beginning in 3 or 4 days, and it forms plaques on monolayers of grivet or baboon cells.

A stable line of rhesus cells shows a CPE after 12 days (Meyer *et al.*, 1962). Adult and embryonic human tissues can also be infected and show various changes including some suggesting malignant transformation (Shein & Enders, 1962; Koprowski *et al.*, 1962). Syncytia are not prominent.

Pathogenicity. Virus has been recovered from cultures of "normal" rhesus and less frequently from cynomolgus and cerco-pithecus kidneys. It can produce a silent infection in man, leading to antibody formation, especially when given by the respiratory route. Virus may be excreted in stools of children for several weeks. It can produce fibrosarcomata when given to suckling hamsters (Eddy *et al.*, 1961). The tumours are serially transplantable and virus can be recovered from them (Girardi *et al.*, 1962). Ependymomata produced by IC inoculation of baby hamsters yielded virus with greater difficulty (Gerber & Kirschtein, 1962). A chronic latent infection follows inoculation of grivets or baboons.

Control. The virus can exist as a contaminant in cultures of monkey kidney used to make vaccines for man. It can be eliminated by adequate formalinization.

VIRUSES PROVISIONALLY PLACED IN PAPOVAVIRUS GROUP

Bovine Papillomatosis

The virus causing this rather common condition differs from other wart-viruses in that connective tissue proliferation is an important component of the warts; the agent is not strictly host-specific and has been cultivated in eggs. It is possibly related to the deer fibroma (Shope *et al.*, 1958).

Morphology. Resembles other papovaviruses (L. Crawford, quoted by Rowe *et al.*, 1961).

Physico-chemical characters. The agent is filterable.

Antigenic properties. No antibodies to the virus are demonstrable in affected cattle but have been found in serum of inoculated horses.

Cultivation in fertile eggs.
The virus grows on the CAM of hens' eggs: epithelial thickenings are rich in virus. Egg-grown virus has been used as a vaccine without great success (Olson *et al.*, 1960).

Pathogenicity. Bovine warts, sometimes in immense numbers, occur on head and neck of calves, less commonly elsewhere on the skin. They regress after some months. Warts on teats, penis and vagina are less common and may not be due to the same agent.
The agent has been transmitted to horses causing connective tissue tumours (Olson & Cook, 1951; Segre *et al.*, 1955). These produced warts on inoculation back to calves.

Ecology. Transmission is believed to be by direct contact.

Control. Wart-suspensions, autogenous or otherwise, made up in glycerol saline or formalinized, have been used as vaccines, either for prophylaxis or cure. Several groups report success but in a disease which clears up spontaneously, judgment is difficult.

Genital Papilloma of Pigs

Description: Parish (1961).

Morphology. The virus passed a filter with average pore-size 175 mμ.

Physico-chemical characters. Survival was poor at −20° or +4°. Heating for 30′ at 50° inactivated. The virus was ether-resistant. Parish (1961) reports inactivation by 0·58 per cent. formaldehyde, 0·5 per cent. phenol and other chemicals in 6 hours at room temperature.

Hæmagglutination. None detected.

Antigenic properties. Neutralizing antibodies were detected in sera of hyperimmunized pigs and rabbits, not in those of recovered pigs. Conglutinating complement absorption tests were also positive; and antigen was detected in gel-diffusion tests at the stage of maximal growth (Parish, 1962). Recovered pigs were immune to challenge.

Pathogenicity. The natural lesions consisted of papillomata in the genital region of boars. Infection was transmitted in series by scarification or injection into the genital skin of adult pigs; the incubation period was about 8 weeks. Injections elsewhere into the skin were without effect, nor were a man, a calf, rabbits, guinea pigs, mice or embryonated eggs susceptible. Cytoplasmic inclusions were observed in papillomatous lesions.

Oral Papillomatosis of Rabbits

Description: Parsons & Kidd (1943).

Physico-chemical characters. Filtrable through Berkefeld V and N candles. Survives at least 2 years in 50 per cent. glycerol at 4° C; stable when freeze-dried. Survives heating for 30′ at 65°; some infectivity persists after heating to 70° for 30′.

Antigenic properties. Recovered animals are immune for at least some months: there is no cross-immunity with the Shope papilloma.

Pathogenicity. Frequent in domestic rabbits in New York. Papillomas up to 5 mm across are found in the mouth, usually beneath the tongue. They usually persist only for a month or two, but may do so for longer.

On inoculation into the oral mucosa, papillomata appear after 5–38 days. *Sylvilagus* and *Lepus* spp. are susceptible though only tame rabbits (*Oryctolagus*) have been found naturally infected. The virus will not "take" on the skin.

Basophilic inclusions have been found near the nucleus of superficial cells of the papillomas of tame rabbits.

Ecology. Infection does not spread readily in animal quarters but may do so from doe to sucklings. Virus has been recovered from mouth-washings of rabbits free from papillomas.

Canine Papillomatosis

Affects mucous membranes, especially of young dogs.

Morphology. Resembles polyoma (L. Crawford, quoted by Rowe *et al.*, 1963).

Physico-chemical characters. The agent is filterable, survives well in 50 per cent. glycerol or when frozen or dried. It survives heating for an hour to 45° but not to 58°.

Antigenic properties. Recovered dogs are immune.

Pathogenicity. Warts, which may become cauliflower-like, usually begin on lips and spread to the inside of the mouth and pharynx: they disappear after 4–21 weeks. They can be transferred to other young dogs, the incubation period being 4 to 8 weeks: only oral mucosa and neighbouring skin could be infected. Other species were insusceptible (McFadyean & Hobday, 1898; DeMonbreun & Goodpasture, 1932; Chambers & Evans, 1959).

Ecology. The disease readily spreads in kennels.

Control. Wart suspensions given intramuscularly along with adjuvants had prophylactic but no curative value (Chambers, Evans & Weiser, 1960).

Equine Papillomatosis

Affects nose and lips but is transferable to skin of neck. Wart usually numerous, not more than 1 cm. across. Readily transmitted to horses, not to other species. Agent survived 75 days at 4° and frozen at −35° for 185 days. Recovered animals are immune (Cook & Olson, 1951).

Papillomatosis of Chamois

Attacks chamois in the Tyrol affecting lips, nose and mouth Reported transmission to a rabbit; but the natural oral papillo matosis of rabbits may have misled the investigator (Kumer, 1935)

Papillomatosis of Goats

Affects some herds (Davis & Kemper, 1936) but is uncommon.

REFERENCES

Allison, A. C. (1961) *Virology*, **15**, 47.
Allison, A. C., & Armstrong, J. A. (1960) *Brit. J. Cancer*, **14**, 313.
Barabadze, Y. M. (1960) *Probl. Virol.*, **5**, 103 and 105.
Beard, J. W., & Rous, P. (1935) *Proc. Soc. exp. Biol. (N.Y.)*, **33**, 191.
Bernhard, W., Febvre, H. L., & Cramer, R. (1959) *C.R. Acad. Sci. (Paris)*, **249**, 483.
Bloch, D. P., & Godman, G. C. (1957) *J. exp. Med.*, **105**, 161.
Breedis, C., Berwick, L., & Anderson, T. F. (1962) *Virology*, **17**, 84.
Boiron, M., Paoletti, C., Thomas, M., Rebière, J. P., & Bernard, J. (1962) *C.R. Acad. sci. (Paris)*, **254**, 2097.
Brodsky, I., Rowe, W. P., Hartley, J. W., & Lane, W. T. (1959) *J. exp. Med.*, **109**, 439.
Bryan, W. R., & Beard, J. W. (1940) *J. nat. Cancer Inst.*, **1**, 607.
Bunting, H., Strauss, M. J., & Banfield, W. G. (1952) *Amer. J. Path.*, **28** 985.
Chambers, V. C., & Evans, C. A. (1959) *Cancer Res.*, **19**, 1188.
Chambers, V. C., Evans, C. A., & Weiser, R. S. (1960) *Cancer Res.*, **20**, 1083.
Chapman, G. B., Drusin, L. M., & Tod, J. C. (1963) *Amer. J. Path.*, **42**, 619.
Cook, R. H., & Olson, C. (1951) *Amer. J. Path.*, **27**, 1087.
Dalmat, H. T. (1958) *J. exp. Med.*, **108**, 9.
Davis, C. L., & Kemper, H. E. (1936) *J. Amer. vet. med. Ass.*, **88**, 175.
Deinhardt, F., Henle, G., & Marks, M. (1960) *J. Immunol.*, **84**, 599.
Deinhardt, F., & Henle, G. (1960) *J. Immunol.*, **84**, 608.
de Maeyer, E. (1962) *Science*, **136**, 985.
De Monbreun, W. A., & Goodpasture, E. W. (1932) *Amer. J. Path.*, **8**, 43.
Di Mayorca, G. A., Eddy, B. E., Stewart, S. E., Hunter, W. S., Friend, C., & Bendick, A. (1959) *Proc. nat. Acad. Sci. (Wash.)*, **45**, 1805.
Eddy, B. (1960) *Advanc. Virus Res.*, **7**, 91.

Eddy, B., Borman, G. S., Berkeley, W. H., & Young, R. D. (1961) *Proc. Soc. exp. Biol. (N.Y.)*, **107**, 191.

Eddy, B., Stewart, S. E., Kirschstein, R. L., & Young, R. D. (1959) *Nature (Lond.)*, **183**, 766.

Evans, C. A., Gorman, L. R., Ito, Y., & Weiser, R. S. (1962) *J. nat. Cancer Inst.*, **29**, 277 and 287.

Fischer, R. G. (1949) *Proc. Soc. exp. Biol. (N.Y.)*, **72**, 323.

Fischer, R. G., & Green, R. G. (1947) *Proc. Soc. exp. Biol. (N.Y.)*, **64**, 452.

Fisher, E. R., & Kilham, L. (1953) *Arch. Path.*, **55**, 14.

Fogel, M., & Sachs, L. (1960) *J. nat. Cancer Inst.*, **24**, 839.

Gerber, P. (1962) *Virology*, **16**, 96.

Gerber, P., & Kirschstein, R. L. (1962) *Virology*, **18**, 582.

Girardi, A. J., Sweet, B. H., Slotnick, V. B., & Hilleman, M. R. (1962) *Proc. Soc. exp. Biol. (N.Y.)*, **109**, 649.

Gotlieb-Stematsky, T., & Leventon, S. (1960) *Brit. J. exp. Path.*, **41**, 507.

Greene, H. S. N. (1953) *Cancer Res.*, **13**, 681.

Greene, H. S. N. (1955) *Cancer Res.*, **15**, 748.

Habel, K. (1962) *Virology*, **18**, 553.

Harris, R. J. C., Chesterman, F. C., & Negroni, G. (1961) *Lancet*, **1**, 788.

Hartley, J. W. (1958) *Virology*, **6**, 249.

Holt, D. (1959) *Aust. J. exp. Biol. med. Sci.*, **37**, 183.

Horne, R. W., & Wildy, P. (1961) *Virology*, **15**, 348.

Howatson, A. F. (1962) *Brit. med. Bull.*, **18**, 193.

Ito, Y. (1960) *Virology*, **12**, 596.

Kidd, J. (1938) *J. exp. Med.*, **68**, 703.

Kilham, L. (1961) *Virology*, **15** 389.

Kilham, L., & Murphy, H. W. (1953) *Proc. Soc. exp. Biol. (N.Y.)*, **82**, 133.

Knight, C. A. (1950) *Proc. Soc. exp. Biol. (N.Y.)*, **75**, 843.

Koprowski, H., Ponten, J. A., Jensen, F., Ravdin, R. G., Moorhead, P., & Zakscha, E. (1962) *J. cell. comp. Path.*, **59**, 281.

Kumer, L. (1935) *Wien. med. Wschr.*, **48**, 890.

Lyell, A., & Miles, J. A. R. (1912) *Brit. med. J.*, **1**.

McFadyean, J., & Hobday, F. (1898) *J. comp. Path.*, **11**, 341.

Mattern, C. F. T., Allison, A. C., & Rowe, W. P. (1963) *Virology*, **20**, 413.

Melnick, J. L. (1962) *Science*, **135**, 1128.

Meyer, H. M., Hobbs, H. E., Rogers, N. G., Brooks, B. E., Bernheim, B. C., Jones, W. P., Nisalak, A., & Douglas, R. D. (1962) *J. Immunol.*, **88**, 796.

Moore, D. H., Stone, R. S., Shope, R. E., & Gelber, D. (1959) *Proc. Soc. exp. Biol. (N.Y.)*, **101**, 575.

Munroe, J. S., & Windle, W. F. (1963) *Science*, **140**, 1415.

Negroni, G., Dourmashkin, R., & Chesterman, F. C. (1959) *Brit. med. J.*, **2**, 1359.

Noyes, W. F. (1959) *J. exp. Med.*, **109**, 423.

Noyes, W. F., & Mellors, R. C. (1957) *J. exp. Med.*, **106**, 555.

Olson, C., & Cook, R. H. (1951) *Proc. Soc. exp. Biol. (N.Y.)*, **77**, 281.

Olson, C., Segre, D., & Skidmore, L. V. (1960) *Amer. J. vet. Res.*, **21**, 233.

Parish, W. E. (1961) *J. Path. Bact.*, **81**, 331.

Parish, W. E. (1962) *J. Path. Bact.*, **83**, 429.

Parsons, D. F. (1963) *Virology*, **20**, 385.

Parsons, R. J., & Kidd, J. (1943) *J. exp. Med.*, **77**, 233.

Rendtorff, R. C., & Wilcox, A. (1957) *J. infect. Dis.*, **100**, 119.

Rogers, S. (1959) *Nature (Lond.)*, **183**, 1815.

Rous, P., & Beard, J. W. (1934) *J. exp. Med.*, **60**, 701.

Rouse, P., & Beard, J. W. (1935) *J. exp. Med.*, **62**, 523.

Rowe, W. P., Allison, A. C., Kilham, L., & Melnick, J. L. (1964) *Virology* in the Press.

Rowe, W. P., Hartley, J. W., Brodsky, I., & Huebner, R. J. (1958) *Science,* **128,** 1339.

Rowe, W. P., Huebner, R. J., & Hartley, J. W. (1961) in *Perspectives in Virology,* II, 177. Minneapolis: Burgess.

Sachs, L., & Fogel, M. (1960) *Virology,* **11,** 722.

Segre, D., Olson, C., & Hoerlein, A. B. (1955) *Amer. J. vet. Res.,* **16,** 517.

Sharp, D. G., Taylor, A. R., & Beard, J. W. (1946) *J. biol. Chem.,* **163,** 289.

Sharp, D. G., Taylor, A. R., Beard, D., & Beard, J. W. (1942) *J. biol. Chem.,* **142,** 193.

Shein, H. M., & Enders, J. F. (1962) *Proc. Soc. exp. Biol. (N.Y.),* **109,** 495.

Shope, R. E. (1933) *J. exp. Med.,* **58,** 607.

Smith, J. D., Freeman, G., Vogt, M., & Dulbecco, R. (1960) *Virology,* **12,** 185.

Stewart, S. E. (1960) *Advanc. Virus Res.,* **7,** 61.

Stewart, S. E., Eddy, B. E., & Borgese, N. G. (1958) *J. nat. Cancer Inst.,* **20,** 1223.

Stoker, M. G. P. (1962) in Ciba foundation symposium *Tumour Viruses of Murine Origin,* p. 52. London: Churchill.

Stoker, M. G. P., & MacPherson, I. (1961) *Virology,* **14,** 359.

Stone, R. S., Shope, R. E., & Moore, D. H. (1959) *J. exp. Med.,* **110,** 543.

Strauss, M. J., Shaw, E. W., Bunting, H., & Melnick, J. L. (1949) *Proc. Soc. exp. Biol. (N.Y.),* **72,** 46.

Sweet, H., & Hilleman, M. R. (1960) *Proc. Soc. exp. Biol. (N.Y.),* **105,** 420.

Syverton, J. T., Berry, G. P., & Warren, S. L. (1941) *J. exp. Med.,* **74,** 223.

Ullman, E. V. (1923) *Acta oto-laryng. (Stockh.),* **5,** 317.

Vogt, M., & Dulbecco, R. (1960) *Proc. nat. Acad. Sci.,* **46,** 365.

Watson, J. D., & Littlefield, J. W. (1960) *J. molec. Biol.,* **2,** 161.

Wildy, P., Stoker, M. G. P., MacPherson, I. A., & Horne, R. W. (1960) *Virology,* **11,** 444.

Williams, R. C., Kass, S. J., & Knight, C. A. (1960) *Virology,* **12,** 48.

Winocour, E. (1963) *Virology,* **19,** 158.

11
Herpesviruses

There will first be considered in this chapter, 5 viruses, included under the group-name *Herpesvirus* by the International Nomenclature Committee (Andrewes, 1954). These are *Herpesvirus hominis*, *H. simiæ* (B virus), *H. suis* (pseudorabies), *H. cuniculi* (Virus III) and *H. varicellæ* (varicella-zoster). Next will come a number of viruses which may well prove to be related to Herpesviruses and were included along with them in the provisional group NITAvirus—the name being derived from the Nuclear Inclusion Type A (Cowdry, 1934) which is characteristically present (Andrewes *et al.*, 1961).

However, at a meeting held subsequently, the virus subcommittee of the International Nomenclature Committee for Bacteria and Viruses decided instead to retain the older term Herpesvirus to include all these related viruses.

Morphology and development. These have been studied in detail only for a few of the group. The viruses have an icosahedral form with 162 cylindrical capsomeres on its surface. It seems to be general in the group that, in contrast to poxviruses, virus begins to be formed in the nucleus. Virus particles surrounded by a single membrane first appear in the nucleus; later they appear in the cytoplasm, usually with a double membrane. Measurements of size vary: probably there is a capsid of fairly uniform size surrounded by protein coats of varying degrees of hydration, the whole virus being readily distorted by drying for electron-micrography. Most estimates lie between 100 and 150 mμ. Release of virus from cells is probably gradual without involving cell destruction.

Chemical composition. There is evidence that members of the group are DNA viruses.

Physico-chemical characters. Ether-sensitive. Rather labile at room temperature and readily inactivated at 56° C.

211

Hæmagglutination. No typical hæmagglutination is described for most members of the group.

Antigenic properties. There are serological cross-reactions between the trio herpes simplex, pseudo-rabies and B virus (Sabin, 1934) but though neutralization and complement-fixation tests are very useful, there is no antigen common to the whole group.

Cultivation. The viruses all grow in tissue culture and most of them also do so in fertile eggs. Those most closely related to herpes simplex produce pocks on chorioallantoic membranes.

Pathogenicity. Lesions produced are at most briefly prolifera-tive, soon necrotic. Many members grow in the central nervous system of their hosts or of experimental animals and some travel along nerves to reach the CNS from a peripheral lesion. The char-acteristic intranuclear inclusions of Cowdry's Type A (1934) are formed by all the agents included here. These are really fixation artefacts in which a single homogeneous eosinophilic mass occupying most of the central area of the nucleus is separated by a clear halo from marginated basophilic chromatin. They are not visible as such in fresh preparations. Pereira (1962) suggests that the definition must be based on knowledge of the whole cycle of development. Nuclear changes in canine hepatitis (an adenovirus) and in yellow fever (an arbovirus) do not fit into this definition, but those of measles (a myxovirus) do so more nearly. Type A inclusions are not necessarily peculiar to the group.

If viruses provisionally included in this group and dealt with in this chapter prove to differ from herpesvirus in nucleic acid com-position or in fundamental morphology, they will have later to be classified elsewhere.

Herpes Simplex

Synonyms: Herpes febrilis, genitalis, labialis, etc. Fever blisters.
Herpesvirus hominis.
Review: Scott *et al.* (1959).
Doerr (1924–5).

Morphology and developmental cycle. Dense particles in the nucleus, 30–40 mμ across appear early in development. They then acquire single membranes and a diameter of 70–100 mμ. Later, particles with double membranes penetrate the nuclear membrane and are found in the cytoplasm; these have now a diameter of 120–130 mμ and as mature particles leave the cell altogether (Morgan *et al.*, 1954). The virus's development seems to be virtually completed in the nucleus (Morgan *et al.*, 1959). Virus infection of adjacent cells may take place by direct transfer. The complete virus (Wildy *et al.*, 1960) when negatively stained is seen to have an icosahedral core with 162 capsomeres on its surface. These are hollow prisms 12·5 × 9·5 mμ in diameter. Outside the capsid is a membrane appearing up to 180 mμ across. Some strains have different appearances: with one the cytoplasmic particles had only single membranes (Reissig & Melnick, 1955): with another particles were found in the nucleus in crystalline array (Morgan *et al.*, 1958). Most virus has left the nucleus by the time the intranuclear inclusion is formed. Particles may be found with and without nucleoids and with and without membranes (Watson *et al.*, 1963).

Chemical composition. Ben-Porat & Kaplan (1962) and Russell (1962) have shown that this is a DNA virus. The DNA has a high content of guanine and cytosine (74 per cent.). The nuclear inclusions are thought to represent a mass of amorphous deoxyribose nucleoprotein. Much DNA accumulates in the nucleus during the eclipse phase, too much to be all of viral origin, but DNA and viral antigen accumulate in the same parts of the cell, the DNA accumulating first (Ross & Orlans, 1958).

Physico-chemical characters. The specific gravity is estimated at 1·27–1·29 and the iso-electric point at pH 7·2–7·6. The virus is fairly heat labile, being inactivated in 30′ at 50–52° C, in 50–80 hours at 41·5° but it withstood 90° C for 30′ when dried (Holden, 1932). According to Scott *et al.* (1961) several biologically different strains were alike in having a half-life of 1½ hours at 37° C, 3¾ hours at 30–31° C. It survives well in 50 per cent. glycerol in the cold; apparently killed preparations may be reactivated with reducing agents such as cysteine (Perdrau, 1931). Readily preserved by lyophilization, or in skim milk at −20° or −70° C. It is ether-sensitive and is also inactivated by phosphatases (Amos, 1953). Inactivation by various other chemicals is described by Holden (1932).

Antigenic properties. Specific complement fixation and neutralization are readily shown. For the latter, various workers have used

15

titration in rabbits' skins, in mouse brains, on chorioallantoic membranes, in egg-yolks and in tissue culture, a plaque-counting method being applicable. There is a soluble antigen separate from the virus particles (Hayward, 1949): this is largely destroyed in 1 hour at 56° C but a little survives boiling for 5'. Virus-treated tanned sheep RBC's are agglutinated by specific antisera. The reaction is best carried out at 25° C and a pH of 6·4 (Scott *et al.*, 1957). An antigen has heen prepared giving specific skin-tests in susceptible persons (Nagler, 1944, 1946). Studies on human sera reveal the curious fact that those susceptible to recurrent herpes have good titres of neutralizing and CF antibody while those not subject to it have no antibodies: attacks of recurrent herpes do not usually affect the titre, while primary attacks lead to a rise. Several workers have reported antigenic differences amongst strains of virus by the neutralization test but the similarities between strains are more obvious than the differences and no consistent separation into serological types is recognized.

Cultivation. *In fertile eggs.* Herpes virus will grow after inoculation by all the usual routes. On the CAM plaques are considerably smaller than those of vaccinia—only 1–2 mm. across. Examination is best made 36–48 hours after incubation at 36° C. Growth also occurs in de-embryonated eggs and on the blastoderm of 1-day eggs (Yoshino, 1956).

In tissue culture. Cultivation is reported in many types of cell—rabbit, chick-embryo and human (HeLa, amnion and others). Cytopathic effects include inclusion body and giant cell formation, later cell destruction. 35° C seems to be the optimal temperature for growth. In monolayers, countable plaques appear and variants producing macro- and micro-plaques are described (Hoggan & Roizman, 1959). There have been several careful studies of various stages of growth—adsorption, eclipse, multiplication, release (Kaplan, 1957; Stoker & Ross, 1958; Hoggan & Roizman, 1959). An early effect in HeLa cells is inhibition of mitosis (Stoker & Newton, 1959).

Pathogenicity. In man, primary infection is mainly in young children and takes the form of acute stomatitis. Many people, including such children, although developing antibodies are subject to recurrent herpes for much of their lives. Such latent infection may be activated by various stimuli such as certain infections, fever, menstruation (*cf.* Doerr, 1924–5). Primary infection may, however, occur in later life: herpes genitalis for example may be a venereal infection. The commonest sites for "fever-blisters" are however the external nares and lips. The lesions, at first vesicular, soon scabbing, heal within a few days without a scar. There are other forms of the disease; Kaposi's varicelliform eruption (eczema herpeticum) is a primary infection especially in children, in which there is widespread herpetic infection of eczematous skin. "Traumatic herpes" may affect burns and other superficial lesions. Herpetic kerato-conjunctivitis may lead to serious corneal opacity. A generalized fatal infection may occur in new-born or under-nourished children and a herpetic meningo-encephalitis in children or adults may be fatal. The view that this virus was the causative agent of encephalitis lethargica is no longer held.

Experimental man-to-man transmission has frequently been carried out; it is more often successful in people subject to herpes.

Rabbits are very susceptible to infection by inoculating either cornea, skin, brain or testis. Neurotropic strains travel along nerves to the CNS from cornea or other peripheral sites and cause convulsions and death from encephalitis. Some strains produce necrotic foci in adrenals. A latent infection in rabbits may be activated by severe allergic reactions. Guinea pigs, mice, particularly suckling mice, monkeys of several genera and other species, including even tortoises, are susceptible. Some strains cause myelitis in mice after IP or ID injection; but the virus is readily modified in the laboratory to produce different effects in different species.

Pathological lesions. Proliferation, then ballooning degeneration of epithelial cells, precede vesicle formation in skin; numerous giant cells may occur and contain many nuclear inclusions. These Type A intranuclear inclusions contain little or no virus and represent a scar—a sequel to virus activity (Lebrun, 1956) (*cf.* p. 215). At an early stage tissues stained with hæmatoxylin and eosin show nuclei filled with homogeneous purple-staining material. Later basophilic material goes to the periphery and eosinophilic matter to form the central inclusion. The inclusions are found in almost all affected tissues. Recombination of strains with different genetic markers has been described by Wildy (1955).

Ecology. Recurrent herpes and associated high antibody levels occur more frequently at lower social-economic levels. Young children are more susceptible than adults; so these are often infected from recurrent lesions in a mother, to acquire themselves a persistent latent infection (Burnet & Williams, 1939). Epidemics amongst children may occur.

Control. Vaccination of man has been attempted without success. Some immunity may be induced experimentally in rodents. Kaufman (1962) has been successful in treating rabbits with herpetic kerato-conjunctivitis by means of 5-iodo-2'-deoxyuridine and there are encouraging reports of its use in similar conditions in man.

B VIRUS

Synonym: *Herpesvirus simiæ*

Morphology. Very like herpes simplex. Particles, presumably early stages, in monkey kidney tissue cultures, were 60–130 mμ across with a dense nucleoid 30 mμ across. Mature particles on the cell surface had a diameter of 130–180 mμ and had double membranes. Some particles had two central masses within one outer membrane (Reissig & Melnick, 1955).

Physico-chemical characters. Labile at room temperature but rather stable at 4° C. Ether-sensitive. Inactivated by 1 : 9000 formaldehyde in 48 hours at 36° C (Pierce *et al.*, 1958): incubation at 36° C for 9 days inactivated virus in the absence of formaldehyde. Readily preserved in 50 per cent. glycerol, at −76° C or by lyophilization. More details of inactivation by formaldehyde and other means are given by Prier & Goulet (1961) and Buthala (1962). Strains are said to vary in their ease of inactivation by formalin.

Hæmagglutinin. None reported.

Antigenic properties. Neutralization tests reveal a group relationship to herpes simplex and pseudo-rabies—not to Virus III, varicella or other viruses. Immune B sera neutralize herpes simplex very well but the contrary is not true: Virus B may be antigenically more complex. Not all B strains are antigenically identical (Prier & Goulet, 1961). Search for evidence of active immunity in cross-protection tests showed little if any between H. *hominis* and H. *simiæ*, but a definite small amount between H. *simiæ* and pseudo-rabies (Sabin, 1934). One of the recorded fatal infections in man was in someone previously known to have antibodies to herpes (Nagler & Klotz, 1958).

Ten per cent. of newly caught rhesus monkeys have antibodies: the percentage rises to 60–70 per cent. when they are confined in "gang-cages" (Hull & Nash, 1960).

Cultivation. *In fertile eggs.* The virus has been serially passed 30 times on chorioallantoic membranes (Burnet *et al.*, 1939).

In tissue culture. It grows readily in cultures of monkey, human and rabbit tissues and has been frequently isolated from cultures of apparently normal rhesus kidneys. The cell-to-cell spread of virus within cultures was studied by Black & Melnick (1955).

Distribution. A natural herpes-like infection of normal Asiatic monkeys (*Macaca mulatta* (rhesus)), *irus*, *cyclopis* and *fuscata* (Endo *et al.*, 1960). A similar virus (SA8) has been recovered in South Africa from kidneys of *Cercopithecus æthiops* (Malherbe & Harbin, 1958).

Pathogenicity. In monkeys (*Macaca* spp.), natural infection, occurring especially in monkeys crowded together, leads to vesicular lesions on tongue and lips, sometimes skin. Lesions in CNS may be found histologically (Keeble *et al.*, 1958).

Infection may occur in human beings 10 to 20 days after a monkey bite, or even in monkey handlers or people working with monkey-tissue cultures in absence of history of bite. There may be local inflammation at the site of a bite, followed by ascending myelitis (Sabin, 1949); or there may be acute encephalitis or encephalo-myelitis. In one reported case there was early infection of the respiratory tract (Love & Jungherr, 1962). Almost all cases have been fatal; there has been much residual disability in the few survivors (Breen *et al.*, 1958).

Experimentally, cortisone treated monkeys have been infected intraspinally. Rabbits are readily infected by various routes and usually die with encephalitis or encephalomyelitis. Skin lesions are more necrotic than those of herpes simplex and may not appear for 10–12 days. The first symptom of CNS involvement may be severe pruritus. Virus probably reaches the CNS along nerves (Sabin, 1934). Mice under 3 weeks old can be infected IC (Sabin, 1958), also day-old chicks. The virus is irregularly fatal for guinea pigs.

Pathological lesions. Besides local necrotic lesions in the skin of rabbits and inflammatory and destructive lesions in brain and cord, there may be necrotic foci in liver, spleen and adrenals. Typical Type A nuclear inclusions may be found whenever the virus is active in any of its hosts.

Ecology. The virus spreads by direct contact between monkeys especially in captivity. Incidence of antibodies under various conditions has already been mentioned (p. 216). The virus has not been found in stools or urine of infected monkeys.

Control. Precautions are possible to avoid infection of monkey handlers. Monkeys are best caged by ones or twos, not in gangs; and quarantined before use in experiments. Really safe gloves are difficult to devise and some workers only inoculate anæsthetized animals.

Attempts have been made to produce formolized vaccines for those working with monkeys; their efficiency is unproved.

Marmoset Virus

A herpes-like virus has been repeatedly isolated from throat-swabs and autopsy material of marmosets (Holmes, Dedman & Deinhardt, 1963). It was inhibited by DNA-inhibitors, was ether-sensitive, inactivated in 2 hours at 60°. It multiplied in marmoset, rabbit and human cells, poorly in rhesus kidney. Pocks were produced on the CAM. It was pathogenic for rabbits and mice IC and for suckling mice IP. Herpes-like intranuclear inclusions appeared in these species. No serological crossing with herpes simplex and a number of other viruses was found.

VIRUS III OF RABBITS

Synonym: *Herpesvirus cuniculi.*

This virus is so-called as the discoverers (Rivers & Tillett, 1923, 1924) mainly studied the third strain they isolated. It exists as a latent infection of some stocks of rabbits.

Morphology and chemical composition. No information.

Physico-chemical characters. Inactivated after heating 10' at 55° C or 30' at 45° C. Survives in 50 per cent. glycerol for at least 24 days or for 16 months after freeze-drying, but it is doubtful whether any virus is in existence in laboratories today.

Antigenic properties. Recovered rabbits are solidly immune and their sera contain neutralizing antibodies. Such antibodies occur in sera of many of the rabbits of stocks in which the virus is endemic.

Complement-fixing antibodies also are described. Partly immune animals show an allergic response.

Interference. Virus III is reported to interfere with rabbit fibroma virus in the rabbit's skin (Andrewes, 1940).

Cultivation. The virus has not been grown in eggs but multiples in tissue culture of rabbit testis, producing nuclear inclusions (Andrewes, 1929: this was perhaps the earliest report of production of a specific virus change in tissue-culture). Growth occurs also in other rabbit tissues (Ivanovics & Hyde, 1936).

Distribution. It has been found in some but not all stocks of rabbits in the United States, Britain and Switzerland, but isolation has not been reported since 1940.

Pathogenicity. Virus III is not known to produce any natural disease in rabbits, being only activated after serial "blind passages" of tissues. Once exalted in this way it produces lesions after inoculation by various routes. Given intradermally it gives rise to slightly raised erythematous lesions; intratesticular injections produce acute orchitis and fever; intrathoracic inoculation leads to pericarditis (Miller *et al.*, 1924) and IC injection to encephalitis (Rivers & Stewart, 1928). In all these tissues the acute inflammatory lesions are associated with Type A intranuclear inclusions, those in the testis being largely in the interstitial tissues. Cowdry (1930) has reported on minor differences between the inclusions of Virus III and herpes. While only persisting for a few days after inoculation into normal rabbits, the virus may be carried for some time in transplanted tumours (Rivers & Pearce, 1925; Andrewes, 1940). Species other than rabbits are insusceptible.

PSEUDORABIES

Synonyms: Aujeszky's disease. Mad itch. Infectious bulbar paralysis. *Herpesvirus suis.*
Review: Galloway (1938).

Morphology. 100–150 mμ in diameter, as estimated by gradocol filtration. Resembles *Herpesvirus hominis* by electron-microscopy.

Chemical composition. Contains DNA with a relatively high content of guanine and cytosine (Ben-porat & Kaplan, 1962).

Physico-chemical characters. Survives on hay for 30 days in summer, 46 days in winter (Solomkin & Tutushin, 1956). Virus dried and stored *in vacuo* survives at least 2 years. It will survive also for at least 3 years in 50 per cent. glycerol in the cold (Galloway, 1938). It also survives for some time in 3 per cent. phenol and may persist in a swine fever vaccine. 0·5 per cent. NaOH inactivates it rapidly. It is fairly stable between pH 5 and 9 and is best preserved at $+4°$ or below $-30°$ (Zuffa & Skoda, 1962).

Antigenic properties. Antisera have usually been prepared in pigs since the virus is so lethal to most other species and inactivated virus does not readily immunize. Neutralizing antibodies have been tested for in guinea pigs rather than in the very sensitive rabbit. Tissue culture techniques are, however, now available. Sabin (1934) found evidence of a group antigen common to this and herpes. There is also evidence suggesting that monkeys with antibodies to B virus may be resistant to pseudorabies (Hurst, 1936).

All strains, including the American Mad Itch, seem alike antigenically.

Interference. There may be interference between strains virulent and less virulent for chick embryo cells in culture.

Cultivation. In fertile eggs, the virus grows on the chorioallantoic membrane producing white plaques (Bang, 1942) or a hæmorrhagic reaction and death of the embryo by the fourth day (Glover, 1939). It can also be cultivated in the yolk sac.

The virus can be grown in cultures of chick, rabbit, guinea pig, pig and dog tissues and doubtless those of other species. It causes cell-destruction and plaques are produced in monolayers of pig kidney or chick embryo cells. Less virulent strains are reported to produce larger plaques. Of two strains cultivated by Tokumaru (1957) one caused rounding-up of cells, the other giant-cell formation.

Intranuclear inclusions are found both in infected eggs and in tissue cultures.

Distribution. The virus is prevalent in most of Europe, in South Africa, North and South America; it is rare in Britain but sporadic in Northern Ireland.

Pathogenicity. Cattle, sheep, pigs, dogs, cats and mink are naturally affected. In pigs the infection is commonly inapparent, but at times 5 to 10 per cent. may have nervous symptoms with fever, convulsions and paralysis; even so recovery is the rule. In cattle, sheep and carnivores the disease is usually fatal, the predominant symptom being intense pruritus causing the animal to gnaw or scratch part of the body—usually head or hind quarters—until great tissue destruction is caused. Other symptoms of encephalomyelitis, violent excitement, fits and paralysis, precede death which usually occurs within a few days. Horses are doubtfully susceptible. There are three reports of infection of laboratory workers; in the best authenticated instance, local pruritus occurred, there were aphthæ in the mouth and virus was recovered from the blood (Aksel & Tuncman, 1940).

Experimentally the disease can be reproduced in the susceptible species just mentioned. Rabbits are extremely susceptible to infection by various routes. Intracerebral injection leads to fatal meningitis or encephalitis without pruritus, but after peripheral inoculation, intense pruritus is the rule, death following very soon. Guinea pigs are slightly more resistant, rats and mice even more so; chicks and ducks can also be infected. Virus spreads centripetally from primary peripheral lesions but spread by blood-stream may occur also.

Pathological lesions. In all species pruritus and consequent self-mutilation result in severe destructive œdematous lesions. The pruritus is apparently due to lesions of spinal ganglia and posterior horn cells in the cord. Here, and elsewhere in the CNS, A-type intranuclear inclusions are found (Hurst, 1933, 1936). Focal necrotic lesions occur in cerebrum, cerebellum, adrenals and other viscera in rabbits and in this species severe pulmonary œdema may be a cause of death (Shope, 1931).

Ecology. The disease does not spread amongst infected sheep or cattle; these often contract infection from pigs with inapparent infections, having virus in their nasal secretions (Shope, 1935a). Pigs in their turn may contract infection through eating carcases of infected rats (Shope, 1935b). Animals can certainly be infected by eating infected material. Possibly cattle may pick infection up directly from rats. Most workers have failed to recover virus from urine; some have succeeded, especially with pigs.

Control. Attempts to make attenuated or inactivated vaccines have given little encouragement. The most promising report is from

Beladi & Ivanovics (1954) who inactivated virus grown in chick embryos with UV irradiation, and were able to immunize guinea pigs and mice. These are, of course, not the most susceptible species. It has lately been tested in cattle (Skoda, 1962).

VARICELLA

Synonym: *Herpesvirus varicellæ.*
The virus causes disease of two clinical types: (i) Varicella, chickenpox or Windpocken; (ii) Herpes zoster or zona.
Review: Downie (1959).

Morphology. Tournier *et al.* (1957) describe in their sections of biopsy material and tissue-cultures intranuclear bodies 30–40 mμ in thickness, surrounded by a membrane giving a total diameter of 70–110 mμ. These particles apparently reach the cytoplasm acquiring a second, thicker, membrane and attaining a total width of 150–200 mμ. Earlier workers, however, estimated the size of the virus as 210 × 240 mμ. The particles seem to be more rounded, less brick-shaped than those of poxviruses. Almeida *et al.* (1962) have described bodies about 200 mμ across with hollow capsomeres, probably 162, on the surface, closely resembling what is described for herpes simplex by Wildy *et al.* (1960).

Physico-chemical characters. Virus from vesicle fluid survives many months at −70° C but tissue-culture suspensions may prove inactive after a few days (Taylor-Robinson, 1959). The virus is inactivated by heating for 30′ at 60° C.

Antigenic properties. Viruses obtained from varicella and zoster are identical by all serological tests. These include agglutination of partly purified virus suspensions (Amies, 1934), complement-fixation (Netter & Urbain, 1926), precipitation and neutralization tests. C-F antigen is better shown with vesicle fluid than with material from tissue cultures. An antigen separable from the virus particles is concerned (Taylor-Robinson & Downie, 1959; Caunt *et al.*, 1961). Gel-diffusion tests in agar reveal the presence of 3 lines of precipitation (Taylor-Robinson & Rondle, 1959). Virus antigen can be revealed also by the aid of fluorescent antibody and in neutralization tests in tissue culture: the latter was best achieved by incorporating antisera in the culture system (Weller, 1958). The earliest antigen detected by immunofluorescence by Slotnik and Rosanoff (1963) was in the perinuclear region of the cytoplasm. Convalescent zoster sera tend to have higher antibody titres than post-varicella sera, probably because a secondary antigenic stimulus is concerned.

Cultivation. The virus has not been cultivated in eggs except that Goodpasture & Anderson (1944) reported development of inclusions in human skin grafted on the chick CAM. Weller (1953, 1958) succeeded in propagating strains from varicella and zoster in tissue cultures of human embryo skin and muscle and of prepuce. The virus has since been grown in HeLa cells and various monkey tissues. Cytopathic effects appear in 2 days, are focal in character, involving the cell-sheet gradually. Virus in culture, in contrast to that in vesicle fluid, is mostly cell-bound and serial cultivation is only achieved by passing material containing tissue. Infection apparently passes to contiguous cells rather than through the fluid medium. Intranuclear inclusions develop in culture and may be seen in all the nuclei of giant cells.

Pathogenicity. Varicella affects chiefly children, causing a papular rash, which soon becomes vesicular and then scabby. The incubation period is 14–16 days, rarely up to 21 days. Pneumonitis, sometimes fatal, may occur, especially in adults. Encephalitis is a rare complication. The disease may be fatal in children on cortisone therapy.

Zoster is a painful local condition, usually in adults; skin lesions resemble those of varicella. Zoster ophthalmicus may be very serious. Zoster may follow exposure to varicella but usually behaves as if it were a latent infection, activated by such stimuli as arsenic treatment or tumour growth: virus is suspected to lie dormant in the body after an attack of varicella. Zoster rarely complicates varicella in children and a generalised rash rarely occurs in zoster in adults. Typical varicella may be contracted from exposure to a zoster case and zoster material has experimentally produced varicella in children (Kundratitz, 1925).

Animals other than man seem to be generally insusceptible. There is, however, a report (Rivers, 1926) of production of nuclear inclusions in testes of inoculated *Cercopithecus* monkeys.

Pathological lesions. Ballooning degeneration of skin epithelium precedes the formation of vesicles. Here and elsewhere are found the characteristic Type A intranuclear inclusions. In zoster, the skin lesions are preceded by inflammatory changes in posterior root ganglia and posterior columns of the cord. Anterior columns are not commonly affected and paralytic symptoms are rare, though they do occur. In fatal cases of varicella in children, focal lesions, with inclusions, are found in various viscera.

Ecology. Spread of varicella is probably mainly through the air. The origin of zoster has been discussed above.

Control. No method of active immunization is yet available. Convalescent serum has not been successful in prevention nor treatment.

INFECTIOUS BOVINE RHINOTRACHEITIS

Synonyms: IBR (but these initials also stand for Inclusion body rhinitis—of pigs, p. 241). Necrotic rhinitis. Red nose. The causative virus can also give rise to infectious pustular vulvovaginitis or bovine coital exanthema.
Review: McKercher (1959).

Morphology. Bodies seen in cell nuclei are 90 × 50 mμ across with a nucleoid. More mature particles seen in the cytoplasm are 130–180 mμ across and have a surrounding membrane (Knocke & Liess, 1961). Armstrong et al. (1961) describe intranuclear particles 115 mμ across with a single membrane and cytoplasmic ones, 150 mμ across, with double membranes. They draw attention to morphological and other similarities between this and herpes virus.

Chemical composition. The observations of Armstrong et al. (1961) suggest that this is a DNA virus.

Physico-chemical characters. Ether-sensitive. Inactivated in 21′ at 56° C, 10 days at 37° C, 50 days at 22° C. Very stable at pH 6–9 but labile at pH 4–5 to 5 (Griffin et al., 1958).

Antigenic properties. Neutralization tests in tissue culture show that the virus is antigenically homogeneous, only minor differences existing between strains (York et al., 1957). The virus is antigenically distinct from herpes simplex but shows some relation to that of equine rhino-pneumonitis (p. 226) in complement-fixation and gel-diffusion tests (Carmichael and Barnes, 1961).

Cultivation. No growth in fertile eggs. The virus has been cultivated in bovine embryo tissues—kidney, testis, lung, skin, producing CPE within 1–2 days (Madin *et al.*, 1956). The disease was reproduced with culture material after 21 but not 40 passages (Schwarz *et al.*, 1957). Intranuclear inclusions were produced in culture. Growth also occurs in pig, sheep, goat and horse kidney tissue cultures, in rabbit spleen, in human amnion and, after adaptation, in HeLa cells. Similar results are reported with a strain from coital exanthema (Greig *et al.*, 1958). Plaques may be found in bovine kidney monolayers.

Distribution. Infectious rhinotracheitis occurs as such chiefly in the western half of the United States; also in Britain, Germany and New Zealand. As pustular vulvovaginitis or coital exanthema it is recorded from the eastern United States and Canada, several European countries and North Africa.

Pathogenicity. "IBR" may be mild and unrecognized or very acute, involving the whole respiratory tract with acute inflammation, exudate and mucosal necrosis. There are fever, depression and often also bloody diarrhœa. The natural incubation period is 4–6 days: experimentally it may be as little as 18 hours. The natural course is 10–14 days. In severe outbreaks mortality may be 75 per cent. but is usually much lower.

Only cattle are naturally susceptible. Virus from cases of rhinotracheitis or vulvovaginitis may reproduce either disease according to the route of inoculation (Brown & Bjornson, 1959). Infection produced by cultivated virus is milder than the natural disease.

In calves the virus may cause only conjunctivitis (Quin, 1961). There is a suggestion also that it may be related to an agent causing kerato-conjunctivitis in cattle (Sykes *et al.*, 1962); that virus, however, was said to be ether-resistant.

Young goats may be infected experimentally and develop fever (McKercher, 1959).

Rabbits inoculated intradermally or intratesticularly with tissue culture material developed local lesions, but inclusions were not found and attempts at serial passage were unsuccessful (Armstrong *et al.*, 1961).

The *pathological lesions* are those of acute inflammation and necrosis of affected mucous membranes, which may be covered with glairy muco-purulent exudate. There may be patchy pneumonia and ulceration of the abomasum is frequent. Occasional involvement of

CNS and adrenals (Webster & Manktelow, 1959) supports the idea of placing this in the Herpesvirus group. Histologically there occur typical Type A intranuclear inclusions in epithelial cells; these are, however, too transient to be of much value in diagnosis.

Ecology. Transmission is by contact, especially where there is overcrowding. Virus may still be present in nasal secretions for several months after an attack.

Control. Unmodified virus will immunize without producing disease if given intramuscularly. However, it is better to use virus which has been attenuated by cultivation in bovine (Schwarz *et al.*, 1957) or porcine (Schwarz *et al.*, 1958) tissue culture.

EQUINE RHINOPNEUMONITIS

Synonyms: Mare abortion. Equine abortion. Equine influenza (in part).
The name equine rhinopneumonitis proposed by Doll *et al.* (1959) seems preferable since another virus, that of equine arteritis (*cf.* p. 305), can also cause abortion in mares.

Morphology. Particles have been described, chiefly in nuclei, of affected hepatic cells of hamsters. Some, with double membranes, were 146 mμ across; others were 90 mμ across and there were nucleoids within 40 mμ across (Bracken *et al.*, 1958). Tajima *et al.* (1961) describe virus bodies 95 mμ in diameter within nuclei and 115 mμ ones in cytoplasm and outside cells. Particles in nuclei may be in crystalline array (Arhelger *et al.*, 1963). It is hard to assess the significance of the bodies seen in hamster plasma and liver extracts by Sharp & Bracken (1960). These were 170 mμ across and many had tails up to 340 mμ long, said not to be artefacts due to use of strong salt in the medium.

Chemical composition. Contains 9·2 per cent. DNA (Darlington & Randall, 1963). The mature inclusion bodies are said not to contain DNA (this is also so in herpes).

Physico-chemical characters. Virus in infected tissues survives for over a year at −18° C. The virus is labile in saline suspensions in the absence of serum. It is inactivated by 0·35 per cent. formaldehyde. Density 1·18.

Hæmagglutination. Horse RBC's are agglutinated between 4° and 37° C by tissues of affected hamsters (McCollum *et al.*, 1956). The hæmagglutinin is labile at 56° C. It is not neutralized by convalescent horse sera but is by sera of horses hyperimmunised with infected hamster tissue. Semerdjiev (1962) described agglutination of horse, and also guinea pig cells, preferably after treatment with formalin.

Antigenic properties. Specific CF antigens occur in lungs of infected hamsters and in infected eggs and there are CF antibodies in sera of infected horses, though these only persist for a few months. Neutralization tests may be carried out in hamsters, and presumably also in tissue culture.

Complement-fixation and gel-diffusion, but not neutralization tests indicate that an antigen is shared by this and infectious bovine rhinotracheitis virus (p. 224) (Carmichael & Barnes, 1961).

Cultivation. *In fertile eggs.* The virus has been adapted to growth on the chorioallantoic membrane, in the yolk sac and amnion (Doll & Wallace, 1954; Randall, 1955).

In tissue culture it grows in fœtal horse tissue; also in HeLa cells, human amnion, sheep, pig and cat tissue. Inclusion bodies are formed *in vitro* (McCollum *et al.*, 1962).

In roller tube cultures of horse kidney cells a specific CPE is produced (Shimizu *et al.*, 1958).

Distribution. The disease is reported from several European countries, South Africa and the United States; probably occurs elsewhere under the guise of equine influenza.

Pathogenicity. In mares, the disease is usually inapparent but abortion occurs, especially in the 8th, 9th and 10th months of pregnancy. Symptoms affecting the central nervous system have been recorded, but rarely.

Only equines are naturally affected.

Experimentally, suckling Syrian hamsters are readily infected IP with production of fatal hepatitis (Anderson & Goodpasture, 1942; Doll *et al.*, 1953). Later it was found possible to adapt the virus to produce fatal infection in adult hamsters; also to go intracerebrally in baby mice (Kaschula *et al.*, 1957). The virus will also cause abortion in pregnant guinea pigs (Doll *et al.*, 1953).

No lesions have been found in aborting mares, but aborted fœtuses show multiple necrotic foci in the liver and petechiæ elsewhere. Type A intranuclear inclusions occur abundantly in infected epithelial cells, in liver and elsewhere; in infected hamsters 99 per cent. of hepatic cells may contain them.

Ecology. Probably transmitted by the respiratory route. Transmission by "carrier" stallions has been alleged but is not generally accepted.

Control. It is safe and effective to give living virus to mares when neither they nor their stable companions are pregnant (Doll *et al.*, 1955); use of virus attenuated by intracerebral mouse-passage has also been suggested (Byrne *et al.*, 1958).

Equine Herpesvirus 2

This name is suggested for a second equine Herpesvirus, described by Plummer & Waterson (1963). It was isolated from a horse with catarrh and by electron-microscopy was similar to equine rhinopneumonitis though antigenically distinct.

VIRUSES LESS CERTAINLY RELATED TO HERPES

We now come to a number of viruses all of which produce nuclear inclusions of Cowdry's A type, are of size comparable with that of herpesviruses and resemble them in other ways. They may be provisionally included in the Herpesvirus group. It is, however, necessary to know the nucleic acid composition and more about their structure before one can have any confidence that a natural group is being delineated.

INFECTIOUS LARYNGO-TRACHEITIS (AVIAN)

Not to be confused with infectious bronchitis of chicks (p. 353).

Morphology. A diameter of 45–85 mμ has been put forward on the basis of filtration (Gibbs, 1935); and of 64 mμ from electron-micrography (Filmer & Hanson, 1959). Watrach (1962), however, describes larger bodies seen in sections of infected chorioallantoic membranes. There were bodies in the nucleus 35 mμ across, or larger ones with a thin surrounding membrane, 81–99 mμ in diameter. Filaments up to 900 mμ long, 65 mμ wide were also seen in the nucleus: they had an opaque core, 22 mμ across. In the cytoplasm (Watrach *et al.*, 1959) were still larger ones 150–240 mμ across, having an opaque 50–80 mμ core and an outer capsule 35–30 mμ thick. This description recalls that of Herpes and suggests a developmental cycle beginning in the nucleus and continuing in the cytoplasm. By negative staining techniques, the virus appears to resemble other Herpesviruses (Cruickshank *et al.*, 1963).

Physico-chemical characters. Survives drying from the frozen state. Inactivated by heating 10′–15′ at 55·5° C, or 2′ or 3′ at 60° C. Ether-sensitivity not reported. Said not to persist long on infected premises.

Hæmagglutination. None detected.

Antigenic properties. Neutralization by antisera is readily measured in tests on the chorioallantoic membrane (Burnet, 1936). No serological types are described but some strains though fully antigenic are poorly neutralized by antisera, a situation recalling the P–Q phase variation of influenza viruses (Pulsford, 1953). A neutralization test involving counting plaques on tissue culture monolayers is described but is less satisfactory (Chomiak *et al.*, 1960). The gel-diffusion test is also useful in diagnosis (Woernle & Brunner, 1961).

Cultivation. *In fertile eggs.* On the CAM plaques of two kinds appear, larger ones with an opaque white periphery and necrotic centre—from more virulent strains; and smaller ones without necrosis—from less virulent viruses (Burnet, 1936). Amniotic inoculation causes production of lesions with intranuclear inclusions in trachea and bronchi (Burnet & Foley, 1941).

In tissue culture growth occurs in kidney and muscle of day-old chicks with CPE; also in HeLa cells without CPE (Webster, 1959). A long eclipse phase is followed by sudden virus release after 18 hours (Pulsford, 1960). Atherton & Anderson (1957) grew the virus in chick-embryo tissue and found activity particularly associated with the tissue in the culture; transmission was thought to be largely from cell to cell. Nuclear inclusions are formed in tissue cultures, as in the CAM; giant cells may appear also.

Distribution. It occurs in North America, Australia and several European countries.

Pathogenicity. Naturally affects mainly fowls and pheasants causing hæmorrhagic tracheitis with gasping and coughing. Virus is mainly in the respiratory tract: in smaller quantity in liver and spleen (Beach, 1931). In some outbreaks hæmorrhagic conjunctivitis occurs. The incubation period lasts for 2–6 days. Mortality may be anything up to 70 per cent., the course of infection in survivors being 2–3 weeks. Egg-production suffers.

A less severe disease with nothing worse than coughing or sneezing is caused by a less virulent strain occurring in Australia and the United States.

Most accounts say that only fowls and pheasants are susceptible, but occasional infection of ducks, pigeons and turkeys is reported.

No mammals have been infected.

Hæmorrhagic inflammation and œdema of larynx, trachea, bronchi and sometimes conjunctiva occur in severe forms; or there may be a caseous exudate in the air-passages and air-sacs. Type A intranuclear inclusions occur in groups of epithelial cells and may be seen as early as 12 hours after inoculation. Though these are homogeneous as seen after ordinary staining, silver staining may reveal argentophilic granules (Seifried, 1931).

Ecology. Transmission is by the respiratory route. The disease is often highly infectious. It may be endemic in some areas, apparently because some recovered birds continue to excrete virus for long periods. Indirect transmission through human agency is also suspected; and transmission occurs through the egg, or perhaps by contamination of the outside of the egg-shell.

Control. *Vaccination.* Living virus has been successfully applied as a vaccine to the bursa of Fabricius off the cloaca (Beaudette & Hudson, 1933). It is best to use a strain attenuated by cultivation in eggs (Cox, 1952).

Since carriers exist, it is clearly rash to mix recovered birds with clean stock.

Pacheco's Disease (of Parrots)

This infection of parrots, clinically similar to psittacosis, is due to quite a different agent, possibly related to infectious laryngotracheitis.

Review: Pacheco (1930–31).

Morphology: nothing known. The agent passes Berkefeld V and N candles.

Physico-chemical characters. Survives freeze-drying and can be preserved for at least 4 months in 50 per cent. glycerol in the cold. Stable at 55° C (Pacheco, 1930–31). Effect of ether not reported. No serological studies are reported.

Cultivation in series is reported on CAM of 10-day chick embryos; opaque white lesions are produced. Many embryos die after 3–5 days.

Distribution. Only reported from South America, affecting parrots especially those of the genus *Amazona*.

Pathogenicity. Symptoms in affected parrots—weakness, wing-drooping, indifference to stimuli, diarrhœa, finally coma and death.
Experimentally the infection is transmissible to budgerigars (*Melopsittacus*) by intramuscular or intracerebral inoculation. Symptoms begin 3–4 days after inoculation; birds showing symptoms rarely recover. Young chicks may be slightly susceptible. Lesions with nuclear inclusions were induced in a few, but serial transmission was not reported. Mammals could not be infected.
Lesions include necrotic foci in liver and spleen and accumulations of fluid in serous cavities. Histologically one sees proliferation of mesenchymatous cells, sometimes syncytia. Type A nuclear inclusions occur in mononuclear cells; these, according to Meyer's (1931) figures are at times crescentic in outline.

Disease of Owls

Green & Shillinger (1936) have described a fatal disease of wild horned owls (*Bubo virginianus*). There were small necroses of liver and spleen. The disease was transmitted with material which was unfiltered but apparently free from bacterial pathogens to another horned owl, a screech owl (*Otus*) but not to a barred owl (*Strix*). Large eosinophilic nuclear inclusions were found in the hepatic cells.

Inclusion Disease of Pigeons

Smadel *et al.* (1945), in the course of studies of ornithosis in pigeons, encountered another virus, which produced intranuclear inclusions in infected cells. It was separated from the ornithosis agent either by filtration through Seitz EK filters, which allowed it alone to pass; or by rapid passage on chorioallantoic membranes of fertile eggs. The virus caused focal necrosis of parenchymatous tissue of the liver in pigeons, but was not transmitted to any other species. In eggs, titres of 10^7/ml. were reached, embryos dying 4 days after inoculation. It could be stored for several months at $-20°$ C. Complement-fixing but not neutralizing antibodies could be demonstrated.

Inclusions in kidneys of normal pigeons described by Nicolau & Kopciowska (1938) may be caused by the same agent.

Cormorant Virus

French (personal communication, 1954) has described a virus which may fall into the same family as the avian viruses just described. It was isolated on the CAM of a fertile hen's egg inoculated with the blood of a little pied cormorant (*Phalacrocorax melanoleucos*) three weeks old. It produced pocks on the membrane and could also be grown in the amniotic and allantoic cavities. There was no regular lethal effect. Neither chicks, pigeons, parrots nor laboratory rodents could be infected. The virus passed a 0.6μ gradocol membrane without loss of titre. It survived storage at $-70°$ C and lyophilization. 30 minutes at $55°$ C inactivated it. No neutralising antisera could be prepared.

Lesions on the CAM were at first proliferative, later necrotic. Eosinophilic intranuclear inclusions were found but these were thought to represent enlarged nucleoli rather than Cowdry Type A inclusions.

There is no evidence that the virus is pathogenic for cormorants.

Feline Viral Rhinotracheitis

An upper respiratory infection of kittens, distinct from panleucopenia (p. 345) and feline pneumonitis (p. 374).

Physico-chemical characters. Survives drying or storage 3 months at $-60°$ C. It is most stable at pH 6, inactivated in 4–5 minutes at $56°$ and ether-sensitive. 0.018 per cent. formalin inactivates in 3 days at $4°$ (Miller *et al.*, 1962).

Antigenic properties. Neutralizing antibodies appear in recovered animals. Distinct from various other cat viruses by CF and neutralization tests (Hersey & Maurer, 1961).

Cultivation. *In tissue culture* grows in cultures of cat kidney, lung and testis, producing focal lesions in 40–48 hours; the whole cell-sheet was affected and fell off the glass in 120 hours. Plaques were formed in monolayers. No CPE in cultures of bovine, human and monkey cells. Intranuclear inclusions and giant cells were formed in culture (Crandell & Maurer, 1958; Crandell *et al.*, 1960).

Pathogenicity. Causes fever, lacrimation and nasal discharge in kittens. Incubation period 1–3 days. Epithelial cells contain Type A intranuclear inclusions.

MALIGNANT CATARRH

Synonyms: Malignant catarrhal fever. Snotsiekte (South Africa).
           Bovine epitheliosis.
Reviews: Schofield & Bain (1941). Stenius (1952).
           Berkman *et al.* (1960)—pathology.

Morphology. The agent is filtered with difficulty. It has at best passed a 430 mμ membrane (Plowright *et al.*, 1960). There are other, unconvincing, reports as to its size and filterability. Recent morphological studies, using electron-microscopy, suggest that it is related to the Herpesvirus group (Armstrong, personal communication, 1963).

Physico-chemical characters. A very unstable organism, not surviving for more than a few days at −60° or after lyophilizing. It can be kept for a few days in citrated blood at 5° C (Piercy, 1953) and in general only survives well within cells under conditions where these can be kept alive. Readily inactivated by alternate freezing and thawing.

Antigenic properties. Immunity of cattle which survive an attack persists for at least a few months (Piercy, 1954). No serological tests for virus have been described.

Cultivation. No continued cultivation in eggs is convincingly reported. The virus may, however, be grown in cultures of thyroids or adrenals from infected cattle (Plowright *et al.*, 1960); syncytia and Cowdry A-type inclusions form in cultures. Once growth has been thus initiated cultivation has proved possible in sheep thyroid, calf testis or adrenal, rabbit and wildebeest kidney. Cultures up to the 19th in calf kidney were still infectious.

Distribution. Occurs sporadically in every continent.

Pathogenicity. An extremely fatal, sporadic disease. After 1 or 2 days' fever, acute inflammation of nasal and oral mucous membranes begins. There occur ulceration, exudation and nasal obstruction and the lesions may spread to pharynx and lungs. Keratitis and various other eye lesions are common. Most cases show nervous symptoms, usually stupor, but there may be excitement. Death may occur within 24 hours but the disease may last a fortnight or more. Mortality is over 90 per cent.

These severe symptoms are seen in cattle but wildebeests and sheep may have inapparent infections. Huck *et al.* (1961) report a similar disease amongst Père David's deer; an agent was transmitted to other deer, calves and rabbits.

Experimental transmission has been achieved almost wholly by workers in Africa, a fact suggesting the possibility that more than one disease is concerned. Piercy (1952) readily transmitted the disease to cattle, also to rabbits (Piercy, 1955; Plowright, 1953); the latter showed little apart from fever, but after 9 rabbit passages virus still infected cattle. The agent transmitted to various species by Daubney & Hudson (1936) seems to have been something different.

Pathological lesions are those of destructive inflammation of mucous membranes of the respiratory and upper intestinal tracts (Berkman *et al.*, 1960). Bronchopneumonia may occur; and the brain shows evidence of meningo-encephalitis. Cytoplasmic inclusions have been seen in various tissues but the striking intranuclear inclusions which are seen in tissue cultures have not been found in animals infected *in vivo*.

Ecology. Much circumstantial evidence suggests that infection is transmitted when cattle are kept in contact with sheep, which may have symptomless infections; and that in Africa it may follow contact with wildebeest (*Gorgon taurinus*). Plowright *et al.* (1960) isolated virus from a blue wildebeest. Contact transmission amongst cattle seems not to occur. Arthropod transmission seems unlikely, at least in North America, where it is a winter disease.

Renal Carcinoma of the Leopard Frog

Reviews: Lucké (1934, 1938).

Adenomata or adenocarcinomata occur in the kidneys of *Rana pipiens* from certain areas. They are caused by a virus, but the properties of the agent itself have been little studied.

Physico-chemical characters. The active agent in tumour tissue survives desiccation or suspension in 50 per cent. glycerol. Filtration has not been reported.

Cultivation. The virus grows in cultures of frog tissue, preferably at 35° C; nuclear inclusions were not formed *in vitro* (Lucké, 1939; Lucké *et al.*, 1953).

Distribution. Natural occurrence is mainly in *R. pipiens* from parts of Vermont and adjacent areas of Canada.

Pathogenicity. The naturally occurring kidney tumours are found in 2 per cent. of Vermont frogs, especially those 30–100 gm. in weight. They are commonly bilateral and may involve almost all the kidney tissue. They are usually progressive and fatal metastases are recorded; but regression can occur.

Attempted subcutaneous transplantation of the tumour apparently fails but many inoculated frogs develop renal tumours several months later. Other frog species and even another subspecies of *R. pipiens* proved insusceptible (Lucké, 1938). However, Rose & Rose (1952) inoculated young salamanders (*Triturus*) or regenerating limb-buds of older ones and produced osteochondromata.

The tumour cells characteristically contain intranuclear inclusion bodies, often in large numbers. Though Duryee *et al.* (1960) liken these to enlarged nucleoli, Lucké's (1934) pictures leave little doubt that they are Type A intranuclear inclusions.

Ecology. There is a suggestion (Rafferty & Rafferty, 1961) that cross-infection may occur within a laboratory, but probably not between adult frogs. Rafferty (1963), however, raises the question of whether injection of tumour extracts may not act merely by accelerating the occurrence of tumours which would develop anyway.

CYTOMEGALOVIRUSES

There is a group of agents affecting various animals and all highly species-specific. Many of them have a particular affinity for salivary glands. The names salivary gland virus or submaxillary virus are used for these agents; and for the human infection cytomegalic inclusion disease, visceral disease, inclusion body disease, salivary gland virus disease, giant-cell pneumonia and other names. Weller *et al.* (1960) suggest the name Cytomegalovirus for the human agents; but the term, if to be of use, will have to include related viruses attacking other species.

Cytomegalic Inclusion Disease of Man

Synonyms: See above.
Reviews: Smith (1959). Rowe (1960). Nelson & Wyatt (1959).

Morphology. Thin sections of infected fibroblast cultures showed particles within the nuclear inclusion interspersed within a skein of granular material. The presumed virus particles were 65–110 mμ across with a central dot and outer shell. In the cytoplasm were similar but larger "target-like" particles 100–180 mμ across. This description is like that on record for herpesviruses. There were, however, also dense homogeneous spherical bodies 300–500 mμ across. Both types occurred within vacuoles. Still larger bodies 2–2·8 μ in diameter had superficial blebs, often containing the smaller particles just described (Luse & Smith, 1958). Stern & Friedman (1960) give 80–120 mμ as the particle size and state that membranes are single within the nucleus and double in cytoplasm.

Electron microscopy, using negative staining techniques, revealed a structure like that of herpes with, probably 162 capsomeres. Only a very small proportion of particles had complete cores (Smith & Rasmussen, 1963).

Chemical composition. Probably a DNA-virus (McAllister *et al.*, 1963).

Physico-chemical characters. Rather sensitive to freezing and thawing and to prolonged storage at −70° C. Ether-sensitive.

Inactivated at 56° C in 10 or 20 minutes. Fairly stable between pH 9 and 5, quickly inactivated at pH 4.

Hæmagglutinin. None found.

Antigenic properties. CF and neutralizing antibodies (the latter tested in tissue-culture) are recorded. Neutralizing antibodies alone may be present in infants' sera but older children's and adult sera are commonly positive by both tests. Antibodies are recorded from 80 per cent. of normal adult sera. Strains may differ antigenically (Weller *et al.*, 1960). The viruses are serologically distinct from those affecting other species except for reports of a cross with a cercopithecus virus (Rowe, 1960; Black *et al.*, 1963).

Cultivation. *In tissue culture.* Cytomegaloviruses of various species grow preferably in fibroblasts, usually only in tissues from natural hosts (but *cf.* Black *et al.*, 1963). Human strains have been cultivated in fibroblasts from human myometrium, adenoid tissue, embryonic skin-muscle tissue and foreskin. Focal lesions consisting of a few enlarged cells appear, sometimes not for many weeks; it may be two months before the whole culture degenerates. Effects develop more quickly after passage but tend to be erratic. Virus is closely associated with tissue and is often not demonstrable in the fluid phase. Inclusion bodies are abundantly formed in cells in the culture. Titres of virus remain low—$10^{3 \cdot 5}$/ml. (References in Smith, 1959.)

Distribution: probably world-wide.

Pathogenicity. Four types of disease in man are recognized. (*a*) Inapparent infection especially of salivary glands; (*b*) overwhelming neonatal infection (cytomegalic inclusion disease); (*c*) more chronic disease in older children or adults, associated with other diseases such as tumours, leukæmia and pertussis; (*d*)—very rarely localized granulomata. In severe, usually fatal, neonatal infections, liver and spleen are much enlarged and anæmia and hæmorrhages occur. More chronic infections lead to microcephaly, intracerebral calcification and hydrocephalus (Weller & Hanshaw, 1962).

Large cells up to 40 μ across bear intranuclear inclusions 8–10 μ across. These are less acidophilic than those of the Herpesviruses, but the amount of basophilia varies. Small basophilic granules may occur in cytoplasm. The nuclear inclusions are usually in epithelial cells (in contrast to what one might expect from tissue-culture findings). In their most characteristic form they occur in salivary glands, but may be in almost any organ. In the rare cases in adults they are commonest in lungs. They may also be found in the brains of sporadic cases of encephalitis of which they are the apparent cause. Cellular infiltrations surround the inclusion-bearing tissues.

Ecology. Serological studies of sera from various countries suggest that the infection is commoner where socio-economic conditions are poor (Rowe, 1960).

The virus can be recovered from oral swabs of infected infants and has been found over periods of 2 to 5 months. It is also excreted in the urine and has been recorded up to 2 years in recovered cases. It has also been recovered from the urine of apparently normal children. Infection may be contracted *in utero* (Rowe *et al.*, 1958; Weller *et al.*, 1957).

Salivary Gland Virus of Guinea Pigs

Synonym: Submaxillary virus.
Review: Smith (1959).

Physico-chemical characters. Inactivated by heating to 54° C for 1 hour; or 56° C for 10–20 minutes. Rather sensitive to freezing and thawing and not surviving long storage at −70° C. Stable at pH 5–9. Ether-sensitive (Smith, 1959).

Antigenic properties. Virus neutralized by sera of infected guinea pigs including apparently normal animals of infected stocks. A complement-fixing antigen is present in infected tissue cultures. Serologically unrelated to salivary viruses of other speceis.

Cultivation. Multiplied in fibroblasts derived from embryonic guinea pig muscle (Hartley *et al.*, 1957). Small foci of enlarged cells appeared in 10 days, the whole cell sheet being affected in 28 days. After serial passage, using fluid together with ground cells, cytopathic effects were seen in 1–2 days. Nuclear inclusions appeared in most cells. Titres of $10^{5 \cdot 8}$/ml. were obtained.

Pathogenicity. In the natural host the disease is usually inapparent, the inclusions in salivary ducts only being discovered on histological examination. What may correspond to the generalized disease caused by the human virus was described in two guinea pigs by Pappenheimer & Slanetz (1942) and in some guinea pigs being treated by aminopterin by Smith & Velios (1940). The disease can normally be passed in series by inoculating the virus peripherally, allowing it to localise in the salivary glands and using these for transfer a few weeks later. Intracerebral inoculation will produce fatal meningitis in susceptible young guinea pigs but serial IC passage has been only once recorded and then only for 2 or 3 passages (Hudson & Markham, 1932). Intratracheal inoculation has produced a pneumonia with inclusions and an unusually virulent strain killed with generalized infection when inoculated by various routes, though serial transmission was no better than usual (Rosenbusch & Lucas, 1939). Generalized disease was produced by inoculating fœti (Markham & Hudson, 1936)—another analogy with disease in man.

Pathological lesions. The very large nuclear inclusions in much enlarged salivary duct cells resemble those of the human virus. Cytoplasmic bodies are also seen. Nuclear inclusions produced in mononuclear cells of meningeal exudates after intracerebral injection are not particularly large, and, being acidophilic, are more like typical Type A inclusions.

Ecology. Many but not all stocks of guinea pigs are latently infected. Virus is normally present in salivary glands; also in the kidneys and probably urine of young animals.

Salivary Gland Virus of Mice

Review: Smith (1959).

Morphology. Appearances closely resemble those seen in electron-micrographs of tissue infected with the human virus (Luse & Smith, 1958). Similar target-like forms were contained within membranous sacs, 2–3·2 μ across; the presumed virus bodies were 120–180 mμ in diameter. There were also present, especially in spleen, dense spheres 250–400 mμ across and there was better evidence than for the human virus of formation of the target-like forms within these spheres.

Physico-chemical characters. Ether-sensitive and inactivated by heat and other agents as for the human and guinea pig viruses (Smith, 1959).

Antigenic properties. Unrelated to other salivary viruses. No neutralizing or CF antibodies are found in latently infected mice, but these may be produced by hyperimmunizing rabbits (Mannini & Medearis, 1961).

Cultivation. Grows in fibroblasts in cultures of mouse embryonic tissue (Smith, 1954), and of mouse salivary gland (Grand, 1958). Focal destruction occurs in the cultures, degeneration being diffuse in 9–12 days. After passage this only took 3 or 4 days. Inclusion bodies are formed in the cultures *in vitro*. Virus is released into the fluid phase of cultures much more freely than with the human and guinea pig viruses and titres of $10^{7\cdot5}$/ml. may be recorded.

Pathogenicity. Normally a wholly latent infection.

Experimentally, young mice of a clean stock can be infected by any route, as with guinea pig virus, the agent localizing in salivary glands, with which tissue alone serial passage is possible (Kuttner & Wang, 1934). However, large doses given intraperitoneally will kill in 4 to 7 days, inclusion bodies are to be found in various viscera and there is evidence of limited multiplication in liver and spleen, though insufficient to make serial passage possible (McCordock & Smith, 1936). Intracerebral inoculation of suckling mice with quite small doses is fatal.

Ecology. Probably ubiquitous in wild mice but present perhaps only in a minority of stocks of laboratory mice. There is prolonged excretion of virus in saliva (Brodsky & Rowe, 1958).

Cytomegalo-viruses in Other Species

An allied virus may cause abortions of *laboratory rats* (Lyon *et al.*, 1959). It occurs in salivary glands (Thompson, 1932; Kuttner & T'ung, 1935—these did do some transmissions).

Rattus norvegicus. In kidneys of wild rats (Syverton & Larson, 1947). Kuttner & Wang (1934) transmitted an agent from wild to tame white rats.

Chinese hamsters (*Cricetulus griseus*). In salivary glands (Kuttner & Wang, 1934). Transmission from hamster to hamster was reported. The results of intracerebral and subcutaneous injections were the same as have been described for the guinea pig virus. Heating the virus for 30 minutes to 56° C inactivated it.

Australian opossums (*Trichiurus*) (Hurst *et al.*, 1943). Inclusions in kidneys were found only in animals which had been some while in the laboratory, not in wild ones.

Intranuclear inclusions likely to have been caused by related viruses have also been described in various organs of chimpanzees (Vogel & Pinkerton, 1955), in monkeys of several genera (Covell, 1932; Cowdry & Scott, 1935), field mice (*Apodemus*) (Raynaud & Raynaud, 1945), ground-moles (Lucas, 1936), moles (Rector & Rector, 1933), dogs (Haberman *et al.*, 1960), sheep (Hartley & Done, 1963) and chicks (Lucas, 1957).

Inclusion Body Rhinitis of Pigs

Synonyms: IBR (but IBR is also used for infectious bovine rhinotracheitis, *v.*, p. 224).
Perhaps related to atrophic rhinitis.
Review: Gwatkin (1948).

Morphology: unknown. Reports as to the filterability of the agent are conflicting.

Physico-chemical characters. 65° for 1 hour inactivates the agent.

Cultivation. Grows in pig tissues but, unlike the other cytoplasmic disease viruses, does so better in epithelial than in fibroblastic cells (J. T. Done, personal communication, 1961). Switzer *et al.* (1961) have cultivated a number of viruses from noses of pigs: two of eleven were ether-sensitive.

Distribution. North America, Europe.

Pathogenicity. Affects particularly 2-week old piglets; mortality may be very high. Symptoms include sneezing, nose-bleeding and distortion of the snout from atrophy of turbinate bones; this last feature is characteristic of atrophic rhinitis, the relation of which to inclusion-body rhinitis is obscure. *Pasteurella multocida* occurs as a secondary invader.
Transmission is possible only to very young pigs.
There occur inclusions in a swollen nucleus; these resemble those of other cytomegalic diseases.

A pneumonia of pigs distinct from that mentioned on p. 310 is described by Goodwin & Whittlestone (1962) under the name "Respiratory Disease type XI". Rhinitis was also present often with cytomegalic inclusions in the nasal mucosa. Bakos *et al.* (1960) also describe an association between rhinitis and pneumonia in piglets.

REFERENCES

Aksel I. S. & Tuncman Z. (1940) *Z. ges. Neurol. Psychiat.*, **169**, 598.
Almeida, J. D., Howatson, A. F., & Williams, M. G. (1962) *Virology*, **16**, 353.
Amies, C. R. (1934) *Brit. J. exp. Path.*, **15**, 314.
Amos, H. (1953) *J. exp. Med.*, **98**, 365.
Anderson, K., & Goodpasture, E. W. (1942) *Amer. J. Path.*, **18**, 555.
Andrewes, C. H. (1929) *Brit. J. exp. Path.*, **10**, 188.
Andrewes, C. H. (1940) *J. Path. Bact.*, **50**, 227.
Andrewes, C. H. (1954) *Nature (Lond.)*, **173**, 620.
Andrewes, C. H., Burnet, F. M., Enders, J. F., Gard, S., Hirst, G. K.. Kaplan, M. M., & Zhdanov, V. M. (1961) *Virology*, **15**, 52.
Arhelger, R. B., Darlington, R. W., & Randall, C. C. (1963) *Amer. J. Path.*, **42**, 703.
Armstrong, J. A., Pereira, H. G., & Andrewes, C. H. (1961) *Virology*, **14**, 276
Atherton, J. G., & Anderson, W. (1957) *Aust. J. exp. Biol. med. Sci.*, **35**, 335.
Bakos, K., Obel, A-L., Swahn, O., & Walzl, H. (1960) *Zbl. Vet.-Med.*, **7**, 262.
Bang, F. B. (1942) *J. exp. Med.*, **76**, 263.
Beach, J. R. (1931) *J. exp. Med.*, **54**, 809.
Beaudette, F. R., & Hunson, C. B. (1933) *J. Amer. vet. med. Ass.*, **82**, 460.
Beladi, J., & Ivanovics, G. (1954) *Acta microbiol. Acad. Sci. hung.*, **2**, 151.
Ben-Porat, T., & Kaplan, A. S. (1962) *Virology*, **16**, 261.
Berkman, R. N., Barner, R. D., Morrill, C. C., & Langham, R. F. (1960) *Amer. J. vet. Res.*, **21**, 1015.
Black, F. L., & Melnick, J. L. (1955) *J. Immunol.*, **74**, 236.
Black, P. H., Hartley, J. W., & Rowe, W. P. (1963) *Proc. Soc. exp. Biol. (N.Y.)*, **112**, 601.
Bracken, E. C., & Norris, J. L. (1958) *Proc. Soc. exp. Biol. (N.Y.)*, **98**, 747.
Breen, G. E., Lamb, S. G., & Otaki, A. T. (1958) *Brit. med. J.*, **2**, 22.
Brodsky, I., & Rowe, W. P. (1958) *Proc. Soc. exp. Biol. (N.Y.)*, **99**, 654.
Brown, A. L., & Bjornson, C. B. (1959) *Amer. J. vet. Res.*, **20**, 985.
Burnet, F. M. (1936) *J. exp. Med.*, **63**, 685.
Burnet, F. M. & Foley, M. (1941) *Aust. J. exp. Biol. med. Sci.*, **19**, 235.
Burnet, F. M., Lush, D., & Jackson, A. V. (1939) *Aust. J. exp. Biol. med. Sci.*, **17**, 35.
Burnet, F. M., & Williams, S. W. (1939) *Med. J. Aust.*, **1**, 637.
Buthala, D. A. (1962) *J. infect. Dis.*, **111**, 95.
Byrne, R. J., Quan, A. L., & Kaschula, V. R. (1958) *Amer. J. vet. Res.*, **19**, 655.
Carmichael, L. F., & Barnes, J. D. (1961) *Proc. 65th ann. Meeting U.S. sanitary livestock Ass.*, 384.
Caunt, A., Rondle, C. J. M., & Downie, A. W. (1961) *J. Hyg. (Lond.)*, **59**, 249.
Chomiak, T. W., Luginbuhl, R. E., & Helmboldt, F. F. (1960) *Avian Dis.*, **4**, 235.
Covell, W. P. (1932) *Amer. J. Path.*, **8**, 151.

Cowdry, E. V. (1930) *Arch. Path.*, **10**, 23.
Cowdry, E. V. (1934) *Arch. Path.*, **18**, 527.
Cowdry, E. V., & Scott, G. H. (1935) *Amer. J. Path.*, **11**, 647.
Cox, H. R. (1952) *Ann. N.Y. Acad. Sci.*, **55**, 236.
Crandell, R. A., Ganaway, J. R., Nieman, W. H., & Maurer, F. D. (1960) *Amer. J. vet. Res.*, **21**, 504.
Crandell, R. A., & Maurer, F. D. (1958) *Proc. Soc. exp. Biol.* (*N.Y.*), **97,** 487.
Cruickshank, J. G., Berry, D. M., & Hay, B. (1963) *Virology*, **20**, 376.
Darlington, R. W., & Randall, C. C. (1963) *Virology*, **19**, 322.
Daubney, R., & Hudson, J. R. (1936) *J. comp. Path.*, **49**, 63.
Doerr, R. (1924–5) *Z. Haut- u. Geschl.-Kr.*, **13**, 417, **15**, 1, 129, 239, **16**, 481.
Doll, E. R., Crowe, M. E. W., Bryans, J. T., & McCollum, W. H. (1955) *Cornell Vet.*, **45**, 387.
Doll, E. R., Crowe, M. E. W., McCollum, W. H., & Bryans, J. T. (1959) *Cornell Vet.*, **59**, 49.
Doll, E. R., Richards, M. G., & Wallace, M. E. (1953) *Cornell Vet.*, **43**, 551.
Doll, E. R., & Wallace, M. E. (1954) *Cornell Vet.*, **44**, 453.
Done, J. T. (1955) *Vet. Rec.*, **67**, 525.
Downie, A. W. (1959) *Brit. med. Bull.*, **15**, 197.
Duryee, W. R., Long, M. E., Taylor, H. C., McElway, W. P. & Ehrmann, R. L. (1960) *Science*, **131**, 276.
Endo, M., Kanimura, T., Aoyama, Y., Hayashida, T., Kinjo, T., Ono, Y., Kotera, S., Suzuki, K., Tajima, Y., & Ando, K. (1960) *Jap. J. exp. Med.*, **30**, 227.
Epstein, M. A. (1962) *J. exp. Med.*, **115**, 1.
Filmer, D. L., & Hanson, R. P. (1959) *J. Bact.*, **78**, 297.
Friedman-Kiem, A. E., Rowe, W. P., & Barfield, W. G. (1963) *Science*, **140**, 1335.
Galloway, I. A. (1938) *Vet. Rec.*, **50**, 745.
Gibbs, J. (1935) *J. Bact.*, **30**, 411.
Glover, R. E. (1939) *Brit. J. exp. Path.*, **20**, 150.
Goodpasture, E. W., & Anderson, K. (1944) *Amer. J. Path.*, **20**, 447.
Goodwin, R. F. W., & Whittlestone, P. (1962) *J. comp. Path.*, **72**, 389.
Grand, N. G. (1958) *Amer. J. Path.*, **34**, 775.
Green, R. G., & Shillinger, J. E. (1936) *Amer. J. Path.*, **12**, 405.
Greig, A. S. (1958) *Canad. J. Microbiol.*, **4**, 487.
Griffin, T. P., Howells, W. V., Crandell, R. A., & Maurer, F. D. (1958) *Amer. J. vet. Res.*, **19**, 990.
Gwatkin, R. (1948) *Advanc. vet. Sci.*, **4**, 211.
Hartley, J. W., Rowe, W. P., & Huebner, R. J. (1957) *Proc. Soc. exp. Biol.* (*N.Y.*), **96**, 281.
Hartley, W. J., & Done, J. T. (1963) *J. comp. Path.*, **73**, 84.
Hayward, M. E. (1949) *Brit. J. exp. Path.*, **30**, 520.
Hersey, D. F., & Maurer, F. D. (1961) *Proc. Soc. exp. Biol.* (*N.Y.*), **107**, 645.
Hoggan, M. D., & Roizman, B. (1959) *Virology*, **8**, 508.
Hoggan, M. D., & Roizman, B. (1959) *Amer. J. Hyg.*, **70**, 208.
Holden, M. (1932) *J. infect. Dis.*, **50**, 218.
Holmes, A. W., Dedman, R. E., & Deinhardt, F. (1963) in preparation.
Huck, R. A. (1961) *Bull. Off. int. Épiz.*, **56**, 5.
Huck, R. A., Shand, A., Allsop, P. J., & Paterson, A. B. (1961) *Vet. Rec.*, **73**, 457.
Hudson, N. P., & Markham, F. S. (1932) *J. exp. Med.*, **55**, 405.
Hull, R. N., & Nash, J. C. (1960) *Amer. J. Hyg.*, **71**, 15.
Hurst, E. W. (1933) *J. exp. Med.*, **58**, 415.
Hurst, E. W. (1936) *J. exp. Med.*, **63**, 449.

Hurst, E. W., Cooke, B. T., Mawson, J., & Melvin, P. (1943) *Aust. J. exp. Biol. med. Sci.*, **21**, 149.
Ivanovics, G., & Hyde, R. R. (1936) *Amer. J. Hyg.*, **23**, 55.
Kaplan, A. S. (1957) *Virology*, **4**, 435.
Kaschula, V. R., Beaudette, F. R., & Byrne, R. J. (1957) *Cornell Vet.*, **47**, 137.
Kaufman, H. E. (1962) *Proc. Soc. exp. Biol.* (*N.Y.*), **109**, 251.
Keeble, S. A., Christofinis, G. J., & Wood, W. (1958) *J. Path. Bact.*, **76**, 189.
Knocke, K. W., & Liess, B. (1961) *Zbl. Bakt. I. Abt. Orig.*, **181**, 429.
Kundratitz, K. (1925) *Mschr. Kinderheilk.*, **29**, 516.
Kuttner, A. G., & T'ung, T. (1935) *J. exp. Med.*, **62**, 805.
Kuttner, A. G., & Wang, S. H. (1935) *J. exp. Med.*, **60**, 773.
Lebrun, A. C. (1956) *Virology*, **2**, 496.
Love, F. M., & Jungherr, E. (1962) *J. Amer. med. Ass.*, **179**, 804.
Lucas, A. M. (1936) *Amer. J. Path.*, **12**, 933.
Lucas, A. M. (1947) *Amer. J. Path.*, **23**, 1005.
Lucké, B. (1934) *Amer. J. Cancer*, **20**, 352.
Lucké, B. (1938) *J. exp. Med.*, **68**, 457.
Lucké, B. (1939) *J. exp. Med.*, **70**, 270.
Lucké, B., Berwick, L., & Nowell, P. (1953) *J. exp. Med.*, **97**, 505.
Luse, S. A., & Smith, M. G. (1958) *J. exp. Med.*, **107**, 623.
Lyon, H. W., Christian, J. J., & Miller, C. W. (1959) *Proc. Soc. exp. Biol.* (*N.Y.*), **101**, 164.
McAllister, R. M., Straw, R. M., Filbert, J. E., & Goodheart, C. R. (1963) *Virology*, **19**, 521.
McCollum, W. H., Doll, E. R., & Bryans, J. T. (1956) *Amer. J. vet. Res.*, **17**, 267.
McCollum, W. H., Doll, E. R., Wilson, J. C., & Johnson, C. B. (1962) *Cornell Vet.*, **52**, 164.
McCordock, H. A., & Smith, M. G. (1936) *J. exp. Med.*, **63**, 303.
McKercher, D. G. (1959) *Advanc. vet. Sci.*, **5**, 299.
Madin, S. H., York, C. J., & McKercher, D. G. (1956) *Science*, **124**, 721.
Malherbe, H., & Harbin, R. (1958) *Lancet*, **2**, 530.
Mannini, A., & Medearis, D. N. (1961) *Amer. J. Hyg.*, **73**, 329.
Markham, F. S., & Hudson, N. P. (1936) *Amer. J. Path.*, **12**, 175.
Meyer, J. R. (1931) *Arch. Inst. Biologico* (*São Paulo*), **4**, 25.
Miller, C. P., Andrewes, C. H., & Swift, H. F. (1924) *J. exp. Med.*, **40**, 773.
Miller, G. W., & Crandell, R. A. (1962) *Amer. J. vet. Res.*, **23**, 351.
Morgan, C., Rose, H. M., Holden, M., & Jones, E. P. (1959) *J. exp. Med.*, **110**, 643.
Morgan, C., Jones, E. P., Holden, M., & Rose, H. M. (1958) *Virology*, **5**, 568.
Morgan, C., Ellison, S. A., Rose, H. M., & Moore, D. H. (1954) *J. exp. Med.*, **100**, 195.
Nagler, F. P. O. (1944) *J. Immunol.*, **48**, 213.
Nagler, F. P. O. (1946) *Aust. J. exp. Biol. med. Sci.*, **24**, 103.
Nagler, F. P. O., & Klotz, M. (1958) *Canad. med. Ass. J.*, **79**, 743.
Nelson, J. S., & Wyatt, J. P. (1959) *Medicine*, **38**, 223.
Netter, A., & Urbain, A. (1926) *C.R. Soc. Biol.* (*Paris*), **94**, 98.
Nicolau, S., & Kopciowska, L. (1938) *Ann. Inst. Pasteur*, **60**, 308.
Pacheco, G. (1930) *C.R. Soc. Biol.* (*Paris*), **105**, 109, **106**, 372.
Pappenheimer, A. M., & Slanetz, C. A. (1942) *J. exp. Med.*, **76**, 299.
Perdrau, J. R. (1931) *Proc. roy. Soc.* (*B*), **109**, 304.
Pereira, H. G. (1962) *Advanc. Virus Res.*, **9**, 245.
Pierce, E. C., Peirce, J. D., & Hull, R. N. (1958) *Amer. J. Hyg.*, **68**, 242.
Piercy, S. E. (1952) *Brit. vet. J.*, **108**, 35, 214.

Piercy, S. E. (1953) *Brit. vet. J.*, **109**, 59.
Piercy, S. E. (1954) *Brit. vet. J.*, **110**, 87.
Piercy, S. E. (1955) *Brit. vet. J.*, **111**, 484.
Plowright, J. (1953) *J. comp. Path.*, **63**, 318.
Plowright, J., Ferris, R. D., & Scott, G. R. (1960) *Nature (Lond.)*, **188**, 1167.
Prier, J. E., & Goulet, N. R. (1961) *Amer. J. vet. Res.*, **22**, 1112.
Pulsford, M. F. (1953) *Nature (Lond.)*, **172**, 1193.
Pulsford, M. F. (1960) *Aust. J. exp. Biol. med. Sci.*, **38**, 153.
Quin, A. H. (1961) *Vet. Med.*, **56**, 192.
Rafferty, K. A. (1963) *J. nat. Cancer Inst.*, **30**, 1103.
Rafferty, K. A., & Rafferty, N. S. (1961) *Science*, **133**, 702.
Randall, C. C. (1955) *Proc. Soc. exp. Biol. (N.Y.)*, **90**, 176.
Raynaud, A., & Raynaud, J. (1944) *Ann. Inst. Pasteur*, **71**, 344.
Rector, L. E., & Rector, E. J. (1933) *Proc. Soc. exp. Biol. (N.Y.)*, **31**, 192.
Reissig, M., & Melnick, J. L. (1955) *J. exp. Med.*, **101**, 341.
Rivers, T. M. (1926) *J. exp. Med.*, **43**, 275.
Rivers, T. M., & Pearce, L. (1925) *J. exp. Med.*, **42**, 523.
Rivers, T. M., & Stewart, F. W. (1928) *J. exp. Med.*, **48**, 603.
Rivers, T. M., & Tillett, W. S. (1923) *J. exp. Med.*, **38**, 673.
Rivers, T. M., & Tillett, W. S. (1924) *J. exp. Med.*, **39**, 777.
Rose, S. M., & Rose, F. C. (1952) *Cancer Res.*, **12**, 1.
Rosenbusch, C. T., & Lucas, A. M. (1939) *Amer. J. Path.*, **15**, 303.
Ross, R. W., & Orlans, E. (1958) *J. Path. Bact.*, **76**, 393.
Rowe, W. P. (1960) in *Viral Infections of Infancy and Childhood*. Ed. Rose.
  Symposium No. 10. *N.Y. Acad. med.* p. 205. New York: Hoeber–Harper.
Rowe, W. P., Hartley, J. W., Waterman, S., Turner, H. E., & Huebner,
  R. J. (1958) *Proc. Soc. exp. Biol. (N.Y.)*, **92**, 418.
Russell, W. C. (1962) *Virology*, **16**, 355.
Sabin, A. B. (1934) *Brit. J. exp. Path.*, **15**, 248, 268, 321, 372.
Sabin, A. B. (1949) *J. clin. Invest.*, **28**, 808.
Schofield, F. W., & Bain, A. F. (1961) *Canad. J. comp. Med.*, **5**, 294.
Schwarz, A. J. F., York, C. J., Zirbel, L. W., & Estela, L. A. (1957) *Proc.
  Soc. exp. Biol. (N.Y.)*, **96**, 453.
Schwarz, A. J. F., Zirbel, L. W., Estela, L. A., & York, C. J. (1958) *Proc.
  Soc. exp. Biol. (N.Y.)*, **97**, 680.
Scott, L. V., Felton, F. G., & Barney, J. A. (1957) *J. Immunol.*, **78**, 211.
Scott, T. F. McN., Macleod, D. L., & Tokumaru, T. (1961) *J. Immunol.*,
  86, 1.
Scott, T. F. McN., Coriell, L. L., & Blank, H. (1959) in *Diagnosis of Viral
  and Rickettsial Infections*. Ed. Horsfall, p. 83. New York: Columbia Univ.
  Press.
Seifried, O. (1931) *J. exp. Med.*, **54**, 817.
Semerdjiev, B. (1961) *Zbl. Bakt. I. Abt. Orig.*, **185**, 316.
Sharp, D. G., & Bracken, E. C. (1960) *Virology*, **10**, 419.
Shimizu, T., Ishizaki, R., Kono, Y., Ishii, S., & Matumoto, M. (1958)
  Jap. J. exp. Med., **27**, 175.
Shope, R. E. (1931) *J. exp. Med.*, **54**, 233.
Shope, R. E. (1935a) *J. exp. Med.*, **62**, 85.
Shope, R. E. (1935b) *J. exp. Med.*, **62**, 101.
Skoda, R. (1962) *Acta virol.* (Eng. Ed.), **6**, 189.
Slotnick, V. B., & Rosanoff, E. (1963) *Virology*, **19**, 589.
Smadel, J. E., Jackson, E. B., & Harman, J. W. (1945) *J. exp. Med.*, **81**, 385.
Smith, K. O., & Rasmussen, L. (1963) *J. Bact.*, **85**, 1319.
Smith, M. G. (1954) *Proc. Soc. exp. Biol. (N.Y.)*, **86**, 435.
Smith, M. G. (1959) *Progr. med. Virol.*, **2**, 171.
Smith, M. G., & Vellios, F. (1950) *Arch. Path.*, **50**, 862.

Solomkin, P. S., & Tutushin, M. I. (1956) *Veterininariya*, **33**:4, 49.
Stenius, P. I. (1952) *Monogr. Inst. Path. vet. Coll., Helsinki*.
Stern, H., & Friedman, I. (1960) *Nature (Lond.)*, **18**, 768.
Stoker, M. G. P., & Newton, A. (1959) *Virology*, **7**, 438.
Stoker, M. G. P., & Ross, R. W. (1958) *J. gen. Microbiol.*, **19**, 250.
Switzer, W. P., Roberts, E. D., & d'Ecuyer, C. (1961) *Amer. J. vet. Res.*, **22**, 67.
Sykes, J. A., Dmochowski, L., Grey, C. E., & Russell, W. O. (1962) *Proc. Soc. exp. Biol. (N.Y.)*, **111**, 57.
Syverton, J. T., & Larson, C. L. (1947) *Arch. Path.*, **43**, 541.
Tajima, M., Shimizu, T., & Ishizaki, R. (1961) *Amer. J. vet. Res.*, **22**, 250.
Taylor-Robinson, D. (1959) *Brit. J. exp. Path.*, **40**, 521.
Taylor-Robinson, D., & Downie, A. W. (1959) *Brit. J. exp. Path.*, **40**, 398.
Taylor-Robinson, D., & Rondle, C. J. M. (1959) *Brit. J. exp. Path.*, **40**, 517.
Thompson, J. (1932) *J. infect. Dis.*, **50**, 162.
Tokumaru, T. (1957) *Proc. Soc. exp. Biol. (N.Y.)*, **96**, 55.
Tournier, P., Cathala, F., & Bernhard, W. (1957) *Presse méd.*, **65**, 1230.
Vogel, F. S., & Pinkerton, H. (1955) *Endocrinology*, **60**, 251.
Watrach, A. M. (1962) *Virology*, **18**, 324.
Watrach, A. M., Vatter, M. E., Hanson, L. E., Watrach, M. A., & Rhodes, H. E. (1959) *Amer. J. vet. Res.*, **20**, 537.
Watson, D. H., Russell, W. C., & Wildy, P. (1963) *Virology*, **19**, 250.
Webster, R. G. (1959) *N.Z. vet. J.*, **7**, 67.
Webster, R. G., & Manktelow, B. W. (1959) *N.Z. vet. J.*, **7**, 143.
Weller, T. H. (1953) *Proc. Soc. exp. Biol. (N.Y.)*, **83**, 340.
Weller, T. H. (1958) *Harvey lectures*. Academic Press, New York.
Weller, T. H., & Hanshaw, J. B. (1962) *New Engl. med. J.*, **266**, 1233.
Weller, T. H., Hanshaw, J. B., & Scott, D. E. (1960) *Virology*, **12**, 130.
Weller, T. H., MacCauley, J. E., Craig, J. M., & Wirth, P. (1957) *Proc. Soc. exp. Biol. (N.Y.)*, **94**, 4.
Wildy, P. (1955) *J. gen. Microbiol.*, **13**, 346.
Wildy, P., Russell, W. C., & Horne, R. W. (1960) *Virology*, **12**, 204.
Woernle, H., & Brunner, A. (1961) *Tierärztl. Umsch.*, **16**, 245.
Yoshino, K. (1956) *J. Immunol.*, **76**, 301.
York, C. J., Schwarz, A. J. F., & Estela, L. A. (1957) *Proc. Soc. exp. Biol. (N.Y.)*, **94**, 740.
Zuffa, A., & Skode, R. (1962) *Vet. Cas.*, **11**, 155.

12

Poxviruses

Poxviruses are rather large viruses, chemically more complex than most smaller ones; they probably all contain DNA. Some of those affecting mammals may be modified and adapted to different hosts, so that there is doubt as to how many should be regarded as distinct entities. Attempted transformation of one to another has often been carried out under conditions in which contamination with another poxvirus (particularly vaccinia) cannot be excluded.

Reviews: Downie & Dumbell (1956). Fenner & Burnet (1957) (a short taxonomic description of the group and some of its members).

The poxviruses can be conveniently but tentatively divided into six groups, as shown in Table 5. The table also indicates the special characters of each group.

Morphology and growth cycle. Rather large oval viruses—oval when hydrated, "brick-shaped" when dried for electron-microscopy. 250–300 mμ × 200–250 mμ in diameter. There is a central electron-dense pepsin-resistant body, the "nucleoid". Details as to a developmental cycle are available particularly for vaccinia: a similar cycle is likely for the other poxviruses. Virus multiplication, so far as is known, is all within the cytoplasm.

Chemical composition. DNA viruses. Fuller details of chemical composition available especially for vaccinia.

Physico-chemical characters. Rather stable viruses, relatively resistant to heat, very stable at −75° C, less so at −10°. In contrast to other virus groups poxviruses are not uniform in their resistance to ether: most in the group are, however, quite resistant.

A **hæmagglutinin** separable from the virus particle itself is described for some members.

247

Table 5

POXVIRUSES

	Group I	Group II	Group III	Group IV	Group V	Group VI
	Viruses closely related to variola	Viruses related to CPD	Other viruses affecting ungulates	Avian poxes	Viruses related to myxoma	Unclassified pox-viruses
Members of group	Variola Alastrim Vaccinia Rabbit pox Monkey pox Ectromelia Cow pox	Contagious pustular dermatitis Bovine papular dermatitis	Sheep pox Goat pox Lumpy skin disease Swine pox Horse pox Camel pox	Fowl pox Canary pox and other bird poxes	Rabbit myxoma Rabbit fibroma Squirrel fibroma	Molluscum contagiosum Milker's nodes (para-vaccinia) Yaba monkey virus
Special characters of group	All closely related antigenically, similar morphologically and ether-resistant	Similar morphologically (woven pattern). Moderately ether-sensitive	Possibly a heterogeneous group of which some should be transferred to groups I or II. Some are partly ether-sensitive	Large virus particles contained in a matrix, probably lipoprotein. Ether-resistant. Often transmitted by insects	Ether-sensitive. Normally mechanically transferred by insects	Contains those pox-viruses which cannot yet be placed in another group

Antigenic properties. All the viruses contain a common nucleo-protein antigen demonstrable by complement-fixation or fluorescent antibody (Takahashi *et al.*, 1959; Woodroofe & Fenner, 1962). Several viral antigens can be revealed by complement-fixation, precipitation, virus neutralization and hæmagglutinin-inhibition. Some of the viruses, though distinct in biological behaviour, stand very close together antigenically. When two closely related pox-viruses grow in the same cells, hybrids or recombinants having characters derived from both "parents" may be formed (Woodroofe & Fenner, 1960). Also, poxviruses inactivated by heat may have their activity restored within cells in which another poxvirus is multiplying (Joklik *et al.*, 1960). Only other poxviruses have this effect; other viruses tested have been ineffective (Fenner and Wood-roofe, 1960). Here may be a character useful in defining the group.

Cultivation. *In eggs*: most but not all poxviruses have been cultivated in developing chick embryos; those which do so produce "pocks" or focal lesions on chorioallantoic membranes.

Tissue culture of poxviruses has proved possible where seriously attempted.

Habitat. Many mammals and birds are susceptible to one or more poxviruses; there is no evidence that carp "pox" is a member of the group.

Pathology. The epidermis, or at least the superficies of the animal, is characteristically attacked, with formation of focal lesions often proliferative in character. Such proliferative lesions are often followed by necrosis. Generalized infection occurs with most of the group. Many form cytoplasmic inclusions in epidermal or other cells.

Transmission is by the respiratory route or through the skin. Some are mechanically transmitted by arthropods but a developmental cycle in arthropods is unproved.

Prevention. Living attenuated viruses are useful for control of many poxviruses, inactivated vaccines generally much less so.

VACCINIA

The origin of the vaccinia used for protection against smallpox is obscure. A derivation from variola has been claimed but many consider an origin from cowpox more probable. Despite its dubious ancestry it will be considered first, as more is known about its properties than about any other poxvirus.

Synonyms: Vaccinia variolæ. *Poxvirus officinalis.*

Morphology and development. Estimates of the virus diameter by filtration and centrifugation vary: they are mostly around 200 mμ. By electron-microscopy the size appears larger. Ultrathin sections of infected tissue, examined by electron-microscopy, show, at an early stage, oval bodies in the cytoplasm; some of these appear to be hollow, others to contain a central body (Gaylord & Melnick, 1953). These appear to evolve into a mature virus particle of somewhat varying size 240–380 mμ × 170–270 mμ (Peters & Nasemann, 1952); there is a dense outer membrane 9–12 mμ across and an inner body or nucleoid with evidence of a smaller body beside it. The nucleoid seems to consist of threads or hollow tubules, probably nucleoprotein in nature (Nagington & Horne, 1962). The appearance of the nucleoid is changed by desoxyribonuclease and subsequent treatment with pepsin leaves empty membranes. A "dumbbell" like body within the nucleoid has been described (Peters, 1957). Before liberation from the cell, double membranes may be seen (Morgan *et al.*, 1954) and stalked forms on the surface of the cell have been observed (Robinow, 1950). Negative-staining techniques reveal subunits of the nature of capsomeres on the surface of the particle but within the outer membrane (Noyes, 1962). The precise arrangement of these is obscure but it is not icosahedral. Treatment with various chemicals throws light on their structure (McCrea *et al.*, 1962).

The development of the virus seems to be within the cytoplasm, where the virus attains full maturity. Liberation from the cell need not entail disruption of this.

Chemical composition. The central body contains desoxyribonucleoprotein; the outer parts probably consist largely of protein. Smadel (1952) gives the percentage composition of purified elementary bodies as: carbon 33·7, nitrogen 15·3, phosphorus 0·57, copper 0·05, total lipids 5·7, reducing sugars 2·8, thymonucleic acid 5·6. The virus also contains biotin and flavin. Several enzymes are also present and have not been separable from the virus bodies; but since enzymes may be adsorbed to the virus surface, their relation to it is uncertain. Various antigens contained in the virus are referred to below.

Physico-chemical characters. *Physical properties.* The specific gravity is variously reported as between 1·10 and 1·33. The virus carries a negative charge between pH 5·5 and pH 8·4 (Douglas *et al.*, 1928).

Inactivation by physical agents. The radio-sensitive area of the particle is half that of the whole virus body (Lea & Salaman, 1942) or even less. The virus can be kept indefinitely at −75° in the presence of peptone or other protective colloids and freeze-dried virus survives *in vacuo* or in nitrogen for many years. Ability of dried vaccine to withstand storage at 37° or 45° for many weeks or months (Cross *et al.*, 1957) is of great practical importance in vaccine campaigns in the tropics. Suspensions are inactivated in 10 minutes at 60° C but dried virus withstands 100° C for 10 minutes. Kaplan (1958) and Woodroofe (1960) have studied the kinetics of heat inactivation; apparently virus becomes more resistant to heating on storage. It loses activity in 1 hour at pH 3 but it is fairly stable between pH 5 and 9. It can survive for weeks when dried on cloths or glass. Methods of preserving vaccine intended for immunization have been reviewed by Collier (1954) from the historical and practical aspects.

Inactivation by chemical agents. The virus is very resistant to ethyl ether in the cold and to sodium desoxycholate but is inactivated by chloroform (Wittman & Matheka, 1958). It resists 1 per cent. phenol at 4° C but not at 37° C and is on the whole more resistant to disinfectants than are most bacteria. It is most readily destroyed by oxidising agents such as potassium permanganate or by ethylene oxide. It is inactivated by *p*-iodo-acetamide and other SH-reactive compounds (*cf.* Dunham & MacNeal, 1943)).

Virus inactivated by chemical or physical means is of little value for immunization; that inactivated by U-V radiation is, however, better than formalinized virus (Collier *et al.*, 1955).

Hæmagglutination. After incubation for an hour at 37° C preparations of virus agglutinate the red blood cells of some but not all fowls (Nagler, 1942). There may be partial agglutination of cells of some other species (Clark & Nagler, 1943). The hæmagglutinin, which may be a lipoprotein (Burnet & Stone, 1946), is separable from virus particles by centrifugation, withstands boiling and has an estimated diameter of 65 mμ (Chu, 1948) though there may be two components, the larger of which is more heat stable (Gillen *et al.*, 1950). Some vaccinial strains (also a strain of rabbit pox) do not form hæmagglutinins (Fenner, 1958). Antibodies to the hæmagglutinin, distinct from other vaccinial antibodies, appear in immunized animals and in man.

Antigenic properties. The virus surface contains a complex (LS) antigen with two serologically reactive components L (heat labile), S (heat stable). A third, NP (nucleoprotein) antigen is also recognised (Craigie & Wishart, 1934; Smadel & Rivers, 1942). These are concerned in reactions of precipitation, agglutinins for elementary bodies and complement-fixation. The L and S components of the LS antigen may be degraded separately. These antigens are distinct from the hæmagglutinin. Neutralizing antibody is probably unrelated to any of them; this may be titrated by mixing with virus, titrating intradermally in the rabbits' skin, on the chorioallantoic membrane of hens' eggs or in tissue culture. The last, using a plaque-counting technique, is said to be the best for some purposes (Cutchins et al., 1960).

All tests show that the viruses of vaccinia, variola, cow-pox and ectromelia are very closely related serologically. Differences can, however, be shown by neutralization tests on chorioallantoic membranes (Downie & McCarthy, 1950), by indirect complement-fixation (Downie & Macdonald, 1950) and by double-diffusion in agar (Gispen, 1955). There is of course cross-immunity, when it can be tested, between these viruses in experimental animals and in man. Variola is said to protect less well against vaccinia in monkeys than the other way round (Horgan & Hasseeb, 1939). The practical use of vaccinia is discussed under variola. An antigen particularly concerned with immunity has been described by Appleyard (1961).

Interference. Interference has been reported experimentally between vaccinia and the viruses of fowl-pox, foot-and-mouth disease and influenza (Schlesinger, 1959). In the last instance it seems to be mediated by interferon.

Cultivation. *In developing eggs.* Vaccinia grows well on the chorioallantoic membrane especially of 7 to 13 day-old eggs: dilute suspensions produce isolated focal lesions or pocks, and thus is available a method of virus-titration. Pocks are formed even up to a temperature of 40·5° (Bedson & Dumbell, 1961). Possibilities of increasing the accuracy of this method of titration have been studied by Westwood et al. (1957). Different vaccinia strains produce varying types of lesion; these—with neurovaccinia—may be hæmorrhagic. The death rate of the embryo also varies with strain and conditions of test from

100 per cent. to something quite low. Inoculation into the allantoic cavity and yolk-sac may also be used but these are less sensitive than the chorioallantoic membrane (Cabasso & Moore, 1957).

In tissue-culture. Vaccinia was the first virus to be grown in tissue culture. It can be grown in cultures of chick embryo,, rabbit kidney, testis, and other tissues, bovine embryo, continuous cell-lines such as HeLa and L. and in various other cells. Cytopathic effects are produced as early as 48 hours and include formation of giant cells and reticulum formation from lengthening of cytoplasmic processes. Some of the effects seem to be due to a "toxic" action for which living virus is not necessary (Bernkopf *et al.*, 1959). Ultimately there is cell destruction. With suitable techniques this can be localized so that plaques are formed and can be counted (Noyes, 1953; Porterfield & Allison, 1960). Culture in bovine embryo has been advocated as a practical measure for vaccine production (Wesslén, 1956).

Pathogenicity. *Disease in man* is usually local. A primary vaccinial reaction is a papule developing into a vesicle and then a pustule, the lesion being maximal at the 8th to 10th day. Other reactions are referred to under variola (p. 257). Generalized vaccinia may occur, especially in children and in persons with pre-existing dermatoses: it may be fatal. An even rarer condition, progressive vaccinia, in hypogammaglobulinæmics, is usually fatal.

Disease in experimental animals. Local skin lesions are produced in calves and sheep; these are used for routine production of vaccine. Much work has been done with rabbits. Strains of virus passed by inoculating scarified skin produce abundant papulo-vesicles; those passed by intradermal inoculation give rise to large swellings necrosing centrally; passage by either method soon modifies the virus so that it takes better when inoculated by the accustomed route. Virulence is exalted by intra-testicular or intra-cerebral passage, resulting in production of neurovaccinia. Corneal inoculation leads to keratitis and a vaccinial pneumonia may be produced by intranasal instillation under anæsthesia. With neurovaccinia and some other strains, generalization may occur, giving rise to multiple lesions in skin, mucous membranes and adrenals. Guinea pigs react much as rabbits do. Strains vary in ease of adaptation to mice. Most produce local lesions on inoculation into skin or brain or intranasally but only some can be passed in series or kill. Big doses given IV to suckling mice will kill without necessarily multiplying (Zakay-Roness & Bernkopf, 1962). Fenner (1958) describes the biological characters of 24 different strains used in his genetic studies.

Morbid anatomy and histopathology. Skin lesions induced in rabbits vary with the strain of virus. Levaditi & Nicolau (1923) and others emphasize the affinity for epidermal and other epiblastic tissues with proliferation followed by necrosis, but Ledingham (1924) describes the lesions as "of the order of an infective granuloma" . . . with "no evidence of an elective affinity for epiblastic tissue". Douglas *et al.* (1929) describe the lesions of generalized vaccinia in rabbits. Presence of cytoplasmic inclusions, Guarnieri bodies, usually juxta-nuclear, has been used in diagnosis, particularly their occurrence in the cornea of inoculated rabbits or guinea pigs. Kato *et al.* (1959) describe in poxvirus infections cytoplasmic inclusions of 2 types, A and B (not to be confused with Cowdry's A and B intranuclear inclusions). The A inclusions contain protein, the B inclusions are Feulgen-positive (DNA containing) and also contain different antigens as shown by staining by fluorescent antibody (Loh & Riggs, 1961). Virus particles—elementary bodies or Paschen bodies—can be stained in preparations of infected tissues by Giemsa's stain or Victoria blue.

Ecology: transmission.
The virus may be accidentally transmitted to contacts of vaccinated persons or to laboratory workers, usually through the skin. Generalized vaccinia is said to be unusually common in such cases. Normal rabbits housed alongside infected ones may undergo an immunizing inapparent infection.

Control. Use of vaccinia for immunization is discussed under variola.
Chemotherapy. A number of substances have proved active in the laboratory. Amongst the most promising are thiosemicarbazones (Hamre *et al.*, 1950; Bauer, 1955). IDU (2-iodo-2′-deoxyuridine) is effective against vaccinial kerato-conjunctivitis in rabbits (Kaufman *et al.*, 1962).

RABBIT POX

Epidemics amongst laboratory rabbits, often very fatal, have been described from Holland, United States and elsewhere. The virus, rabbit pox (Greene, 1934) or rabbit plague (Jansen, 1941) is immunologically identical with vaccinia or almost so, but differs in virulence for rabbits. A comparison of its other biological characters with those of a number of vaccinia strains (Fenner, 1958) reveals no other firm basis for separation from vaccinia. It has not been reported amongst wild rabbits and may well be a laboratory "sport" from vaccinia.

MONKEY POX

An epidemic disease has also been described amongst captive monkeys (von Magnus *et al.*, 1959; Prier *et al.*, 1960): there is a generalized variola-like rash. Infected monkeys are not seriously ill. The sporadic appearance amongst stocks of monkeys suggests that the virus may exist as a silent infection (von Magnus *et al.*, 1959). Again, the virus is very close to vaccinia. It is distinct from the Yaba virus (p. 272).

The Danish strain at least may be distinguished from vaccinia by the appearance of the pocks on the CAM, by the type of plaques in chick embryo monolayers and by its failure to grow at temperatures above 39° in the chick embryo (Bedson & Dumbell, 1961).

VARIOLA

Synonyms: Smallpox.

Less virulent forms: variola minor, alastrim, amaas.

Reviews: *cf.* Poxvirus, p. 248. Also Downie & Macdonald (1953).

Morphology and growth cycle; chemical composition. By electron-microscopy the virus particles are approximately 200 mμ in diameter and are indistinguishable from those of vaccinia, Variola virus has been less studied than vaccinia, but doubtless resembles it in other fundamental respects.

Physico-chemical characters. The virus is very stable and has survived in crusts kept at room temperature for over a year. Vesicle fluid remains active for years if kept in sealed tubes in the cold. Most strains are inactivated by heating for 30′ at 55° C; resists most disinfectants, as does vaccinia, and is most readily destroyed by oxidizing agents such as KMnO4.

Hæmagglutination. Hæmagglutinins are like those of vaccinia but may not be readily obtained in such high titre. In tissue cultures hæmadsorption of sensitive fowls RBC's occurs (Vieuchange, 1959).

Antigenic properties. Very similar to vaccinia and cowpox; minor differences can be shown (*cf.* Vaccinia, p. 252). Precipitation, complement-fixation (Gordon, 1925; Craigie & Wishart, 1936) or agar gel-diffusion may be used for diagnosis if smallpox crusts are available. Sera used for diagnosis should be able to detect the heat-stable (S) antigen—*cf.* Vaccinia, p. 252.

Cultivation. *In developing eggs.* "Pocks" on infected chorioallantoic membranes are smaller than those of vaccinia, more dome-shaped, less necrotic and not hæmorrhagic; embryos are usually not killed unless the infecting dose is large. Limited growth is possible after inoculation into the yolk sac or amniotic cavity: allantoic inoculation is unsuccessful (Hahon *et al.*, 1958). Variola major will produce pocks when incubated at 38–38·5°, unlike variola minor (alastrim) which will only do so at temperatures below 38° C (Bedson & Dumbell, 1961).

In tissue culture. Grows, producing CPE, in tissue-cultures of many kinds—chick embryo, HeLa cells, bovine tissues, etc. Foci of proliferation may be seen before cell-destruction sets in. Virus may be isolated directly from human lesions in tissue cultures of human embryo skin and muscle (Marennikova *et al.*, 1959).

Distribution. Variola major is still a widespread and lethal disease, especially in parts of Asia and Africa and in Central America. In other parts of the world variola minor (alastrim) is endemic. Recent outbreaks in Britain have mostly been caused by introduction of variola major: they have been rapidly brought under control. Man is the only natural host but a possible outbreak amongst monkeys in South America has been reported (Blaxall, 1930).

Pathogenicity. The extensive, often confluent, rash produced in man by variola major is familiar. With alastrim, pocks may be very few and may be missed altogether. In vaccinated contacts infection may take the form of pneumonia.

Experimentally, various species of monkeys can be infected with production of a generalized rash, and infection can be propagated in series. Lesions can also be produced in rabbits; but serial passage is achieved with difficulty (K. R. Dumbell, personal communication, 1963). Suckling mice can be infected intracerebrally, intraperitoneally or intranasally. In general, attempted serial propagation in rodents has failed but the virus has been adapted to go serially in suckling mouse brains (Brown *et al.*, 1960). The production of keratitis and Guarnieri bodies in eyes of inoculated rabbits (Paul's test) was formerly used in diagnosis.

The classical account of the pathology is by Councilman *et al.* (1904) and there are good reviews by Lillie (1930) and Bras (1952). First lesions in the skin of man are proliferative, all layers of the skin being involved; later, necrosis and fibrosis lead to the familiar "pitting". Similar lesions occur in mucous membranes. Cytoplasmic inclusions (Guarnieri) bodies occur in epithelial cells in man and experimental animals. They probably consist of collections of virus particles together with matrix. Intranuclear inclusions also are found from time to time but their significance is obscure.

Ecology. Infection is probably airborne. The source of infection, early in the disease, is probably from mouth and nose, later from dried crusts. Contaminated bed-clothes can infect.

Control. Isolation of patients, quarantine of contacts and vaccination are all-important. Vaccination is most frequently carried out with living vaccinia virus propagated on the skin of calves or sheep. Great advantages would accrue from the substitution of virus propagated in a medium free from bacteria such as chick embryo or bovine embryo tissue culture (Wesslén, 1956). Such vaccines are on trial with promising results. Virus propagated wholly in chick embryo loses its effectiveness after too many passes. Scarification and multiple pressure are the techniques recommended: intradermal inoculation is not so good. Lymph is commonly preserved in glycerol but freeze-dried vaccine (Collier, 1955) has far better keeping properties, especially for use in the tropics. Official requirements for smallpox vaccine have been laid down by W.H.O. (1959).

Encephalitis following vaccination is an infrequent complication but an undeniable small risk. It is associated with demyelination and is probably an auto-immune phenomenon analogous to other post-infection encephalitides. It is less frequent when vaccination is carried out in infancy.

Vaccinated persons may show: (i) when fully susceptible, a primary reaction with vesiculation, maximal at 8–10 days; (ii) with partial immunity, a vaccinoid or accelerated reaction, maximal at 3–7 days, with presence of a smaller vesicle; (iii) an early or immediate reaction at 2–3 days, usually only papular; this last may be elicited by live or killed virus and may occur both in people who are immune and in those who are susceptible.

Chemotherapy. Bauer *et al.* (1963) have shown that N-mettyl isatin thiosemicarbazone has prophylactic value when given to contacts.

COWPOX

Now agreed to be a disease distinct both from vaccinia and from milkers' nodes (often called natural cowpox in the United States).

Morphology. Similar to vaccinia by electron-microscopy.

Chemical composition. The virus DNA is, at least for the most part, double-stranded (Joklik, 1962).

Physico-chemical characters. Resistance to physical and chemical agents the same as that of vaccinia, so far as tested.

Hæmagglutination. Though to lower titre, is against the same range of fowl red cells as with vaccinia.

Antigenic properties. Very close to vaccinia but distinguishable by refined tests using complement-fixation, agar gel-diffusion and antibody-adsorption (Downie, 1939; Downie & McCarthy, 1950; Gispen, 1955; Rondle & Dumbell, 1962).

Cultivation. *In eggs.* Hæmorrhagic pocks are produced on chorioallantoic membranes but not above 40° (Bedson & Dumbell, 1961); with large doses the embryo may be killed. Several variant strains have been isolated causing white pocks on the membrane; these owe their colour to the more rapid necrosis produced and absence of hæmorrhage (Downie & Haddock, 1952).

In tissue culture. Plaques are produced on monolayers of chick embryo cultures, as with vaccinia (Porterfield & Allison, 1960); also in human and bovine cells.

Pathogenicity. *Natural host range.* Affects the skin, particularly teats and udders of cows. Frequently spreads to milkers affecting their hands, sometimes arms and face, and even the eye. In cattle, papules develop into vesicles on a firm inflamed base. Crusting follows and may not clear up for several weeks. Lesions in man resemble those of primary vaccination.

Readily infects rabbits, guinea pigs, mice and monkeys—other species have probably not been tested: skin and testis have been used as sites for infection. There is less rapid epithelial necrosis than with vaccinia, more invasion of mesodermal tissue and more hæmorrhage (Downie, 1939). Mice inoculated intraperitoneally are killed more regularly than by vaccinia (Moritsch, 1956). Lesions on rabbit cornea are smaller.

Large cytoplasmic inclusions in the lower epidermal layers are larger than the Guarnieri bodies of vaccinia and variola (Downie, 1947). Kato *et al.* (1959) suggest that the larger inclusions are of the nature of their protein A inclusions (*cf.* Vaccinia, p. 254) and not analogues of Guarnieri bodies.

Ecology. Infection is readily spread amongst a herd of cattle, probably by the hands of milkers, who may in turn be infected themselves. Man to man infection is rare. Occasionally cattle may be infected with true vaccinia virus coming from a recently vaccinated subject (Dekking quoted by Downie, 1959).

MILKERS' NODES

Synonyms: Pseudo-cowpox. Paravaccinia.
Review: Lipschütz (1920).
A pock-like disease occurs on udders of cows and is often confused with cowpox, especially as, like it, it may spread to milkers and cause lesions on their hands. It seems fairly safe to regard milkers' nodes as the same as Lipschütz's (1920) paravaccinia (Becker, 1940).

Morphology. The dimensions of the virus are reported as 296 × 190 mμ (by electron-microscopy): bodies are said to be narrower than those of vaccinia but to show, like them, a dense core after treatment with pepsin. Friedman–Kiem *et al.* (1963) describe a spiral structure as in orf and bovine papular stomititis; the virus is conceivably related to the latter.

Physico-chemical characters. Inactivated in 10′ by chloroform (Friedman–Kiem *et al.*, 1963).

Antigenic properties. It is agreed that there is no cross-immunity between this virus and cowpox or vaccinia. Morozow (1940) has suggested a relationship to contagious pustular dermatitis of sheep. von Pirquet (1916) considered that immunity was transient as lesions could be produced repeatedly in one subject (they may, however, have been allergic). Berger (1955) observed repeated attacks in cattle.

Cultivation. A virus isolated from milkers' nodes in man by Friedman–Kiem *et al.* (1963) multiplied serially in cultures of bovine kidney, causing CPE. Later it was transferred to human embryonic fibroblasts, but failed to grow in rabbit and rhesus kidneys.

Pathogenicity. Lesions in cattle and men take the form of hemispherical cherry-red papules. The incubation period in man is 5 days. Histologically the characteristic lesion is one of endothelial proliferation with formation of new small blood vessels. Juxtanuclear cytoplasmic inclusions occur and more rarely inclusions in nuclei. Lipschütz failed to transmit infection to rabbits, nor has attempted propagation in mice, guinea pigs or chick embryos been successful.

INFECTIOUS ECTROMELIA

Synonym: Mouse-pox. (Pseudo-lymphocytic choriomeningitis is ectromelia.)

Reviews: Marchal (1930)—the original description. Fenner (1949), Briody (1959).

Morphology and developmental cycle. Not distinguishable from vaccinia. Size, estimated by electron-microscopy, 232×172 mμ (Ruska & Kausche, 1933) (100–150 mμ by filtration—Barnard & Elford, 1931). The bodies can be stained by victoria blue (Herzberg, 1934). Formation of hollow spheres may precede formation of mature particles (Gaylord & Melnick, 1953).

Chemical composition. A DNA virus like other poxes.

Physico-chemical characters. Inactivated by heating 30′ at 55° C; also by UV radiation ($\lambda = 2536$ Å) in 4″ (Andrewes & Elford, 1947). Resistant to ether and bile salts: also to 1 per cent. phenol for 50 days. Formalin 0·01 per cent. inactivated in 48 hours. Readily preserved in 50 per cent glycerol at 0° C; at −76° or by freezing and drying (Marchal, 1930).

Hæmagglutination. Agglutinates the same range of fowl and pigeon cell as vaccinia. Reported agglutination of mouse cells

(Burnet & Stone, 1946) has not been generally reproducible. A heat-labile hæmagglutinin-inhibitor occurs in the sera of most normal mice (Briody, 1959).

Antigenic properties. Very close to vaccinia but separable by indirect complement-fixation, antibody adsorption and gel-diffusion (*cf.* Vaccinia). Some tests suggest a closer relation to cowpox than to vaccinia and variola. Antihæmagglutinins may or may not be present in sera of latently infected mice. Recovered mice are solidly immune.

Interference between this virus and vaccinia was studied by Andrewes & Elford (1947).

Cultivation. *In eggs.* The virus grows on the chorioallantoic membrane but only below 39° C. From the membrane it reaches the whole embryo and embryonic fluids.

In tissue-culture. Grows in various types of culture—HeLa cells, L cells, mouse-fibroblasts, chick-embryo (on which it will form plaques—Porterfield & Allison, 1960). There is evidence in culture of cell-to-cell spread and of giant-cell formation (Nii, 1959).

Distribution. An endemic infection of laboratory mice in Europe and Asia; more recently recognized in the United States. The only known recovery from wild mice was in a laboratory where the disease was under study, but latent infection in wild mice would almost certainly be overlooked.

Pathogenicity. *In mice.* The infection is latent in many stocks of laboratory mice and is activated by various stresses, such as transport, X-radiation and especially when in the course of experiments serial passages are made of tumour-cells or tissues. The disease then elicited has many forms and often remains undiagnosed for some time. It may present as conjunctivitis, pneumonia, meningitis or hepatitis rather than in the classical form of œdema and necrosis followed by loss of limb or tail.

With established virus intradermal inoculation into a footpad leads to this œdema and necrosis, signs first appearing about five days after inoculation. With virulent strains generalisation occurs with a "rash" of pocks or, more often, fatal necrosis of liver and spleen. With less virulent strains, though viræmia occurs, visible lesions are only seen locally. Intraperitoneal inoculations lead to

18

death from hepatitis: pancreatic necrosis and ascites also occur. Results after inoculation by other routes are variable. The course of infection is fully described by Fenner (1948a). There are genetic differences in susceptibility between different strains of mice.

In other hosts. Inapparent infection is produced in rats inoculated intranasally (Burnet & Lush, 1936b): virus multiplies in olfactory bulbs. Local lesions are produced in the skins of rabbits, guinea pigs and cotton-rats but serial transmission is not reported. No ill effects have followed inoculation into man: ectromelia was the active agent in a vaccine ostensibly containing attenuated typhus rickettsiæ and given to very many people.

Morbid anatomy. In fatal cases the liver may be an even yellow-grey or may show varying amounts of mottling. The spleen often has large white necrotic areas. White patches over the peritoneum are due to fat necrosis following pancreatic damage. Intestinal hæmorrhages may occur. Early lesions on feet and tail are those of œdema. Whole limbs may fall off after severe damage or only single toes or scabs from the tail. Roberts (1962) has described the course of infection in skin and respiratory tract.

Histopathology. There are characteristic cytoplasmic inclusions, often multiple. They may be found in epithelial cells of many organs, and in fibroblasts. Only exceptional virus strains produce them in the liver: they are not found in the spleen. Intestinal lesions are probably common and important but are not often looked for. The necrotic lesions are secondary to gross damage to blood vessels. Kato's (1955) A and B inclusions are both seen (Kameyama, 1959), virus antigen being revealed by fluorescent-antibody "staining" in the B inclusions.

Ecology. *Transmission* occurs especially from skin lesions (Fenner, 1947b) but the respiratory route may also be important (Briody, 1959). Virus is also present in urine and fæces. Transmission by mosquitoes has been demonstrated in the laboratory but arthropod-transmission is of doubtful importance in nature. Regularity of transmission by contact is variable with different strains. Gledhill (1962) has shown that virus may be recovered from tail-skin and fæces for several months after recovery from infection.

The epizootic behaviour of the disease has been studied by Greenwood *et al.* (1936) and by Fenner (1948a and b).

Control. *Vaccines.* Immunization with vaccinia virus given either intranasally (Fenner, 1947a) or into the tail (Salaman *et al.*, 1957) is effective in preventing deaths—more doubtfully in eliminating the infection from a stock.

Chemotherapy. Isatin-β-thiosemicarbazone, while experimentally effective against vaccinia in mice, is useless against ectromelia. On the other hand, several derivatives of the drug (Bauer & Sadler, 1961) act against ectromelia, not vaccinia.

Wholesale slaughter may be necessary to get rid of infection.

ORF

Synonyms: Contagious pustular dermatitis (of sheep) (C.P.D.). Contagious ecthyma of sheep. Sore mouth. Scabby mouth. Contagious pustular stomatitis. Infectious labial dermatitis.

(Contagious pustular dermatitis or stomatitis of the horse is probably a different disease, *cf.* p. 269.)

Morphology. Size by electron-microscopy 252 × 158 mμ, with rounded ends and dense sub-polar regions—less brick-shaped in dried preparations than vaccinia (Abdusalam & Coslett, 1957). Nagington & Horne (1962) have described an appearance in electron-micrographs suggesting a ball of yarn; this seems to be due to the spiral arrangement of nucleo-protein threads or tubules.

Physico-chemical characters. Dried scabs can remain virulent out of doors for months; or may survive at room temperature for 15 years (Hart *et al.*, 1949). Heat for 30' at 55° did not inactivate but 30' at 58°–60° did so. Reports on ether-resistance are divergent; it is apparently intermediate in its behaviour between ether-sensitive viruses and those such as vaccinia which are fully resistant. It is inactivated by chloroform (Lisse, 1962).

Hæmagglutination. Abdusalam (1958) tested cells of a number of species but found none sensitive.

Antigenic properties. Sera of immunized sheep and rabbits agglutinate elementary body suspensions, precipitate soluble antigen and fix complement specifically (Abdusalam, 1958). There is a small amount of cross-reaction shown by complement-fixation and gel-diffusion with vaccinia and ectromelia; also orf antisera showed some neutralization of ectromelia (Webster, 1958). Goat-pox will immunize against orf but not vice versa (Bennett *et al.*, 1944). Goat-pox antisera were found by Shama & Bhatia (1959) to neutralize orf but the reverse neutralization test was negative. All strains of orf may not be identical serologically (Horgan & Hasseeb, 1947) but in practice there seems to be good cross-immunity between strains from different continents.

Cultivation. No success has been met with in cultivating the virus in eggs.

Tissue-culture with CPE is reported by Greig (1957) in fibroblast monolayers derived from sheep embryo skin and muscle. Growth in primate cells is described by Nagington & Horne (1962).

Distribution. The disease occurs in all continents but is apparently absent from Scandinavia and almost so from the Caribbean area.

Pathogenicity. In the *natural hosts*, the disease mainly affects young lambs and kids, though adults are not resistant. Lips and mouth are mainly involved with vesicles followed by pustules and ulcers or by proliferative wart-like lesions. Malignant aphtha is probably a severe form. Exceptionally there may be considerable mortality amongst lambs. Other parts of the skin may be affected including eyes, anus and, in suckling ewes, the udder (Glover, 1930). Lesions usually regress in 3–4 weeks.

Natural host range. The only other species to be naturally infected is man, who may contract a local skin lesion from affected animals— usually on face or hands.

Experimentally sheep, goats and man can be readily infected by scarification, lesions appearing in 2–5 days, being maximal (in lambs) on the 8th day. There is dispute as to whether calves are susceptible; most workers have failed to infect them. Evidence as to susceptibility of rabbits is confused as some published work describes the reaction to a fungus infection rather than orf. However, Abdusalam (1957a) apparently did propagate the virus in series in rabbits.

Pathological lesions. Lesions in epithelium show ballooning of cells leading to degeneration and vesicle formation. Later the lesion may be granulomatous. No specific inclusions bodies are described (Wheeler & Cawley, 1956; Abdusalam, 1957b).

Ecology. Virus persists in the soil of an affected pasture for some months, and infection is probably by direct contact of the mouth with the virus.

Control. A living virus vaccine has been applied by scarification to immunize lambs and kids.

Balano-prosthitis of Sheep

A filtrable agent causing venereal infection of sheep in America was described by Tunnicliff & Matishek (1941) and by Tunnicliff (1949). It could cause ulcerative dermatitis as well as balanitis and ulcerative vulvitis. Similar conditions are described from Australia, South Africa and Britain (Glover, personal communication, 1962) but their relation to each other and to known viruses is obscure. Trueblood *et al.* (1963) grew an "ulcerative dermatosis" virus in monolayers of bovine embryo kidney and could not distinguish it from "contagious ecthyma" (orf) except by the results of cross-immunity tests. They thought that the two might be considered as strains of one virus.

GOAT-POX

This seems to be an entity but little is known of the properties of the virus.

The virus is ether-resistant (Bennett *et al.*, 1944); the Kedong strain of "sheep-pox" (really goat-pox) is sensitive (Plowright & Ferris, 1959). Elementary body suspensions are agglutinated by immune sera.

Reported to immunize against orf (*q.v.*, p. 263) and against sheep-pox (Rafyi & Ramyan, 1959); but the reverse protection is said to operate in neither case. Protects cattle against lumpy skin disease (*v.*, p. 267) (P. B. Capstick, personal communication, 1963).

Cultivation on the chorioallantoic membrane of 12-day eggs produces opaque pocks: the virus is said to be attenuated for goats after 4 to 8 passes (Rafyi & Ramyan, 1959).

It grows in lamb testis, producing CPE and cytoplasmic inclusions like those of sheep-pox. Some reports concerning "sheep-pox" (Plowright *et al.*, 1959) in fact concern goat-pox (P. B. Capstick, personal communication, 1963).

Distribution. Prevalent particularly in North Africa and the Middle East—in fact where there are most goats. Also from a few European countries particularly Scandinavia—where orf is said to be absent(!)—and Australia. See p. 267 for a possible relationship to African strains of sheep-pox.

Pathogenicity. It produces generalized pocks on mucous membranes and skin. Is transmissible to sheep and allegedly to calves, rabbits and other species; but other workers deny this and it requires confirmation. A virus dermatitis in goats (Haddow & Idnani, 1948) is said to be more severe than ordinary goat-pox.

Control. Virus attenuated by cultivation in eggs has been used to immunize (Rafyi & Ramyan, 1959).

SHEEP-POX

Synonyms: Clavelée. Variola ovina.

Morphology. 194 × 115 mµ by electron microscopy——said to be more elongated than other poxviruses (Abdusalam, 1957).
Inactivated in 15′ by 2 per cent. acid or 2 per cent. phenol (Angeloff *et al.*, 1956).

Antigenic properties. All strains are serologically alike (Ježić, 1932). For cross-protection by goat-pox vaccine *cf.* Goat-pox (p. 265).
Neutralization by antisera was studied by Borrel (1903) and incompletely neutralized virus used for immunisation (sero-clavelization). Specific complement-fixation is reported.

Cultivation. *Developing eggs.* Adapted, apparently with some difficulty, to growth on chorioallantoic membranes (Yuan *et al.*, 1957; Sabban, 1957). Sabban found no change in properties but the Chinese workers report attenuation after 90 passes, so that the virus could be used for immunization. Others report failure to cultivate the virus in eggs.
In tissue culture. Growth is reported in skin, kidney and testis of sheep, goats and calves with complete CPE in most tissues in 4–12 days and a peak titre 10⁶/0·2 ml.) in 4 to 5 days. Virulence for sheep unchanged (Plowright & Ferris, 1958; Boúe *et al.*, 1957). Aygün (1955) on the other hand reports attenuation after 15 passages in sheep embryo cultures and that this attenuated virus has been used for immunization in Turkey.

Distribution. Prevalent in parts of Africa, Asia, the Middle East: in Europe only in the South-East and in the Iberian peninsula. Strains of sheep-pox from Eastern and Southern Africa are said to be more closely related to goat-pox than to classical sheep-pox (P. B. Capstick, personal communication, 1963).

Pathogenicity. Produces a generalized pock disease in sheep, with often tracheitis and caseous nodules in the lungs. Breeds of sheep vary greatly in susceptibility; mortality varies from 5–50 per cent.

Only sheep are naturally infected.

Local lesions can be produced experimentally in goats and gazelle and, with some strains, in cattle.

Subcutaneous inoculation of sheep produces œdematous swellings and on passage a virus is obtained adapted to growth in mesodermal tissues. There are many contradictory claims to have succeeded— or otherwise—in infecting other species; success should be regarded as unproved.

Pathological lesions. The characteristic cytoplasmic inclusion body, not unlike the Guarnieri body, occurs in "cellules claveleuses"; there is also condensation of chromatin on the nuclear membrane. These changes are seen also in cells in tissue-culture.

Control. As this is an economically very important diesase, many attempts at producing a vaccine have been made since the 'sero-clavelization' of Borrel (1903). That widely used in Egypt is the dried Roumanian virus given intradermally under the tail. Reactions are slight and immunity good for 14 months (Sabban, 1960). An Iranian strain is similarly used. Virus attenuated in eggs or tissue-culture (see above) may in time prove better.

LUMPY SKIN DISEASE
(Neethling strain)

Of several viruses isolated from lumpy skin disease of cattle in Africa, the Neethling virus proves to be closely related to African sheep-pox, which itself lies near goat-pox (P. B. Capstick, personal communication, 1963).

The virus withstands 3 cycles of freezing and thawing. It is sensitive to 20 per cent. ether (Plowright & Ferris, 1959).

The virus is serologically related to African sheep-pox.

Cultivation. *In eggs.* Multiplies in the embryo and chorioallantoic membrane, producing pocks (van Rooyen *et al.*, 1959).

In tissue culture of embryonic calf and lamb kidney and in calf and lamb testis. CPE appears slowly in early cultures, but as early as 24 hours after adaptation spindle cells appear and later round up. Inclusions like those of sheep-pox are formed (Plowright & Witcombe, 1959), but no syncytia.

Distribution. South and East Africa. First seen in N. Rhodesia and Madagascar in 1929; it appeared in the Transvaal in 1945; it was widespread there for a number of years before being recognized in Kenya.

Pathogenicity. *In cattle.* Fever with formation of multiple nodules in the skin, lesions in mucous membranes and viscera, adenitis: these seem constant features but are not described in detail as the clinical picture has not been disentangled from that due to the Allerton virus, an agent possibly belonging to an Herpesvirus group.

Experimentally the cultivated virus produces fever and local reaction in cattle; and in rabbits a transient local reaction with some generalized lesions (Alexander *et al.*, 1957).

Pathological lesions. Cytoplasmic inclusions like those of sheep-pox are found in epithelial cells and histiocytes.

Ecology. The first outbreak in cattle in Kenya was apparently in association with a disease in sheep (Burdin & Prydie, 1959).

Control. The Isiolo or Kedong strains of "sheep-pox" have been given to cattle intradermally to produce immunity to Neethling virus (Capstick *et al.*, 1959). These are, in fact, nearer to goat-pox. True sheep-pox does not protect as well (P. B. Capstick, personal communication, 1963).

STOMATITIS PAPULOSA
(of cattle)

Probably the same disease as ulcerative stomatitis, papular stomatitis, pseudo-aphthous stomatitis, erosive stomatitis of cattle, but it is possible from discrepancies in accounts that more than one agent is concerned.

Morphology. Particles seen 125–150 mμ in diameter by electron-microscopy (Pritchard *et al.*, 1958). Passed a 0·4 μ gradocol membrane (Mason & Neitz, 1940). Reczko (1957) describes pox-virus-like bodies 207 and 215 mμ in diameter, with single or double membranes, not brick-shaped.

Nagington *et al.* (1962) describe a ball of yarn appearance as for orf. A rather similar structure is reported by Reczko (1962).

Physical characters. Survives freeze-drying. Ether-resistance partial (Plowright, 1959).

Antigenic properties. No cross-reactions with other viruses are reported, except for the common pox nucleoprotein antigen.

Cultivation. *In eggs.* It grows on the CAM (Mason & Neitz, 1940) but not according to Schaaf *et al.* (1940).

In tissue culture. Grows in calf testis and other bovine tissues—with slow-growing foci appearing on the 5th day, more rapidly (1 to 3 days) after passage. Reported also (Pritchard *et al.*, 1958) to grow in human tissue-cultures but not indefinitely.

Habitat. Reported from N. America, Africa and Europe.

Pathogenicity. Lesions in mouths of cattle somewhat resemble those of foot-and-mouth disease. There may be crateriform ulcers up to 1 cm. across. There is no generalization.

The agent causing ulcerative stomatitis in Ruanda-Urundi (Huygelen *et al.*, 1958) was reported to infect sheep and goats but a virus from Holland (Jansen *et al.*, 1959) failed to do so. No transmission to other species is reported.

Pathological lesions. A number of writers describe cytoplasmic inclusions. According to Plowright & Ferris (1959) there is a para-nuclear acidophilic part, partly surrounded by a hoop-like baso-philic part.

HORSE-POX

Synonym: Contagious pustular dermatitis (of the horse). Contagious pustular stomatitis. Grease or grease-heel is often considered as a synonym but may be due to a different virus.

Antigenic properties. No reliable information as to crossing with other poxes. Numerous reports of cross-immunity with vaccinia and other poxes must be regarded with suspicion.

Distribution. The disease is now quite rare. In 1959 the F.A.O. only recorded it, at low incidence, from Norway, Hungary, Spain, Lebanon and Jordan (F.A.O., 1959).

Pathogenicity. Papular lesions developing into vesicles develop on the lips and buccal mucosa, sometimes in the nose. There is fever, drooling of saliva; a few die. Course 10–14 days; 3–4 weeks in severe cases. Possibly identical with coital exanthema of the horse. Finger lesions have been reported to occur in attendants (Bub, 1942).

Control. Skin lesions are milder than those on the mouth; and good results have been claimed from vaccinating on the skin.

In *Grease* vesicles turn into pustules and then crusts develop on flexor surfaces of lower parts of legs. Jenner thought this the origin of cow-pox but this is not generally believed. It may or may not be the same as horse-pox: the latter disappeared from Britain some time before grease did (R. E. Glover—personal communication, 1963).

SWINE-POX

Two pox-diseases occur in swine. One is probably vaccinia, the other a distinct entity. Manninger *et al.* (1940) suggest calling the former swine-pox, the latter pseudo-swine-pox. Most other authors refer to the true swine disease as swine-pox and call the other, what it is, vaccinia. We shall follow this as the reasonable course.

Morphology. Reczko (1959) describes bodies 250 mμ revealed by electron-miscroscopy; there are surrounding membranes. Also seen in the cytoplasm were "crystalline" bodies 800 mμ across, not seen with other poxes. Blakemore & Abdusalam (1956) also describe bodies rather larger, even larger than those of vaccinia.

Antigenic properties. The virus is distinct from vaccinia and other poxes. However, Datt & Orlans (1958) by gel-diffusion in agar were able with difficulty to reveal a minor component common to vaccinia and swine-pox.

Cultivation. *In eggs.* Not reported.

In tissue-culture. The virus grows, with CPE, in pig kidney, testis and embryonic lung and brain. On monolayers very small plaques were produced (Kasza *et al.*, 1960). No growth occurred in tissue-cultures of cattle, sheep, mouse, roe-deer (Mayr, 1959).

Distribution. The disease is reported, usually in low incidence, from a few countries in every continent.

Pathogenicity. *In pigs* it affects chiefly very young animals with generalized pocks 1 cm. or more across; these are followed by crusts which soon fall off.

Experimentally the incubation period is 4–5 days from the time of inoculation. Rabbits, guinea pigs and baby mice are insusceptible (Mayr, 1959); so are calves, sheep and goats.

Pathological lesions. Blakemore & Abdusalam (1956) describe cytoplasmic and intranuclear inclusions. Other workers (Lübke, 1960; Kasza *et al.*, 1960) refer to nuclear vacuolation or ballooning as well as cytoplasmic inclusions.

Ecology: transmission. The pig louse (*Hæmatopinus suis*) is of major importance in transmitting the disease (Shope, 1940) but the disease may occur in the absence of lice.

Control. Vaccination is not considered necessary but it is reported that glycerolated virus gives only local lesions (Schwartz, 1958).

CAMEL-POX

Synonym: Photo-Shootur.

Little information is available about this. It occurs in the Middle East, in North East Africa and Pakistan. Camel drivers may contract local lesions on hands and arms from contact with affected animals (Amanschulow *et al.*, 1930; Leese, 1909).

MOLLUSCUM CONTAGIOSUM

Morphology and development. Elementary bodies have a size estimated by electron-microscopy as 302×226 mμ (Boswell, 1947) but other reports give a maximum diameter of up to 360 or even 390 mμ. Dourmashkin & Bernhard (1959) report an eccentric nucleoid and single or double membranes round the particles. The nucleoid is 50–100 mμ across. They also describe stages referred to as "viroplasm with double-leafed cleaving membranes" and "free nucleoid particles". Other reports describe a dense cortex and hollow interior; possibly representing an extra stage of development (Gaylord & Melnick, 1953). The particles are at first scattered but soon come to lie within a protein matrix divided into locules by septa; tryptic digestion reduces this matrix to a gelatinous mass (Goodpasture & Woodruff, 1931). Particles "negatively stained" for electron-microscopy may look like a "ball of yarn", as does orf (Howatson, 1962).

Chemical composition. The studies of Rake & Blank (1950) suggest that the elementary bodies are made up of DNA.

Physico-chemical characters. Virus retains activity for a month in 50 per cent. glycerol.

Antigenic properties. A heat labile soluble antigen can be used for complement-fixation but most patients do not develop complement-fixing antibodies. There are no cross-reactions with other poxes (Mitchell, 1953).

Cultivation. The virus does not grow in eggs but multiplication in tissue cultures of HeLa cells is reported by Dourmashkin & Febvre (1958).

The **distribution** is world-wide.

Pathogenicity. Exclusively a human disease; lesions are confined to the skin. After an incubation period variously estimated at 14–50 days, pimples develop and increase to form nodules having a diameter of 2 mm. They become pearly white and may develop an opening revealing a white core. Lesions persist for months. There is proliferation, hyperplasia of epidermal cells, those nearest the surface containing the large molluscum body up to 24 μ across. The nature of these bodies is described above.

Ecology. Transmission—by direct contact and fomites.

YABA MONKEY VIRUS

Virus of "subcutaneous tumours in monkeys".

Description: Niven *et al.* (1961).

Morphology. Electron-microscopy reveals many particles 250–280 mμ in their long axis, with a limiting membrane and dense internal nucleoid, sometimes dumb-bell shaped. Some sections reveal a lateral structure between the nucleoid and the membrane. Towards the centre of affected cells bodies with incomplete membranes can be seen.

The virus passed a 0·65 μ but not a 0·23 μ gradocol membrane.

Chemical composition. Staining with acridine orange indicates that the particles contain DNA.

Physico-chemical characters. Tests for ether-resistance gave equivocal results.

No **hæmagglutination** was demonstrated.

Antigenic properties. Recovered rhesus monkeys are immune to reinoculation. There is no cross-immunity with vaccinia; the virus is thus different from the pox-like disease in monkeys described by von Magnus *et al.* (1959) (p. 255).

Cultivation. *In eggs.* No specific lesions were produced on chorioallantoic membranes.

Tissue culture. Apparent multiplication took place for 3 passages in primary monkey kidney cells but the virus was then apparently overgrown by a simian virus and lost. Subsequent attempts at cultivation in a cell-line of monkey origin gave no evidence of multiplication (D. M. Chaproniere—unpublished).

Distribution. The disease appeared in a colony of rhesus monkeys housed in the open at Yaba, Nigeria (Bearcroft & Jamieson, 1958). It spread to 20 of 35 rhesus in a few weeks and affected also one baboon (*Papio papio*).

Pathogenicity. The virus causes tumour-like growths particularly on heads and limbs of rhesus and cynomolgus monkeys. These reach a diameter of 25–45 mm. and may project 25 mm. above surrounding skin. They are liable to break down and ulcerate. Regression usually begins in 4–6 weeks and is complete in 6–12 weeks.

They are firm and white on section; local lymph nodes may be enlarged.

Lesions consist of accumulations of large polygonal cells probably derived from fibrocytes. Cytoplasmic inclusions consist of masses of virus particles.

In *Cercopithecus æthiops* monkeys lesions appeared 11 days after inoculation and began to regress a week later. They remained flat and not bigger than 30 mm. across. In inoculated cancer patients and in one accidental laboratory infection in man, the virus produced local skin nodules appearing after 5–7 days, reaching 2 cm. in diameter and regressing after 3–4 weeks. Virus was recovered from the lesions (Grace *et al.*, 1962).

Ecology. The spontaneous disease has only been seen where monkeys were kept out of doors in Africa; the natural host is probably therefore an African mammal, most probably a primate. Spread by arthropod has been neither demonstrated nor excluded.

FOWL-POX

Synonyms: Bird-pox. Epithelioma contagiosum. Fowl diphtheria. Variola Avium. *Borreliota avium. Poxvirus avium.* Avian molluscum. Roup.

Poxviruses affect numerous birds and are not clearly separable. Some strains are rather specific, others attack birds of various families. Canary-pox will be described separately but is not to be sharply distinguished from fowl-pox.

Morphology and development, chemical composition. Elementary bodies or Borrel bodies have an estimated diameter of $0.25\ \mu$—or 332×284 mμ by electron-microscopy (Boswell, 1947). In general they resemble other poxviruses, having a pepsin-resistant core. They are found in a cytoplasmic inclusion body, the Bollinger body, which consists of a matrix in which the virus particles are embedded. This matrix is osmiophilic, very resistant to enzymes but dissolved by sodium lauryl sulphate. It probably contains both protein and lipoid and is said to give a positive Feulgen reaction after previous extraction of lipoids (Todd & Randall, 1958).

The developing virus appears first in the form of fairly undifferentiated particles but soon acquires the characteristic pox-virus appearance of a dumb-bell like structure within an outer membrane (Morgan & Wyckoff, 1950; Eaves & Flewett, 1955).

Physico-chemical characters. Virus is inactivated by 1 per cent. caustic potash but only after being freed from its matrix. It is resistant to ether but sensitive to chloroform, and withstands 1 per cent. phenol and 1 : 1000 formalin for 9 days. Readily preserved by drying or freeze-drying for periods of several years. Inactivated by heating 30' at 50° C or 8' at 60° C.

Hæmagglutination. A hæmagglutinin, more readily separable from the virus bodies than with other poxes, is described by Mayr (1956). Some other workers have failed to demonstrate hæmagglutination.

Antigenic properties. There is some cross-neutralization between fowl, pigeon and canary pox. The bird poxes in fact form a family of viruses of varying degrees of cross-relationship. Fowl and pigeon poxes lie more closely together than either does to canary pox. Neutralization tests can be carried out by testing mixtures on scarified fowl combs or, more conveniently, by a method involving pock-counting on chorioallantoic membranes (Burnet & Lush, 1936). Precipitating antibodies can be revealed by gel-diffusion (Wittman, 1958).

Interference. The virus is said to interfere with vaccinia.

Cultivation. *In eggs.* Pocks are produced on chorioallantoic membranes of hens' and ducks' eggs, the lesions being first proliferative, later necrotic. Growth is best at 37° C, maximal titre being reached in 3 days on 8–12-day embryos (Haig, 1951).

In tissue culture. Both fowl and pigeon pox grow well and produce CPE in chick embryo tissue cultures. Bollinger bodies may be found *in vitro*. Growth in chick fibroblasts was not accompanied by CPE or inclusion formation (Bang *et al.*, 1951).

Pathogenicity. Disease in fowls runs a course of 3 or 4 weeks. There are proliferative lesions followed by scabbing on the skin especially the head, sometimes on feet and vent. Involvement of the trachea is "fowl diphtheria". Various eye lesions. Caseous material may collect in the infra-orbital sinuses. Similar lesions in other birds.

Host-range includes fowls, turkeys, pheasants, partridges, quail, grouse, pigeons, rhea, storks, ducks, sparrows and cormorants.

Experimentally birds of practically any species can be infected by a variety of routes. A strain has been modified by intracerebral passage to give meningo-encephalitis in chicks (Buddingh, 1938). A mutant described by Goodpasture (1959) produced adenoma-like lesions on inoculation into kidneys. Otherwise the experimental disease is much like that occurring naturally. One of four strains of fowl-pox inoculated into canaries produced necrotic lesions and deaths much like those caused by canary-pox itself (Burnet, 1933). The virus may produce local lesions in mammals, e.g. in mouse lungs, but is not propagable in series (Nelson, 1951).

Pathology. The local lesions are caused by heaping up of epithelial cells continuing for some days or even weeks before necrosis sets in. The Bollinger bodies in cytoplasm already described (p. 274) attain a diameter larger than that of the nucleus.

Ecology. Transmission is by direct contact or through mechanical transfer by biting mosquitoes (*Culex* & *Aëdes* spp.). No multiplication in the mosquitoes is reported but they may remain infectious for as long as 210 days (Bos, 1934). Epidemics usually occur in spring, summer or autumn. French & Reeves (1954) isolated 5 bird pox viruses from wild caught mosquitoes; these were related with various degrees of closeness to each other and to fowl-pox.

Control. Pigeon-pox or fowl-pox viruses attenuated by growth in eggs have been widely used as live vaccines by the feather follicle or "stick" method of inoculation. There are varying reports as to efficacy: immunity is not as permanent as could be desired (Glover, 1939).

CANARY-POX

This fatal disease of canaries described by Kikuth & Gollub (1932) was shown by Burnet (1933) to be closely related to fowl-pox.

Morphology. Ruska (1943) reports the diameter as 311×263 mμ. The appearances seen by electron-microscopy are fully described by Herzberg *et al.* (1954, 1955, 1959): rather more detailed structure can be seen in their pictures than is possible in those yet published of fowl-pox.

Hæmagglutination. A strain was found to agglutinate only 1 in 4 of the fowl RBC suspensions agglutinable by vaccinia.

Antigenic properties. *Cf.* Fowl-pox, p. 274.

Cultivation. Lesions on chorioallantoic membranes are like those of fowl-pox. Mayr & Kalcher (1960) have compared the behaviour of fowl-, pigeon-, and canary-pox in cultures of chick fibroblasts.

Pathogenicity. The fatal disease following intramuscular inoculation of canaries is at first sight unlike fowl-pox, but (*cf.* p. 276) fowl-pox itself may behave like this in canaries. There is local necrosis with œdema and exudates over serous membranes, and pneumonia with numerous cytoplasmic inclusions visible in bronchiolar epithelium.

Sparrows are readily infected; chicks and other birds usually not. A pox infecting Juncos in North America gave rise to both nuclear and cytoplasmic inclusions (Beaver & Cheatham, 1963).

MYXOMATOSIS

Reviews: Aragão (1927). Fenner (1959).

Morphology. Indistinguishable from vaccinia by electron-microscopy: brick-shaped on drying and with a pepsin-resistant core (Farrant & Fenner, 1953). Dimensions in osmium-fixed preparations 287×233 mμ (Ruska & Kausche, 1933). Considerably smaller by centrifugation and filtration.

Chemical composition. No direct examination of nucleic acid content is reported: it is almost certainly a DNA virus. The cytoplasmic inclusions believed to consist largely of virus are Feulgen-positive (Kato & Cutting, 1959). A peculiar lipoid was found in a centrifuged deposit of virus particles (Balls *et al.*, 1940).

Physico-chemical characters. The specific gravity is estimated as 1·3.

Inactivated in 25′ at 55° C—rather more quickly than other poxviruses; 50° for 1 hour killed. Very stable in 50 per cent. glycerol or when frozen and dried. It survives for many months in skins of affected rabbits at ordinary temperatures (Jacotot *et al.*, 1955).

It is ether-sensitive—unlike most poxviruses—but, like them, is resistant to sodium desoxycholate (Andrewes & Horstmann, 1949). (With almost all other viruses sensitivity to ether and to bile salts are parallel.) 0·1 m. potassium salicylate inactivates quickly. The action of various antiseptics was described by Moses (1911).

Hæmagglutination not reported.

Antigenic properties. Neutralizing antibodies can be demonstrated by tests in rabbit skins or on chorioallantoic membranes of eggs, but not always very readily. Soluble antigens demonstrable by precipitin tests in tubes (Rivers *et al.*, 1939; Smadel *et al.*, 1940) or by gel-diffusion (Mansi & Thomas, 1958) are present in tissues and sometimes serum of acutely ill rabbits. There are at least two distinct heat-labile antigens, possibly more. Complement-fixation can also be used (Fenner, Marshall & Woodroofe, 1953). The virus is very close antigenically to rabbit fibroma (*q.v.*, p. 280).

Interference is reported by Semliki forest virus (Ginder & Friedewald, 1952).

Cultivation. *In developing eggs.* Pocks are formed on chorioallantoic membranes, as with many other poxviruses. Pock-counting can be used for virus titration but the eggs are $2\frac{1}{2}$ times less sensitive than the rabbits' skin (Fenner & McIntyre, 1956).

In tissue culture. The virus grows and produces CPE in tissue cultures not only of susceptible species (rabbit, cotton-tail) but also in cultures of squirrel, rat, hamster, guinea pig and even human tissues. Plaques develop on monolayers. Tissues of some guinea pigs are susceptible only after they have been cultivated for a few days outside the body. Only tissues of very young rats are susceptible (Chaproniere & Andrewes, 1957).

Distribution. The virus exists in the natural state in Uruguay and Brazil in the local wild rabbits (*Sylvilagus brasiliensis*); also in California in bush rabbits (*Sylvilagus bachmani*). It has now been introduced into Australia and Europe where it is widespread amongst the rabbits, which belong to the genus *Oryctolagus*.

Pathogenicity. In *Sylvilagus* it produces only a local swelling: the disease is not fatal.

In wild and domestic *Oryctolagus* it produces a disease which, on first contact with the new host, is more than 99 per cent. fatal. The first symptoms are those of blepharo-conjunctivitis leading to sealing of the eyelids with inspissated pus. Nose, muzzle, anal and genital orifice swell up. The "myxomata" are subcutaneous gelatinous swellings. Rabbits become thin and apathetic and may die 2–5 days after symptoms appear. With severe infections the discrete tumours may not be seen. Disease of varying degrees of mildness are seen when either the virus has become attenuated or rabbits have become genetically resistant. The disease then runs a slower course and is often not fatal: local lesions differ widely in their character. Grades of virulence of strains are described by Fenner & Marshall (1957).

As already mentioned, *Sylvilagus* species are the natural hosts. Apart from *Oryctolagus*, natural transmission has been reported only —and very rarely—in hares (*Lepus*) in Britain and France. The virus has been propagated as an inapparent infection in brains of suckling mice (Andrewes & Harisijades, 1955), in a guinea pig sarcoma and in homologous tissue grafts in guinea pigs (Chaproniere & Andrewes, 1958). Before the virus was introduced into Australia, Bull & Dickinson (1937) tested the susceptibility of a wide range of mammals and birds and found all but rabbits to be refractory. Hurst obtained an attenuated strain (neuromyxoma) by intracerebral passage in rabbits.

The face and eye swellings give typically affected rabbits a characteristic "leonine" facies. The subcutaneous swellings are firm and whitish and ooze a serous fluid on section. Orchitis is common. The "tumours" consist of proliferation of undifferentiated mesenchymal cells which assume a stellate form: but their bulk is made up of the sero-mucinous exudate. Rivers (1928) described masses of oxyphilic granules in epithelium of skin and elsewhere. The pathological lesions in various organs are described by him, by Hurst (1937) and by Ahlström (1940).

Ecology. *Transmission* in South America is probably through arthropod vectors, mainly mosquitoes. The same is true in Australia, the main vector being *Anopheles annulipes*, though many other insects can carry virus also. Transmission is apparently mechanical. In Britain the rabbit flea *Spilopsyllus cuniculi* is the main vector, though *Anopheles atroparvus* probably plays a role on the South Coast and also in France. Rabbit-to-rabbit spread only occurs across distances of a few inches.

Anopheles freeborni seems to be the main vector of the Californian virus (Grodhaus et al., 1963).

Other aspects. This is not the place to describe the fascinating effects of the interaction of virus and rabbit in Australia, resulting within a few years in great reduction in severity of the disease, due partly to attenuation of virus but even more to increased genetic resistance in the rabbits—see Fenner's review (1959), also Marshall & Fenner

(1958). In Britain, the picture has been different, doubtless because of transmission by fleas rather than mosquitoes (Andrewes, Thompson & Mansi, 1959).

Control. *Vaccination.* Rabbits can be immunized by inoculation of fibroma virus, which produces only a local lesion and usually protects at least against fatal myxomatosis (Shope, 1938).

Other measures. Domestic rabbits can be protected by prevention of access of mosquitoes or fleas from without. The disease does not spread in a rabbit house where these are excluded.

FIBROMATOSIS OF RABBITS

Synonym: Shope fibroma.
Review: Shope (1932)—the original description.

Morphology. By electron-microscopy the virus resembles vaccinia and myxoma. It is depicted as seen in thin sections by Bernhard *et al.* (1954); their estimate of its size is 200–240 mμ, larger than Schlesinger & Andrewes (1937) found by filtration and centrifugation.

Physico-chemical characters. The virus is ether-sensitive. The effect of several antiseptics is described by Pontieri & Chaumont (1954).

Antigenic properties. Several workers have studied the immunological relation with myxoma, which is extremely close. Some find them almost identical, others that there are minor differences revealed in cross complement-fixation or precipitation tests. Comparison of the two viruses by agar gel-diffusion (Fayet *et al.*, 1957; Mansi & Thomas, 1958) suggests that most of their antigens are common but there may exist specific ones also.

Interference is reported by Virus III (Andrewes, 1940), Semliki forest virus, (Ginder & Friedewald, 1951) and by Murray Valley encephalitis virus.

Cultivation. *In developing eggs.* The virus (OA strain) can be propagated on the chorioallantoic membrane but in contrast to myxoma, no characteristic lesions were produced, nor was the embryo invaded.

In tissue culture. Growth occurs in cultures of rabbit and cotton-tail rabbit tissues, with CPE, also in tissue cultures of guinea pig, rat and man (Chaproniere & Andrewes, 1957). Foci of heaped-up cells appear on rabbit-kidney monolayers (Padgett *et al.*, 1962).

Pathogenicity. In cotton rabbits (*Sylvilagus*) the natural host, and in European rabbits (*Oryctolagus*) the virus causes subcutaneous swellings which normally remain localized: in nature they are commonly found on the foot. The lesions are soft and rubbery, appearing 3 to 5 days after intradermal inoculation and persisting for 10–15 days before necrosis and regression begin. Intratesticular inoculation leads to enlargement of the testis to several times its natural size: it may remain large up to 40 days. This description applies to the original (OA) strain.

Experimental infection. An acute disease with generalized lesions, sometimes fatal, is seen when rabbits are treated with tar at the time of inoculation (Ahlström & Andrewes, 1938), cortisone (Harel, 1956) or X-rays (Clemmesen, 1939) or if very young rabbits are injected (Duran-Reynals, 1945).

Fibroma virus has been propagated intracerebrally in 1-day old mice (Dalmat, 1958).

Pathological lesions. Inoculation of virus into various tissues of rabbits leads to an immediate inflammatory reaction quickly followed by fibroblastic proliferation; this is the basis of production of the tumour-like swellings (Ahlström, 1938). A variant, the inflammatory (IA) strain was described by Andrewes (1936); in this the lesions are inflammatory throughout with intense accumulation of small mononuclear cells; fibroblastic proliferation is almost absent. Shope (1932) has described the occurrence in cotton-tails of proliferated epithelium with eosinophilic cytoplasmic inclusions in skin overlying fibromata.

Berry & Dedrick (1936) reported that heat-inactivated myxoma introduced into a rabbit along with fibroma virus led to production of fully virulent myxoma. This is more regularly demonstrable in tissue-culture (Kilham, 1958) and is part of a more general phenomenon of mutual reactivation by pox viruses studied by Joklik *et al.* (1960). The properties of the transforming agent were studied by Kilham *et al.* (1958); it may be a nucleo-protein (Shack & Kilham, 1959).

Ecology: *transmission.* Experimentally *Aëdes and Culex* mosquitoes transmit the disease between cotton-tails or baby domestic rabbits—not readily between adult domestic rabbits (Kilham & Dalmat, 1955; Dalmat, 1959).

Fibromatosis of Hares

A virus, serologically related to myxoma, is described as causing fibromata in hares in North Italy and Southern France (Leinati *et al.*, 1961). It was transmissible to rabbits and serially transmissible in suckling rabbits. It may be identical with the fibrosarcoma of hares described by von Dungern & Coca in 1909.

Squirrel Fibroma

Multiple fibromata occur naturally in grey squirrels (*Sciurus carolinensis*) in North America and are due to an agent serologically related to the rabbit fibroma virus (Kilham *et al.*, 1953). This produces lesions in domestic rabbits for 1 passage only but is serially transmissible in woodchucks (*Marmota monax*). In suckling squirrels the virus will produce not only generalized skin nodules (Kilham, 1955) but also lung adenomata (Kirschstein *et al.*, 1958). Cytoplasmic inclusions are present in the fibroma cells.

Deer Fibroma

Multiple skin nodules occurring in skins of white-tailed deer in North America are histologically fibromata. They are caused by a filtrable agent, but there is no evidence that this is a poxvirus. Experimentally the incubation period of the disease is about 7 weeks. The agent was stable in 50 per cent. glycerol in the cold; it was not transmissible to a calf, rabbits, guinea pigs or sheep (Shope *et al.*, 1958).

REFERENCES

Abdusalam, M. (1957a) *J. comp. Path.*, **67**, 217 and 307.
Abdusalam, M. (1957b) *Amer. J. vet. Res.*, **18**, 614.
Abdusalam, M. (1958) *J. comp. Path.*, **68**, 23.
Abdusalam, M., & Coslett, V. E. (1957) *J. comp. Path.*, **67**, 145.
Ahlström, C. G. (1938) *J. Path. Bact.*, **46**, 461.
Ahlström, C. G. (1940) *Acta path. microbiol. scand.*, **17**, 377.
Ahlström, C. G., & Andrewes, C. H. (1938) *J. Path. Bact.*, **47**, 65.
Alexander, R. A., Plowright, W., & Haig, D. A. (1957) *Bull. epizoot. Dis. Afr.*, **5**, 489.
Amanschulow, S. A., Samarzew, A. A., & Arbusow, L. N. (1930) *Z. Infekt.-Kr. Haustiere*, **38**, 186.

Andrewes, C. H. (1936) *J. exp. Med.*, **63**, 157.
Andrewes, C. H. (1940) *J. Path. Bact.*, **50**, 227.
Andrewes, C. H., & Elford, W. J. (1947) *Brit. J. exp. Path.*, **28**, 278.
Andrewes, C. H., & Harisijades, S. (1955) *Brit. J. exp. Path.*, **36**, 18.
Andrewes, C. H., & Horstmann, D. M. (1949) *J. gen. Microbiol.*, **3**, 290.
Andrewes, C. H., Thompson, H. V., & Mansi, W. (1959) *Nature (Lond.)*, **184**, 1179.
Angeloff, S., Panajotoff, P., Manolowa, N., & Nikoloff, P. (1956) *Arch. exp. vet. Med.*, **10**, 365.
Appleyard, G. (1961) *Nature (Lond.)*, **190**, 465.
Aragão, H. de B. (1927) *Mem. Inst. Oswaldo Cruz*, **20**, 225.
Aygün, S. T. (1955) *Arch. exp. vet. Med.*, **9**, 415.
Balls, A. K., Jansen, E. F. & Axelrod, B. (1940) *Enzymologia*, **8**, 267.
Bang, F. B., Levy, E.. & Gey, G. O. (1951) *J. Immunol.*, **66**, 329.
Barnard, J. E., & Elford, W. J. (1931) *Proc. roy. Soc. B*, **109**, 360.
Bauer, D. J. (1955) *Brit. J. exp. Path.*, **36**, 105.
Bauer, D. J., & Sadler, P. W. (1961) *Nature (Lond.)*, **190**, 1167.
Bauer, D. J., St. Vincent, L., Kempe, C. H., & Downie, A. W. (1963) *Lancet*, **2**, 494.
Bearcroft, W. G. C., & Jamieson, M. (1958) *Nature (Lond.)*, **182**, 195.
Beaver, D. L., & Cheatham, W. J. (1963) *Amer. J. Path.*, **42**, 23.
Becker, F. T. (1940) *J. Amer. med. Ass.*, **115**, 2140.
Bedson, H. S., & Dumbell, K. R. (1961) *J. Hyg.*, **59**, 457.
Bennett, S. C. J., Horgan, E. S., & Hasseeb, M. A. (1944) *J. comp. Path.*, **54**, 131.
Berger, K. (1955) *Zbl. Bakt. I. Abt. Orig.*, **162**, 363.
Bernhard, W., Bauer, A., Harel, J., & Oberling, C. (1954) *Bull. Cancer*, **41**, 423.
Bernkopf, W., Nishmi, M., & Rosin, A. (1959) *J. Immunol.*, **83**, 635.
Berry, G. P., & Dedrick, H. M. (1936) *J. Bact.*, **31**, 50.
Blakemore, F., & Abdusalam, M. (1956) *J. comp. Path.*, **66**, 373.
Blaxall, F. R. (1930) in *A System of Bacteriology*, **7**, 84. London: Med. Res. Counc.
Borrel, A. (1903) *Ann. Inst. Past.*, **17**, 123 and 732.
Bos, A. (1934) *Z. Infekt.-Kr. Haustiere*, **46**, 195.
Boswell, F. W. (1947) *Brit. J. exp. Path.*, **28**, 253.
Boué, A., Baltazard, M., & Vieuchange, J. (1957) *C.R. Acad. Sci. (Paris)*, **244**, 1571.
Bras, G. (1952) *Docum. Med. geogr. trop. (Amst.).*, **4**, 303.
Briody, B. A. (1959) *Bact. Rev.*, **23**, 61.
Brown, A., Elsner, V., & Officer, J. E. (1960) *Proc. Soc. exp. Biol. (N.Y.)*, **104**, 605.
Bub., (1942) *Z. Veterinark.*, **54**, 137.
Buddingh, G. J. (1938) *J. exp. Med.*, **67**, 921 and 933.
Bull, L. B., & Dickinson, C. G. (1937) *J. Coun. sci. ind. Res. (Aust.)*, **10**, 291.
Burdin, M. L., & Prydie, J. (1959) *Nature (Lond.)*, **183**, 949.
Burnet, F. M. (1933) *J. Path. Bact.*, **37**, 107.
Burnet, F. M., & Lush, D. (1936a) *Brit. J. exp. Path.*, **17**, 302.
Burnet, F. M., & Lush, D. (1936b) *J. Path. Bact.*, **42**, 469.
Burnet, F. M., & Stone, J. D. (1946) *Aust. J. exp. Biol. med. Sci.*, **24**, 1.
Cabasso, V., & Moore, I. F. (1957) *Proc. Soc. exp. Biol. (N.Y.)*, **95**, 605.
Capstick, P. B., Prydie, J., Coackley, W., & Burdin, M. L. (1959) *Vet. Rec.*, **71**, 422.
Chaproniere, D. M., & Andrewes, C. H. (1957) *Virology*, **4**, 351.
Chaproniere, D. M., & Andrewes, C. H. (1958) *Virology*, **5**, 120.
Chu, C. M. (1948) *J. Hyg. (Lond.)*, **50**, 42.

Clark, E., & Nagler, F. P. O. (1943) Aust. J. exp. Biol. med. Sci., 21, 103.
Clemmesen, J. (1939) Amer. J. Cancer, 35, 378.
Collier, L. H. (1954) Bact. Rev., 18, 74.
Collier, L. H. (1955) J. Hyg. (Lond.), 53, 76.
Collier, L. H., McClean, D., & Vallet, L. (1955) J. Hyg. (Lond.), 53, 513.
Councilman, W. T., Magrath, G. B., & Brinckerhoff, W. L. (1904) J. med. Res., 11, 12.
Cox, H. R. (1947) Ann. N.Y. Acad. Sci., 48, 393.
Craigie, J., & Wishart, F. O. (1934) Brit. J. exp. Path., 15, 390.
Cross, R. M., Kaplan, C., & McClean, D. (1957) Lancet, 1, 446.
Cutchins, E., Warren, J., & Jones, W. P. (1960) J. Immunol., 85, 275.
Dalmat, H. T. (1958) Proc. Soc. exp. Biol. (N.Y.), 97, 219.
Dalmat, H. T. (1959) J. Hyg. (Lond.), 57, 1.
Datt, N. S., & Orlans, E. S. (1958) Immunology, 1, 81.
Dourmashkin, R., & Bernhard, W. (1959) J. Ultrastruct. Res., 3, 11.
Dourmashkin, R., & Febvre, H. L. (1958) C.R. Acad. Sci. (Paris), 246, 2308.
Douglas, S. R., Smith, W., & Price, L. R. W. (1929) J. Path. Bact., 32, 99.
Downie, A. W. (1939) Brit. J. exp. Path., 20, 158.
Downie, A. W. (1947) J. Path. Bact., 48, 361.
Downie, A. W. (1959) in Virol and Rickettsial Infection of Man. Ed. Rivers and Horsfall. 3rd ed. London: Pitman Medical Publ. Co.
Downie, A. W., & Dumbell, K. R. (1956) Ann. Rev. Microbiol., 10, 237.
Downie, A. W., & Haddock, D. W. (1952) Lancet, 1, 1049.
Downie, A. W., & McCarthy, K. (1950) Brit. J. exp. Path., 31, 789.
Downie, A. W., & Macdonald, A. (1950) J. Path. Bact., 62, 389.
Downie, A. W., & Macdonald, A. (1953) Brit. med. Bull., 9, 191.
Dunham, C. G., & MacNeal, W. J. (1943) J. Lab. clin. Med., 28, 947.
Duran-Reynals, F. (1940) Cancer Res., 5, 25.
Eaves, G., & Flewett, T. F. (1955) J. Hyg. (Lond.), 53, 102.
F.A.O. (1959) Anim. Health Yearbook.
Farrant, J. L., & Fenner, F. (1953) Aust. J. exp. Biol. med. Sci., 31, 121.
Fayet, M. T., Mackowiak, C., Camand, R., & Leftheriotis, E. (1957) Ann. Inst. Pasteur, 2, 466.
Fenner, F. (1953) Nature (Lond.), 171, 562.
Fenner, F. (1947a) Aust. J. exp. Biol. med. Sci., 25, 257.
Fenner, F. (1947b) Aust. J. exp. Biol. med. Sci., 25, 275 and 327.
Fenner, F. (1948a) Brit. J. exp. Path., 29, 69.
Fenner, F. (1948b) J. Hyg. (Lond.), 46, 383.
Fenner, F. (1949) J. Immunol., 63, 341.
Fenner, F. (1958) Virology, 5, 502.
Fenner, F. (1959) Brit. med. Bull., 15, 240.
Fenner, F., & Burnet, F. M. (1957) Virology, 4, 305.
Fenner, F., & McIntyre, G. A. (1956) J. Hyg. (Lond.), 54, 246.
Fenner, F., & Marshall, I. D. (1957) J. Hyg. (Lond.), 55, 149.
Fenner, F., Marshall, I. D., & Woodroofe, G. M. (1953) J. Hyg. (Lond.), 51, 225.
Fenner, F., & Woodroofe, G. M. (1960) Virology, 11, 185.
French, E. L., & Reeves, W. C. (1954) J. Hyg. (Lond.), 52, 551.
Friedman-Kiem, A. E., Rowe, W. P., & Banfield, W. G. (1963) Science, 140, 1335.
Gaylord, W. H., & Melnick, J. L. (1953) J. exp. Med., 98, 157.
Gillen, A. L., Burr, M. M., & Nagler, F. P. O. (1950) J. Immunol., 65, 701.
Ginder, D. R., & Friedewald, W. F. (1951) Proc. Soc. exp. Biol. (N.Y.), 77, 272.
Gispen, R. (1955) J. Immunol., 74, 134.
Gledhill, A. W. (1962) Nature (Lond.), 196, 298.

Glover, R. E. (1930) *Proc. 11th internat. vet. Congress.*

Glover, R. E. (1939) *J. comp. Path.*, **52**, 29.

Goodpasture, E. W. (1959) *Amer. J. Path.*, **35**, 213.

Goodpasture, E. W., & Woodruff, C. E. (1931) *Amer. J. Path.*, **7**, 1.

Gordon, M. H. (1925) Studies of the Viruses of Vaccinia and Variola, *Spec. Rep. Ser. med. Res. Coun. (Lond.)* No. 98.

Grace, J. T., Mirand, E. A., Millian, S. J., & Metzger, R. S. (1962) *Fed. Proc.*, **21**, 32.

Greenwood, M., Hill, A. B., Topley, W. W. C., & Wilson, J. (1936) *Spec. Rep. Ser. med. Res. Coun. (Lond.)* No. 209, p. 64.

Greig, A. S. (1957) *Canad. J. comp. Med.*, **21**, 304.

Grodhaus, G., Regnery, D. C., & Marshall, I. D. (1963) *Amer. J. Hyg.*, **77**, 205.

Haddow, J. R., & Idnani, J. A. (1948) *Indian vet. J.*, **24**, 332.

Hahon, N., Ratner, M., & Kozikowski, M. (1958) *J. Bact.*, **75**, 707.

Hamre, D., Bernstein, J., & Donovick, R. (1950) *Proc. Soc. exp. Biol. (N.Y.)*, **73**, 275.

Haig, D. A. (1957) *Onderstepoort, J. vet. Res.*, **25**, 17.

Harel, J. (1956) *C.R. Soc. Biol. (Paris)*, **150**, 351.

Hart, L., Hayston, J. T., & Keat, J. C. (1949) *Aust. vet. J.*, **25**, 40.

Herzberg, K. (1954) *Zbl. Bakt. I. Abt. Orig.*, **160**, 481.

Herzberg, K., & Kleinschmidt, A. (1954) *Z. Hyg. Infekt.-Kr.*, **139**, 545.

Herzberg, K., & Kleinschmidt, A. (1959) *Zbl. Bakt. I. Abt. Orig.*, **174**, 1.

Herzberg, K., Kleinschmidt, A., Requardt, K., & Vogell, W. (1955) *Arch. ges. Virusforsch.*, **6**, 283.

Horgan, S. E., & Hasseeb, M. A. (1939) *J. Hyg. (Lond.)*, **39**, 615.

Horgan, S. E., & Hasseeb, M. A. (1947) *J. comp. Path.*, **57**, 8.

Howatson, A. F. (1962) *Fed. Proc.*, **21**, 947.

Hurst, E. W. (1937) *Brit. J. exp. Path.*, **18**, 1.

Huygelen, C., Mortelmans, J., Thienport, D., Biche, Y., & Pinckers, F. (1958) *Zbl. Vet.-Med.*, **5**, 859.

Jacotot, H., Vallée, A., & Virat, B. (1955) *Ann. Inst. Pasteur*, **89**, 290.

Jansen, J. (1941) *Zbl. Bakt. I. Abt. Orig.*, **148**, 65.

Jansen, J., & Kunst, H. (1959) *T. Diergeneesk.*, **84**, 947.

Ježić, J. A. (1932) *Z. Immunforsch.*, **75**, 456.

Joklik, W. K. (1962) *J. molec. Biol.*, **5**, 265.

Joklik, W. K., Abel, P., & Holmes, I. H. (1960) *Nature (Lond.)*, **186**, 992.

Kaplan, C. (1958) *J. gen. Microbiol.*, **18**, 58.

Kameyama, S., Takahashi, M., Toyoshima, T., Kato, S., & Kamahora, J. (1959) *Biken's J.*, **2**, 341.

Kasza, L., Bohl, E. H., & Jones, D. O. (1960) *Amer. J. vet. Res.*, **21**, 269.

Kato, S., Takahashi, M., Kameyama, S., & Kamahora, J. (1959) *Biken's J.*, **2**, 353.

Kato, S., & Cutting, W. (1959) *Stanf. med. Bull.*, **17**, 34.

Kaufman, H. E., Nesburn, A. B., & Maloney, E. D. (1962) *Virology*, **18**, 567.

Kikuth, W., & Gollub, H. (1932) *Zbl. Bakt. I. Abt. Orig.*, **125**, 313.

Kilham, L. (1955) *Amer. J. Hyg.*, **61**, 55.

Kilham, L. (1958) *J. nat. Cancer. Inst.*, **20**, 729.

Kilham, L., & Dalmat, H. T. (1955) *Amer. J. Hyg.*, **61**, 45.

Kilham, L., Herman, C. M., & Fisher, E. R. (1953) *Proc. Soc. exp. Biol. (N.Y.)*, **82**, 298.

Kirschstein, R. L., Rabson, A. S., & Kilham, L. (1958) *Cancer Res.*, **18**, 1340.

Lea, D. E., & Salaman, M. H. (1942) *Brit. J. exp. Path.*, **23**, 27.

Ledingham, J. C. G. (1924) *Brit. J. exp. Path.*, **5**, 332.

Leese, A. S. (1909) *J. trop. vet. Sci.*, **4**, 1.

Leinati, L., Cilli, V., Mandelli, G., Castrucci, G., Carrara, O., & Scatozza, F. (1961) *Boll. Ist. sieroter. milan.*, **40**, 295.
Levaditi, C., & Nicolau, S. (1923) *Ann. Inst. Pasteur*, **37**, 1.
Lillie, R. D. (1930) *Arch. Path.*, **10**, 241.
Lipschütz, B. (1920) *Arch. Derm. Syph.*, **127**, 193.
Lisse, B. (1962) *Zbl. Bakt. I. Abt. Orig.*, **185**, 289.
Loh, P. C., & Riggs, J. L. (1961) *J. exp. Med.*, **114**, 149.
Lübke, A. (1960) *Dtsch. tierärztl. Wschr.*, **67**, 113.
McCrea, J. F., Angerer, S., & O'Loughlin, J. (1962) *Virology*, **17**, 208.
Manninger, R., Csontos, J., & Sályi, G. (1940) *Arch. Tierheilk.*, **75**, 159.
Mansi, W., & Thomas, V. (1958) *J. comp. Path.*, **68**, 188.
Marchal, J. (1930) *J. Path. Bact.*, **33**, 713.
Marennikova, S. S., Gurvich, E. B., & Yemasheva, M. A. (1959) *Probl. Virol.*, **4**, 70.
Marshall, I. D., & Fenner, F. (1958) *J. Hyg. (Lond.)*, **56**, 288.
Mason, J. H., & Neitz, W. O. (1940) *Onderstepoort J. vet. Res.*, **15**, 159.
Mayr, A. (1956) *Arch. ges. Virusforsch.*, **6**, 439.
Mayr, A. (1959) *Arch. ges. Virusforsch.*, **9**, 156.
Mayr, A., & Kalcher, K. (1960) *Arch. ges. Virusforsch.*, **10**, 72.
Mitchell, J. C. (1953) *Brit. J. exp. Path.*, **34**, 44.
Morgan, C., Ellison, S. A., Rose, H. M., & Moore, D. H. (1954) *J. exp. Med.*, **100**, 301.
Morgan, C., & Wyckoff, R. W. G. (1950) *J. Immunol.*, **65**, 285.
Moritsch, H. (1956) *Zbl. Bakt. I. Abt. Orig.*, **166**, 427.
Morozow, M. (1940) *J. Microbiol. (Moscow)*, **8**, 25.
Moses, A. (1911) *Mem. Inst. Oswaldo Cruz*, **3**, 46.
Nagington, J., Plowright, W., & Horne, R. W. (1962) *Virology*, **17**, 361.
Nagington, J., & Horne, R. W. (1962) *Virology*, **16**, 248.
Nagler, F. P. O. (1942) *Med. J. Aust.*, **1**, 281.
Nelson, J. B. (1941) *J. exp. Med.*, **74**, 203.
Nii, S. (1959) *Biken's J.*, **3**, 195.
Niven, J. S. F., Armstrong, J. A., Andrewes, C. H., Pereira, H. G., & Valentine, R. C. (1961) *J. Path. Bact.*, **81**, 1.
Noyes, W. F. (1953) *Proc. Soc. exp. Biol. (N.Y.)*, **83**, 426.
Noyes, W. F. (1962) *Virology*, **17**, 282.
Nizamuddin, M. D., & Dumbell, K. R. (1961) *Lancet*, **1**, 68.
Padgett, B. L., Moore, M. S., & Walker, D. L. (1962) *Virology*, **17**, 462.
Peters, D. (1957) *Nature (Lond.)*, **178**, 1453.
Peters, D., & Nasemann, T. (1952) *Z. Tropenmed. Parasit.*, **4**, 11.
Plowright, W. (1959) *Virology*, **7**, 357.
Plowright, W., & Ferris, R. D. (1958) *Brit. J. exp. Path.*, **39**, 424.
Plowright, W., & Ferris, R. D. (1959) *Virology*, **7**, 357.
Plowright, W., MacLeod, W. G., & Ferris, R. D. (1959) *J. comp. Path.*, **69**, 400.
Plowright, W., & Witcomb, M. A. (1959) *J. Path. Bact.*, **78**, 397.
Pontieri, G., & Chaumont, L. (1959) *Ann. Inst. Past.*, **86**, 532.
Porterfield, J. S., & Allison, A. C. (1960) *Virology*, **10**, 233.
Prier, J. E., Sauer, R. M., Malsberger, R. E., & Sillaman, J. M. (1960) *Amer. J. vet. Res.*, **21**, 381.
Pritchard, W. R., Claflin, R. M., Gustafson, D. P., & Ristic, M. (1958) *J. Amer. vet. med. Ass.*, **132**, 273.
Rafyi, A., & Ramyan, H. (1959) *J. comp. Path.*, **69**, 141.
Rake, G., & Blank, H. O. (1950) *J. invest. Derm.*, **15**, 81.
Reczko, E. (1957) *Zbl. Bakt. I. Abt. Orig.*, **169**, 425.
Reczko, E. (1959) *Arch. ges. Virusforsch.*, **9**, 193.
Reczko, E. (1962) *Arch. ges. Virusforsch.*, **12**, 269.

Rivers, T. M. (1928) *Amer. J. Path.*, **4**, 91.
Rivers, T. M. (1939) *J. exp. Med.*, **51**, 965.
Roberts, J. A. (1962) *Brit. J. exp. Path.*, **43**, 451 and 462.
Robinow, C. F. (1950) *J. gen. Microbiol.*, **4**, 242.
Rondle, C. J. M., & Dumbell, K. R. (1962) *J. Hyg. (Lond.)*, **60**, 41.
Ruska, H., & Kausche, G. A. (1943) *Zbl. Bakt. I. Abt. Orig.*, **150**, 311.
Sabban, M. S. (1957) *Amer. J. vet. Res.*, **18**, 618.
Sabban, M. S. (1960) *Bull. Off. int. Épiz.*, **53**, 1527.
Salaman, M. H., & Tomlinson, A. J. H. (1957) *J. Path. Bact.*, **74**, 17.
Schaaf, J., Traub, E., & Beller, K. (1940) *Z. Infekt.-Kr. Haustiere*, **56**, 85.
Schlesinger, M., & Andrewes, C. H. (1937) *J. Hyg. (Lond.)*, **37**, 521.
Schlesinger, R. W. (1959) in *The Viruses* Vol. 3. Ed Burnet and Stanley. New York: Academic Press. p. 157.
Schwartz, L. H. (1958) in Dunne, *Diseases of Swine*. Iowa State Press.
Shack, J., & Kilham, L. (1959) *Proc. Soc. exp. Biol. (N.Y.)*, **100**, 726.
Shama, R. M., & Bhatia, H. M. (1959) *Indian J. vet. Sci.*, **28**, 205.
Shope, R. E. (1932) *J. exp. Med.*, **56**, 803.
Shope, R. E. (1938) *Proc. Soc. exp. Biol. (N.Y.)*, **38**, 86.
Shope, R. E. (1940) *Arch. ges. Virusforsch.*, **1**, 457.
Shope, R. E., Mangold, R., Macnamara, L. G., & Dumbell, K. R. (1958) *J. exp. Med.*, **108**, 797.
Smadel, J. E. (1952) in *Viral and Rickettrial Diseases of Man*, Ed. Rivers. 2nd Ed. Philadelphia: Lippincott.
Smadel, J. E., Ward, S. M., & Rivers, T. M. (1940) *J. exp. Med.*, **72**, 129.
Smadel, J. E., Rivers, T. M., & Hoagland, C. L. (1942) *Arch. Path.*, **34**, 275.
Tunnicliff, E. A. (1949) *Amer. J. vet. Res.*, **10**, 240.
Tunnicliff, E. A., & Matisheck, P. H. (1941) *Science*, **94**, 283.
Takahashi, M., Kameyama, S., Kato, S., & Kamahora, J. (1959) *Biken's J.*, **2**, 27.
Todd, W. M., & Randall, C. C. (1958) *Arch. Path.*, **66**, 150.
Trueblood, M. S., Chow, T. L., & Griner, L. A. (1963) *Amer. J. vet. Res.*, **24**, 42.
Van Rooyen, P. J., Kümm, N. A. L., Weiss, K. E., & Alexander, R. A. (1959) *Bull. epizoot. Dis. Afr.*, **7**, 79.
Vieuchange, J. (1959) *Bull. Soc. Path. exot.*, **52**, 432.
Von Dungern, E., & Coca, A. F. (1903) *Z. Immun.-Forsch.*, **2**, 391.
Von Magnus, P., Anderson, E. K., Petersen, K. B., & Birch-Andersen, A. (1959) *Acta path. microbiol. scand.*, **46**, 156.
von Pirquet, C. (1916) *Z. Kinderheilk.*, **13**, 309.
Webster, R. G. (1958) *Aust. J. exp. Biol. med. Sci.*, **36**, 267.
Wesslén, T. (1956) *Arch. ges. Virusforsch.*, **6**, 430.
Westwood, J. C. N., Phipps, P. H., & Boulter, E. A. (1957) *J. Hyg. (Lond.)*, **55**, 123.
Wheeler, C. E., & Cawley, E. P. (1956) *Amer. J. Path.*, **32**, 535.
W.H.O. (1959) *Requirements for smallpox vaccine*. Techn. Report series no. 180.
Wittman, G. (1958) *Zbl. Vet.-Med.*, **5**, 769.
Wittman, G., & Matheka, H. D. (1958) *Mschr. Tierheilk.*, **10**, 161.
Woodroofe, G. M. (1960) *Virology*, **10**, 379.
Woodroofe, G. M., & Fenner, F. (1960) *Virology*, **12**, 272.
Woodroofe, G. M., & Fenner, F. (1962) *Virology*, **16**, 334.
Yuan, C. J., Lee, P. C., & Cheng, Y. S. (1957) *Acta vet. zootechn. sinica*, **2**, 15.
Zakay-Roness, R. A., & Bernkopf, H. (1962) *J. Immunol.*, **88**, 184.

PART III
Unclassified Viruses

13

Unclassified Viruses Pathogenic for Man

The three infections next to be discussed, infectious mononucleosis, hepatitis and rubella, have certain features in common. All have been difficult to cultivate and they show in varying degrees lymphadenopathy, hepatitis and rash.

INFECTIOUS MONONUCLEOSIS

Synonyms: Glandular Fever. Monocytic Angina.
Review: Evans (1961–62).
This is included as a virus disease by inference. There is no direct evidence of viral causation, still less as to the properties of the infectious agent.

Antigenic properties. The following tests are useful in diagnosis and are described here, though not necessarily directly related to a causative virus.
Many patients develop heterophile antibodies agglutinating sheep RBC's (Paul & Bunnell, 1932). These antibodies, in contrast to those developing in some other infections, can be absorbed by bovine RBC's but not by guinea pig kidney. The Paul–Bunnell test is not positive in all cases. A hæmolysin for bovine RBC's is also described (Mikkelson *et al.*, 1958). Human red cells modified by treatment with an Australian strain of Newcastle disease virus are agglutinated by many recent mononucleosis sera (Burnet & Anderson, 1946).

Cultivation. Attempts at cultivation in numerous kinds of primate cells were unsuccessful (Evans, 1960).

Pathogenicity. The onset of the disease is insidious and its course chronic; symptoms include fever, swollen lymph nodes, especially cervical ones at first, enlarged spleen and sore throat. Rashes and jaundice may occur; some hepatitis is apparently the rule. The blood shows a great increase in mononuclear cells, probably abnormal lymphocytes. Maximal incidence is in the age-group 15–25. There are two schools of thought concerning the disease. Evans (1960, 1961–62) considers that there are 3 phases: (i) a contagious disease with indefinite respiratory symptoms; (ii) an intermediate stage often with rash and increasing adenopathy; (iii) frank disease with positive Paul–Bunnell test, hepatitis and mononucleosis. In children only the first phase may be seen. A second, less convincing, view (Shubert *et al.*, 1954; Hobson *et al.*, 1958) considers that the Paul–Bunnell positive and negative cases represent different diseases, the latter being more infectious and less severe. Experimental transmission to human volunteers and to monkeys has been reported by a few workers, but the results are unconvincing and most attempts have been negative. Reported transmission to mice remains unconfirmed.

Pathological lesions in biopsy material from man have shown various changes in lymph nodes up to great distortion from lymphocytic or reticulo-endothelial hyperplasia; there was also hepatitis. Similar pictures have been seen in the few fatal cases (Custer & Smith, 1948).

Ecology. Most cases are sporadic, rare outbreaks being particularly in closed communities. The disease seems not to be highly infectious. Hoagland (1955) thinks "intimate oral contact" important in transmission.

INFECTIOUS HEPATITIS

Synonyms: Infective hepatitis (hepatitis virus A).
Epidemic jaundice. Catarrhal jaundice.
Reviews: Havens (1948, 1954).
MacCallum (1953, 1955).
Ward & Krugman (1962).

This infection and that next discussed, homologous serum hepatitis, are described separately though they may be related (see p. 294).

Morphology. There is no agreement as to the virus's size. Various workers have described bodies with diameters of 40 × 60 mμ (Gueft, 1961), 42 × 58 mμ (Braunsteiner *et al.*, 1957) or—from tissue culture—12–18 mμ (Rightsel *et al.*, 1961).

Physico-chemical characters. Survives 30′ at 56°; also 1½ years at −10 to 20°. Ether-stable. Residual chlorine 1 part/million inactivates in the absence of impurities.

Hæmagglutination. Sera from infected persons agglutinate rhesus RBC's more frequently than do others but the test is not specific. Schmidt & Lennette (1961) have reviewed the reported HA-tests.

Antigenic properties. Challenge of recovered volunteers with homologous virus shows that there is immunity to that, but apparently none to serum hepatitis. Pools of gamma globulin from randomly obtained human sera show protective action.

Cultivation. Growth of virus in the amniotic cavity of eggs and in chick and rabbit embryo tissue cultures was reported by Henle et al. (1950) but the results were not consistent or reproducible. There have been several recent claims to have cultivated a virus. That of Rightsel et al. (1961) produced CPE in a particular line of human cancer cells (Detroit 6). The virus was said to be ether-resistant, 12–18 mμ across, not inactivated in 30′ at 60°; there were 3 serotypes. A similar virus was described by Ananiev (1962). Davis (1961) isolated from Arizona Indians with hepatitis an agent which only grew with CPE in a cell strain derived from human embryonic lung. Cases of human hepatitis apparently contracted from chimpanzees (Hillis, 1961) yielded an agent causing CPE in chimpanzee kidney cultures (Hillis, 1962). The virus of O'Malley et al. (1961) recovered from serum hepatitis is referred to on p. 295. There are discrepancies between the accounts of different workers and no results from any laboratory have been regularly reproducible elsewhere. The virus described by Chang (1961), though apparently coming from a patient with hepatitis, is unlikely to be causally related to that disease. It multiplied in several cell lines of human origin and had remarkable powers of degrading DNA.

Distribution. Distribution is world-wide: the disease is particularly prevalent in the Middle East and around the Mediterranean.

Pathogenicity. Onset in man may be acute or insidious with anorexia, nausea and abdominal tenderness. There may be a period of improvement before jaundice appears; but many patients, especially children, are anicteric. Mortality is low but cirrhosis or

20

liver atrophy may follow in a few cases. The incubation period is from 15 to 40 days, average 25. A milder form occurring amongst children had a longer incubation—35–56 days (Ward & Krugman, 1962).

Experimentally volunteers have been infected *per os* or parenterally. Virus is present in blood and fæces. Many of the infected persons have had subicteric infection detected by finding abnormalities in liver function tests. There have been claims to have reproduced the disease in rats, guinea pigs, pigs, ducks, canaries and other species; none has been generally confirmed.

Pathological lesions. Focal mid-zonal necrosis of liver parenchyma and portal infiltration have been seen in biopsy specimens. In fulminant cases there is acute yellow atrophy of the liver with multiple hæmorrhages (Lucké, 1944). Regeneration of liver is rapid in convalescence. It is likely that there is a general infection and that liver damage, often its most striking manifestation, may be absent.

Ecology. Infection commonly occurs through fæcal contamination of food or water; infected oysters have caused some serious outbreaks. Opinions differ as to occurrence of virus in the nasopharynx and the importance of infection by the respiratory route. Virus may be present in blood and fæces during the incubation period and for months after recovery; this virus and not only homologous serum hepatitis can thus be transmitted by transfusions.

Control. Improved hygiene should be aimed at. Pooled gamma globulin from normal adults, given during the incubation period, is believed to be effective in preventing illness if not infection (Krugman & Ward, 1961–62). The unexpectedly long duration of its efficacy has suggested that it operates as a passive-active immunising agent, permitting an immunizing subclinical infection in those exposed before its effects have quite worn off (Stokes *et al.*, 1951).

HOMOLOGOUS SERUM HEPATITIS

Synonyms: Hepatitis (virus B). Serum hepatitis.
Reviews: as for Infectious hepatitis (McCallum, 1953, 1955).

Morphology. Passed a 52 mμ gradocol membrane (McCollum, 1952) and diameter therefore likely to be 30 mμ or less.

Physico-chemical characters. Survives heating at 60° for 4, not 10 hours; also, in serum or plasma, at least 6 months at room temperature, and for years when frozen or dried. Withstands 0·25 per cent. phenol for over a year. Ether-resistant. UV-radiation is unreliable as a method of inactivation.

Antigenic properties. No cross-immunity with hepatitis virus A, but there is some evidence of homologous immunity (Neefe et al., 1946). γ-globulin from pooled human sera does not protect.

Cultivation. Results of attempted cultivation in *eggs* inoculated amniotically (Henle et al., 1952) have doubtful significance. O'Malley et al. (1961) cultivated from a pool of icterogenic serum an agent causing CPE in a wide range of tissue-cultures: its significance is obscure.

Pathogenicity. Symptoms in man are not clearly separable from those due to hepatitis virus A. The disease is transmitted, however, only by parenteral injection and the incubation period is considerably longer, commonly 40–150 days. Persons of all ages are susceptible (A virus usually affects younger people) but this difference may reflect the different method of transmission. Some subjects carry virus in the blood for as long as 5 years: they may show abnormalities in liver function tests. Virus has not been detected in stools.

Ecology. Virus is present in the blood of some normal persons, apparently 0·78 per cent. in one survey (Lehane et al., 1949). It may therefore be transmitted by transfusion or by any other injection of human blood, serum or plasma or when several people are injected without proper sterilization of needles or syringes in between. Thousands of cases occurred during the Second World War as a result of injecting yellow fever vaccine containing human serum. One or two reports suggest that the virus may occasionally be present in the throat (MacCallum et al., 1951), but contact infection seems hardly ever to occur. It may be that virus B is unrelated to virus A: its normal method of transmission is in that case obscure. Alternatively virus A may pass into a phase (B) in which it is not neutralized by anti-A antibodies, can persist in the blood for long periods and takes many weeks to produce evidence of infection after it has been injected.

Control. Many infections can be avoided if blood or plasma for transfusions is not pooled; and if syringes and needles are sterilized by autoclaving or boiling for 10 minutes between any two injections. Immersion in alcohol is useless. No satisfactory method of inactivating virus in blood or plasma without destroying their useful properties has been established.

A possibly related condition in horses is referred to on p. 303.

RUBELLA

Synonym: German Measles.
Reviews: (epidemiology and teratology) Ingalls *et al.* (1960). Blattner & Heys (1961).

Morphology. Passed a 300 mμ not a 150 mμ membrane (Parkman *et al.*, 1962; Weller & Neva, 1962). Norrby *et al.* (1963) found by electron-microscopy particles with cores 130 mμ across on the average, surrounded by an envelope outwardly smooth, 120–280 mμ across.

Physico-chemical characters. Almost or quite inactivated in 1 hour at 56°. Very stable at −65°. Sensitive to ether, chloroform or desoxycholate.

Hæmagglutination—none demonstrated.

Antigenic properties. One attack usually confers immunity: reports of second attacks are commonly due to mistaken diagnosis. Neutralizing antibodies, rising in the course of an attack, are demonstrable in tissue cultures. Specific complement-fixation could not be demonstrated (Weller & Neva, 1962; Parkman *et al.*, 1962). Pooled human gamma globulin is said to protect but results are often equivocal (Grayston & Watten, 1959).

Interference with ECHO 11 and Sindbis viruses in tissue culture is reported in the next paragraph.

Cultivation. Reports of cultivation in *eggs* have not been confirmed.

Weller & Neva (1962) reported that they had cultivated virus in primary human amnion or embryonic skin-muscle cultures with production of CPE. Cultures were rotated at 35°. Changes included an unusual kind of aggregation of nuclear material and production of nuclear and cytoplasmic inclusions. It appeared to multiply in human cancer cell-lines (HeLa, Chang liver) but without causing cell changes. The virus interfered with Sindbis virus in culture. Antigenically similar viruses were propagated by Parkman et al. (1962) in cultures of *Cercopithecus* kidney. No cytopathic effects were seen; activity of the virus was recognized by interference with the growth of ECHO 11, titres up to 10^{-4} being obtained. Growth occurred also, though less regularly, in human embryonic kidney and rhesus kidney. Sever et al. (1962) produced rubella with cultivated virus in the only 2 of 10 volunteers without previous antibody.

Pathogenicity. Rubella is a mild infection with generalized rash, enlargement of lymph-nodes, especially the post-cervical. There is usually little fever or constitutional disturbance. The incubation period is 16–18 days. Meningo-encephalitis and other complications are rare. The disease is important because of the high incidence of congenital abnormalities in children whose mothers had rubella during the first 3 or 4 months of pregnancy (Gregg, 1945; Swan et al., 1946). Incidence has been different at different times and places; abnormalities include deaf-mutism, cataract, cardiac and dental malformations and microcephaly.

Experimentally infection has been transmitted to rhesus monkeys (Habel, 1942); these developed leucopenia and, in some cases, a light pink rash. The disease has also appeared in volunteers inoculated SC or IN, after an incubation period of 13–20 days (Anderson, 1949): some infections were apparently subclinical.

Pathological lesions. No characteristic lesions have been seen in lymph nodes removed for biopsy.

Control. Women in early pregnancy should not be exposed to infection. If this does occur, γ globulin from rubella convalescents should be given, though its efficacy cannot be relied on. It has been suggested that non-immune young women should be deliberately exposed to infection before marriage.

EPIDEMIC VIRAL GASTRO-ENTERITIS
(of man)

Synonyms: Acute infectious gastro-enteritis. Winter vomiting disease. Viral dysentery. Infantile diarrhœa (in part) —and various other names.

There is obscurity as to the relationships between neonatal diarrhœa and the diarrhœas of older infants and of adults. A number of viruses are probably concerned; some epidemics, especially in children, are probably caused by enteroviruses (v. p. 16). There is a little information about some others, largely obtained as a result of transmission experiments in human volunteers.

A. Marcy Virus

Stool-filtrates obtained from adults suffering from epidemic diarrhœa were fed to volunteers, most of whom developed severe watery diarrhœa with little or no fever; some had vomiting also. The incubation period was 1 to 5 days, average 3 (Gordon *et al.*, 1947). The infection was transmissible in series. Sufferers reinoculated after 2 weeks proved to be immune, but 2 subjects tested after 10 months were susceptible. Immunity is therefore transient. A virus from Japan is probably identical with Gordon's from the United States (Fukumi *et al.*, 1957).

Virtually nothing is known of the properties of this virus. It could not be cultivated in fertile eggs, nor are there definite reports of growth in tissue culture.

B. F.S. Virus

Another agent, obtained from bacteria-free preparations of stools of adults with diarrhœa, caused rather different symptoms with some fever, more constitutional symptoms, often abdominal pain without diarrhœa (Jordan *et al.*, 1953; Badger *et al.*, 1956). There was no cross-immunity with the Marcy virus.

C. Viruses Isolated from Infantile Diarrhœa

Buddingh & Dodd (1944) recovered a virus from infants under 6 months old. Diarrhœa was associated with stomatitis affecting chiefly the tongue and gums. The virus produced keratitis when inoculated on to the scarified rabbit's cornea. A reaction appeared in 24 hours. There was sometimes iritis but never a keratitis leading to corneal opacity, as in a herpes simplex infection. No inclusions were found. The virus was passed 40 times in series through corneas of young rabbits. Corneal suspensions were still infective after 90 days' storage at 0° C. Recovered rabbits were immune to reinoculation. The virus could not be cultivated in fertile eggs. Neutralizing antibodies were present in sera of recovered patients.

D Other Agents

A virus from infantile diarrhœa was reported to be transmissible to calves by Light & Hodes (1943), but since calves are very liable to diarrhœa and since the agent was said to withstand boiling, confirmation should be awaited. Another agent, cultivable in yolk-sacs of hens' eggs, was reported by Meiklejohn (1947).

DURAND'S DISEASE

This febrile illness, apparently due to a virus and transmitted to several animal species (Findlay, 1942) cannot now be identified.

REFERENCES

Ananiev, V. A. (1962) *Abst. Proc., 8th int., Microbiol. Congr.*, p. 94.
Anderson, S. G. (1949) *J. Immunol.*, **62**, 29.
Badger, G. F., McCorkle, L. P., Curtiss, G., Dingle, J. H., Hodges, R. G., & Jordan, W. S. (1956) *Amer. J. Hyg.*, **64**, 376.
Blattner, R. J., & Heys, F. M. (1961) *Progr. med. Virol.*, **3**, 311.
Braunsteiner, H., Fellinger, K., Beyreder, T., Grabner, G., & Neumayr, A. (1957) *Wien. Z. inn. Med.*, **38**, 231.
Buddingh, G. J., & Dodd, K. (1944) *J. Pediat.*, **25**, 105.
Burnet, F. M., & Anderson, S. G. (1946) *Brit. J. exp. Path.*, **27**, 236.
Chang, R. S. (1961) *Proc. Soc. exp. Biol. (N.Y.)*, **107**, 135.
Custer, R. P., & Smith, E. B. (1948) *Blood*, **3**, 830.
Davis, E. V. (1961) *Science*, **133**, 2059.
Evans, A. S. (1960) *Amer. J. Hyg.*, **71**, 342.
Evans, A. S. (1961–2) *Yale J. exp. Biol.*, **34**, 101.
Findlay, G. M. (1942) *Trans. roy. Soc. trop. Med. Hyg.*, **35**, 303.
Findlay, G. M., & MacCallum, F. O. (1938) *Proc. roy. Soc. Med.*, **31**, 799.
Fukumi, H., Nakaya, R., Hatha, S., Noriki, H., Yunoki, H., Akagi, K., Saito, T., Uchiyama, K., Kobari, K., & Nakamishi, R. (1957) *Jap. J. med. Sci.*, **10**, 1.
Gordon, I., Ingraham, H. S., & Korns, R. F. (1947) *J. exp. Med.*, **86**, 409.
Grayston, J. T., & Watten, R. H. (1959) *New Engl. J. Med.*, **261**, 1145.
Greene, H. S. N. (1934) *J. exp. Med.*, **60**, 427.
Gregg, N. McA. (1945) *Med. J. Aust.*, **1**, 313.
Gueft, B. (1961) *Arch. Path.*, **72**, 61.
Habel, K. (1942) *Publ. Hlth. Rep. (Wash.)*, **57**, 1126.
Havens, W. P. (1948) *Medicine*, **27**, 279.
Havens, W. P. (1954) *Ann. Rev. Microbiol.*, **8**, 289.
Henle, W., Drake, M. E., Henle, G., & Stokes, J. (1952) *Arch. ges. Virusforsch.*, **4**, 612.
Henle, W., Harris, S., Henle, G., Harris, T. N., Drake, M. E., Mangold, F., & Stokes, J. (1950) *J. exp. Med.*, **92**, 271.
Hillis, W. D. (1961) *Amer. J. Hyg.*, **73**, 316.

Hillis, W. D. (1962) *Proc. Soc. exp. Biol.* (*N.Y.*), **108,** 813.

Hoagland, R. J. (1955) *Amer. J. med. Sci.*, **229,** 262.

Hobson, F. G., Lawson, B., & Wigfield, M. (1958) *Brit. med. J.*, **1,** 845.

Ingalls, T. H., Babbott, F. L., Hampson, K. W., & Gordon, J. E. (1960) *Amer. J. med. Sci.*, **239,** 363.

Jordan, W. S., Gordon, I., & Dorrance, L. R. (1953) *J. exp. Med.*, **98,** 461.

Krugman, S., & Ward, R. (1961–2) *Yale J. Biol. Med.*, **34,** 169.

Lehane, O., Kwantes, C. M. S., Upward, M. G., & Thompson, D. R. (1949) *Brit. med. J.*, **2,** 572.

Light, J. S., & Hodes, H. L. (1943) *J. exp. Med.*, **90,** 113.

Lucké, B. (1944) *Amer. J. Path.*, **20,** 471.

MacCallum, F. O. (1953) *Brit. med. Bull.*, **9,** 221.

MacCallum, F. O. (1956) in *Virus and Rickettsial Diseases.* Ed. Bedson, Downie, MacCallum, Stuart-Harris. 2nd Ed. London: Arnold.

MacCallum, F. O., McFarlan, A. M., Miles, J. A. R., Pollock, M. R., & Wilson, C. (1951) *Spec. Rep. Ser. med. Res. Coun.* (*Lond.*), no. 273.

McCollum, R. W. (1952) *Proc. Soc. exp. Biol.* (*N.Y.*), **81,** 157.

Marsh, A. (1937) *J. Amer. vet. med. Ass.*, **91,** 88 and 330.

Meiklejohn, G. (1947) *Calif. Med.*, **67,** 238.

Mikkelsen, W., Tupper, C. J., & Murray, J. (1958) *J. Lab. clin. Med.*, **52,** 648.

Neefe, J. R., Baty, J. B., Reinhold, J. G., & Stokes, J. (1947) *Amer. J. publ. Hlth.*, **37,** 365.

Norrby, E., Magnusson, P., Friding, B., & Gard, S. (1963) *Arch. ges. Virusforsch.*, **13,** 426.

O'Malley, J. P., Meyer, H. M., & Smadel, J. E. (1961) *Proc. Soc. exp. Biol.* (*N.Y.*), **108,** 200.

Parkman, D., Buescher, E. L., & Arnstein, E. S. (1962) *Proc. Soc. exp. Biol.* (*N.Y.*), **111,** 225.

Paul, J. R., & Bunnell, W. W. (1932) *Amer. J. med. Sci.*, **183,** 90.

Rightsel, W. A., Keltsch, R. A., Taylor, A. R., Boggs, J. B., & McLean, I. W. (1961) *J. Amer. med. Ass.*, **177,** 671.

Schmidt, N. J., & Lennette, E. H. (1961) *Progr. med. Virol.*, **3,** 32.

Sever, J. L., Schiff, G. M., & Traub, R. G. (1962) *J. Amer. med. Ass.*, **182,** 663.

Shubert, S., Collee, J. G., & Smith, B. J. (1954) *Brit. med. J.*, **1,** 671.

Stokes, J., Farquhar, J. A., Drake, M. E., Capps, R.B., Ward, C. S., Mills, O. W., & Kitts, A. W. (1951) *J. Amer. med. Ass.*, **147,** 714.

Swan, C., Tostevin, A. L., & Black, G. H. B. (1946) *Med. J. Aust.*, **2,** 889.

Ward, R., & Krugman, S. (1962) *Progr. med. Virol.*, **4,** 87.

Weller, T. H., & Neva, F. (1962) *Proc. Soc. exp. Biol.* (*N.Y.*), **111,** 215.

14

Unclassified Viruses of Ungulates

BORNA DISEASE
(*Named from a locality in Saxony*)

Synonym: Enzoötic encephalomyelitis (of horses, sheep and cattle).
Reviews: Nicolau & Galloway (1928, 1930).

Morphology. Estimated diameter, by filtration 85–125 mμ, by UV microscopy 110–140 mμ (Elford & Galloway, 1933).

Physico-chemical characters. Inactivated in 30′ at 50°–57°, in 10′ at 70°, fairly stable between pH 6·1 and 7·6. Ether- and chloroform-sensitive. Survives drying, storage in 50 per cent. glycerol for 6 months or even 17 years (von Sprockhoff, 1953). One per cent. phenol inactivated in 4 weeks, not in 2 weeks. 0·2 per cent. formalin inactivated a brain suspension in 18 hours at room temperature.

Antigenic properties. Immunologically distinct from viruses causing similar infections. Neutralizing antibodies not readily detected in serum. CF antigen present in brains of infected rabbits; apparently a "soluble antigen" 15–30 mμ across, stable between pH 5 and 8 (von Sprockhoff, 1958).

Cultivation is reported on the CAM of fertile eggs incubated for 5–11 days, preferably at 35°–35·5° (Rott & Nitzschke, 1958). No reports on attempted tissue culture.

Distribution. The main focus of the disease is in Saxony but it is reported from other parts of Germany, Poland, Rumania, Russia and formerly elsewhere in Europe. It occurs in Libya and an encephalitis of donkeys in Egypt (Sabban *et al.*, 1961) may be due to Borna virus or to the "Near East equine encephalomyelitis"—*v.* p. 303. Its occurrence in North and South America has been reported but apparently only on clinical grounds and before the insect-borne encephalitis viruses had been recognized.

Pathogenicity. Affected horses show lassitude, followed by a period of excitation with tonic spasms and later paralysis. The virus may produce similar symptoms in sheep, cattle and probably deer (sporadic bovine encephalomyelitis is due to a different agent *v.* p. 379).

Experimentally the disease can be transmitted to other species, most readily to rabbits (Zwick & Seifried, 1924). Inoculation IC is most effective but infection can be produced by various other routes. The incubation period is from 20–60 days, but in new-born rabbits may be only 12–15 days (von Sprockhoff, 1958). Symptoms consist of depression, somnolence, loss of weight, salivation, later paralysis affecting first the hind limbs and finally death in coma. Infected guinea pigs, rats and mice develop similar symptoms, but are less susceptible than rabbits; older rats and mice are more easily infected than younger ones. Fatal disease may occur in rhesus monkeys inoculated IC. Human infections are not reported. Cats, dogs and ferrets are also resistant. Virus may be found in the nervous system, adrenals and in ganglia in various organs of rabbits, probably travelling along nerves; viræmia is not a regular feature but may occur in rabbits.

Pathological lesions are those of meningo-encephalomyelitis, the characteristic feature being the presence of the Joest-Degen bodies in nerve cells, particularly those of the hippocampus and olfactory lobes. These are small round eosinophilic nuclear inclusions, showing evidence of internal structure. They are not constantly present in horses or rabbits, particularly in later serial passages in rabbits; they occur more regularly in infected rats and guinea pigs.

Ecology. The disease may occur throughout the year and arthropod transmission is improbable. Infection probably passes from oral and nasal secretions. Inapparently infected sheep may infect horses but horses do not seem to infect sheep. Contact infection may occur, though infrequently, between rabbits, and a spontaneous outbreak in laboratory rabbits is reported (Otta & Jentzsch, 1960).

Control. Virus in brain tissue, inactivated with phenol or phenol-glycerol has been used, apparently with success, to control the disease (Razza & Carusillo, 1949). Zwick *et al.* (1929) had previously reported success with a lapinized virus.

Borna disease may conceivably come to be classified along with rabies.

A suggested relation between it and malignant catarrh (*v.*, p. 233) does not seem very likely.

Nigerian Horse Virus

A virus possibly related to Borna and causing "staggers" in Nigerian horses was described by Porterfield *et al.* (1958). It was transmissible to mice inoculated IC, was pathogenic for *Cercocebus* monkeys and was unrelated serologically to 32 other viruses, chiefly arboviruses. It passed a 0·23 mμ membrane, not one of 0·16 mμ.

NEAR EAST EQUINE ENCEPHALOMYELITIS

A virus was isolated by Daubney & Mahlau (1957) from horses, donkeys, cattle and sheep with encephalomyelitis in Egypt and Syria. It passed a 34 mμ membrane. It was transmissible to rabbits, guinea pigs and day-old chicks, and was also apparently cultivated in eggs. The incubation period in rabbits was very variable. The virus was also isolated from herons and other birds and from ticks (*Hyalomma excavatum*). The characteristic Joest-Degen bodies of Borna disease could not be found. The virus is no longer available and a possible relation to arboviruses has not been explored.

HEPATITIS IN HORSES

There are reports of hepatitis in horses following injection of homologous serum or tissues (Findlay & MacCallum, 1938). The disease has followed attempts at immunizing against horse sickness in South Africa, against equine encephalomyelitis in North America (Marsh, 1937) and against *Clostridia* in Scotland. In Marsh's cases the incubation period was 40–72 days in 90 per cent. and the mortality in horses developing symptoms was about 90 per cent. Besides hepatitis, there were diffuse enteritis and renal damage. There are no reports of attempts to recover a transmissible agent.

INFECTIOUS ANÆMIA OF HORSES

Synonym: Swamp fever.
Review: Dreguss & Lombard (1954).

Morphology. Diameter estimated to be 60–95 mμ (Mohlmann & Gralheer, 1954).

Physico-chemical characters. Virus in serum is inactivated in 60′ at 60°. It is resistant to drying and putrefaction but not to sunlight. It survived 158 days in tap water at room temperature (Rodionov & Oleynik, 1946). Ether-sensitivity not reported. 0·1 per cent. formaldehyde inactivated virus in serum in 1 month at 5° but it survived 0·5 per cent. phenol under these conditions (Stein & Gates, 1952). Four per cent. NaOH inactivated it in 15′ but oxidizing agents (hypochlorite and KMno$_4$) were not very effective.

Hæmagglutination of fowl and frog (*Rana esculenta*) cells by infective serum is reported (Fedotov, 1960) but not generally confirmed.

Antigenic properties. Complement-fixation has been reported but is doubtfully specific.

Cultivation. Attempts at growth on eggs have been negative. Multiplication in embryonic horse tissues is reported but without evidence of CPE (Watanabe, 1960).

Habitat. Distribution is world-wide. The disease is more prevalent in low-lying marshy country.

Pathogenicity. Certainly pathogenic only for horses and other *Equidæ*. Horses may have acute or chronic infections, the latter often consisting of a succession of acute episodes with remissions; these may last for years but the disease is usually fatal. The incubation period is usually 12–15 days but it may be much longer before symptoms appear even though viræmia occurs earlier. There occur fever, anæmia, wasting, serous nasal discharge and areas of subcutaneous œdema. Viræmia may be present for years even during remissions. A chronic case of human infection is reported (Peters, 1924); in this the blood remained infectious for horses over a long period.

Experimentally several workers have reported successful transmission to rabbits, rats, mice, swine, pigeons and other species, few or no symptoms being produced; but other workers (e.g. Stein & Mott, 1944) have failed to confirm these claims.

Pathological lesions. In fatal cases one finds numerous hæmorrhages, areas of subcutaneous œdema, degeneration of liver and kidney, replacement of yellow by red bone marrow in long bones.

Ecology. Biting insects, especially *Stomoxys* and *Tabanids*, are suspected of transmitting the virus, probably mechanically; but transmission by contact or even oral infection is believed to be also possible. Virus occurs in milk, semen, saliva and urine. Since viræmia is so prolonged, even up to 18 years, transmission by inadequately sterilized syringes is also to be guarded against.

Control. No specific prophylaxis is at present possible. Infected animals should be slaughtered.

INFECTIOUS ARTERITIS

This has been confused with rhinopneumonitis or equine abortion (p. 226), since it, too, is a cause of abortion in mares.

Synonym: Pink-eye, equine influenza. It may be the commonest cause of so-called equine influenza (but *v.* p. 111).

Description: Doll *et al.* (1957).

Morphology. Passes a Seitz EK filter.

Physico-chemical characters. Survives for 6 years at −20° C, 75 days at 4° C, only 2 days at 37° C, 20' not 30' at 56° C (McCollum *et al.*, 1961).

Antigenic properties. Neutralizing antibodies are demonstrable. It is unrelated to rhinopneumonitis.

Cultivation. None reported in fertile eggs. Grows in monolayers of horse kidney, producing CPE, becoming attenuated so as to be of use for immunisation (McCollum *et al.*, 1961). Later it was adapted to grow in hamster kidney cultures (Wilson *et al.*, 1962).

Pathogenicity. Causes fever, conjunctivitis, rhinitis, œdema of the legs or trunk, enteritis and colitis. Virus is present in the tissues and various body fluids but not in the urine. Is one cause of abortions in mares, virus having invaded the fœtus. Pneumonia may occur and is usually fatal.

Experimentally. The incubation period in horses is 5–10 days. Other species are not susceptible.

Pathological lesions. Bronchopneumonia and pleural effusions are seen in fatal cases. Gelatinous swellings occur round the larynx and elsewhere. The essential lesions are those of medial necrosis of smaller arteries; when endothelial intima is involved thrombosis and infarction follow with the characteristic hæmorrhages and œdema.

Ecology. It is believed to be this virus which has caused widespread epizoötics in the past. It is extremely contagious, infecting mainly young animals, probably through the respiratory tract. Some maintain that recovered stallions may be carriers and transmit infection.

Control. Prospects for a vaccine made from virus attenuated in tissue culture seem good (McCollum *et al.*, 1961).

Other Respiratory Infections of Horses

The literature on this subject is most confusing. Differentiation of entities is almost wholly on a clinical basis. There are described (apart from the conditions listed as synonyms of infectious arteritis), infectious bronchitis, Hoppegartener husten (or racing-stable cough), contagious pleuropneumonia of horses and numerous other ailments. The agent of Hoppegartener husten is said to be transmissible to cattle and young pigs (Waldmann & Kobe, 1934). There is, however, no firm basis for describing any respiratory virus infection of horses other than true horse influenza, due to Myxovirus *Influenzæ-A equi* (*v.* p. 111), infectious arteritis (*v.* p. 305) and infectious rhinopneumonitis (*v.* p. 226).

Other Virus Diseases of Horses

Elsewhere in this book are described:
Rhinopneumonitis (p. 226).
Vesicular stomatitis (p. 318).
African horse-sickness (p. 322).
Horse-pox (p. 269).
A coital exanthema affecting horses is described by Reisinger & Reimann (1928); this may possibly be due to the agent affecting cattle (p. 306).

Equine encephalomyelitis: Eastern (p. 51)
Western (p. 54)
Venezuelan (p. 57).
Rhinovirus of horses (p. 26).

SWINE FEVER

Synonym: Hog cholera.
Reviews: Dunne (1958).
Wilsdon (1958) (Symptoms and Control).

Morphology. Size estimated by Pehl & Gralheer (1956) at 15–25 mμ. Other estimates all suggest that it is a small virus but none are very convincing. Dinter (1963) gives a diameter of 50 mμ.

Chemical composition. Probably RNA (Dinter, 1963).

Physico-chemical characters. A very stable virus, more so in blood held between pH 4·8 and 5·1 than at neutral pH (Chapin et al., 1939). A pH <1·4 or >13 is necessary to kill it within an hour (Slavin, 1938). When dried in vacuo and sealed in ampoules it survives well even at 37° but is soon inactivated when dried in air in the field; however, it persists a long time in infected pork or garbage. Virus keeps well in the cold when mixed with glycerol or in the presence of 0·5 per cent. phenol. Ether-sensitive according to Dinter (1963).

Antigenic properties. Neutralization and CF tests are applicable; also precipitation in agar gel-diffusion tests (Molnar, 1954; Mansi, 1957), lymph nodes or pancreas from infected pigs being the best antigens for this last test. Gel-diffusion tests also reveal an antigenic component in common with mucosal disease of cattle (v., p. 311) (Darbyshire, 1962). Recovered pigs are permanently immune. A variant virus is reported from the United States giving rise to "breaks" in the course of attempted immunization. It is poorly neutralized by specific antisera but no distinct stable antigenic type has been distinguished. Variant virus may be analogous to the Q variant of influenza virus which is poorly neutralized by homologous sera (v., p. 108).

Cultivation. Adaptation of virus to duck embryos (Coronel & Albis, 1950) and to chick embryos (Fontanelli et al., 1959) has been claimed, but further studies are not yet reported. On the other hand it is generally agreed that the virus will multiply in cultures of swine kidney, testis, bone-marrow and "buffy coat"; also (Lang *et al.*, 1960) in testis cultures from young rabbits. Unfortunately it usually produces no cytopathic effects or only (Gustafson & Pomerat, 1957) minimal ones. However, Gillespie *et al.* (1960b) adapted one strain to pig kidney tissues in lamb serum and saw definite CPE. Kumagai *et al.* (1961) report that in the presence of swine fever, the CPE of Newcastle disease virus on swine testis monolayers is greatly accelerated.

Distribution. The disease apparently first appeared in mid-western North America about 1833 and thence in the course of the nineteenth century spread all over the world. Its possible origin is discussed by Hanson (1957).

Pathogenicity. Usually exceedingly contagious and fatal amongst herds of pigs. These show fever, apathy, vomiting, eye-discharge, diarrhœa, cutaneous hæmorrhages, but mild strains have been reported (Keast *et al.*, 1962). Symptoms referable to encephalomyelitis are frequent. Some strains of virus are unusually neurotropic. Pigs may die of the virus infection, or, after secondary infection with *Salmonella choleræ-suis* or other bacteria, of pneumonia or ulcerative enteritis. Only pigs are naturally affected.

Experimentally the disease is easily reproduced by inoculating pigs by various routes, the incubation period being from 3 to 7 days. Zichis (1939) produced a transmissible inapparent infection in sheep; and several authors have achieved the same thing in rabbits. Some (Baker, 1946; Koprowski *et al.*, 1946) have succeeded by zigzagging, i.e. making alternate passages between pigs and rabbits; others have found this unnecessary. Infected rabbits show nothing but transient fever. Lapinized virus is attenuated for pigs and has been used for immunization.

Pathological lesions comprise degeneration of small blood vessels leading to small hæmorrhages in kidney, bladder, skin, lymph-nodes and infarction especially in the spleen; but pigs dying early of pure virus infection show very little macroscopically. Characteristic lesions, including cuffing and microgliosis, may, however, be found in the CNS (Done, 1957). With later deaths there are seen pneumonia and "button ulcers" in intestines. Leucopenia is the rule. Inclusion bodies have been described but are doubtfully specific.

Ecology. Spread is by direct contact and by feeding contaminated garbage. Virus apparently disappears between outbreaks; Shope (1958) has produced evidence suggesting that it may persist in swine lung-worms.

Control. Hyperimmune sera can be used to give temporary protection when the disease appears in a herd. Several methods of active immunization are used: (i) Simultaneous inoculation of virulent virus and antisera at separate sites; this method is being replaced by others, since it leads to persistence of infection in the locality; (ii) Virus inactivated by crystal violet (McBryde & Cole, 1936) is widely and successfully used; also Boynton's (1933) eucalyptol-treated vaccine. These, however, give only temporary immunity; (iii) Viruses attenuated by passage in rabbits (Baker, 1947) or in tissue-culture (Casselberry et al., 1953) give much promise. They may be given with or without antisera. There is still doubt, however, as to whether the character of attenuation is stable. Attenuated virus may cause abortions, or malformations amongst litters (Bontcheff et al., 1959; Young et al., 1955) and may be dangerous when given to baby pigs (Baker & Sheffy, 1960). The virus of mucosal disease of cattle, shown to be antigenically related to swine fever, is being tested for its ability to immunize swine.

TRANSMISSIBLE GASTRO-ENTERITIS
(of pigs)

Review: Doyle (1958).

Morphology. Size estimated at 200 mμ by gradocol filtration (Young et al., 1955).

Physico-chemical characters. Survives drying 3 days at room temperature, or $3\frac{1}{2}$ years at $-28°$. 0·05 per cent. formaldehyde inactivates in 20' at 37° C. Heating for 30' at 56° inactivates (Bay et al., 1962; Haeltermann & Hutchings, 1956).

Antigenic properties. Convalescent serum from recovered pigs neutralizes the virus (Goodwin & Jennings, 1959).

Cultivation is reported in pig kidney tissue culture but without CPE (Lee, 1956).

21

Distribution. Occurs in Britain, United States, Japan and U.S.S.R.

Pathogenicity. A very fatal disease in young pigs, causing acute diarrhœa, vomiting, dehydration and often death after 5 to 7 days. Incubation period 12 to 18 hours. May affect older pigs causing scarring; and may take a chronic course. Recovery is usual in pigs over 3 weeks old.

Species other than pigs are insusceptible.

Experimental infection is successful when virus is given *per os* but not parenterally. Virus is mainly found in intestines and kidneys.

Pathological lesions. Acute enteritis involving the whole gut with hyperæmia and some necrosis but particularly distension of the gut with fluid. May be degenerative lesions in heart, muscle and kidney.

Ecology. Spread is by direct or indirect contact—imperfectly cleaned buildings may retain infection. Virus may be excreted in fæces of recovered cases up to 10 weeks.

Control. Probable protection by colostrum: young of recovered sows usually survive. Proper management, with breaks between farrowing seasons, usually eliminates infection.

Other Diseases of Pigs

Vesicular exanthema (p. 29).
Inclusion-body rhinitis (p. 241).
Swine influenza (p. 110).
Foot-and-mouth disease (p. 31).
Porcine enteroviruses (ECSO) (p. 18).

"Virus pneumonia" of pigs is not considered here as the common form is almost certainly caused by a *Mycoplasma* (pleuro-pneumonia-like organism). Another respiratory disease affecting suckling pigs is referred to on p. 242.

VIRUS-DIARRHŒA
(in cattle)

Synonyms: Mucosal disease. Pneumo-enteritis of calves. Bovine diarrhœa (New York, Oregon and Indiana strains).

There is no certainty as to how many different agents are concerned in causing in cattle—particularly calves—diarrhœa with or without pneumonia. Where data are reported, the name used by the author for the particular agent will be given.

Review: Johnston (1959).

Morphology. Pneumo-enteritis virus passes a filter with pore-size 50–80 mμ (Brandly *et al.*, 1956). Mucosal disease virus was not more than 30 mμ across (Huck, 1961) or was between 275 and 400 mμ in diameter (van Bekkum, 1959). Bovine diarrhœa (Oregon strain) was 40 mμ across by electron-microscopy (Hermodsson & Dinter, 1962).

Chemical composition. Probably an RNA virus (Dinter, 1963).

Physico-chemical characters. Sensitive to ether and chloroform, according to Hermodsson & Dinter (1962); the same strain was reported as ether-stable by Taylor *et al.* (1963). They also found it inactivated in 35′ at 56°.

Antigenic properties. Different reports state that the New York and Indiana strains do not cross-immunize (in cattle) or do show cross-neutralization (in tissue culture) (Gillespie *et al.*, 1960a). There is also said to be cross-neutralization with mucosal disease (Gillespie *et al.*, 1961; Taylor *et al.*, 1963).

Gel-diffusion tests show an antigen in common between mucosal disease virus and swine fever (Darbyshire, 1960) and Sheffy *et al.* (1962) have found that mucosal disease virus will give some protection to pigs against swine fever.

Cultivation. Cultivation of mucosal disease virus has been reported in trypsinized bovine kidney and fœtal skin (Noice & Schipper, 1959; van Bekkum, 1959) also of bovine diarrhœa (Gillespie *et al.*, 1959, 1960a). Darbyshire (1963) encountered a strain which would multiply and produce pocks on chorio-allantoic membranes of eggs.

Pathogenicity. The disease picture described for mucosal disease includes, besides diarrhœa, fever and oral ulcerations. There is intestinal catarrh, and necrotic lesions occur in the mucosa together with lesions in the hooves, lymph nodes and elsewhere. The disease transmitted experimentally is usually mild (Huck, 1957). Transmission to other species is not reported.

The agent described as pneumo-enteritis of calves has an incubation period of 9–10 days and a mortality of 4–8 per cent. Besides diarrhœa we again read reports of ulcers in the upper respiratory and upper intestinal tracts and pneumonia. Transmission to mice with production of pneumonia after 3 passages is reported (Baker, 1943) and production of disease in calves with mouse-passed material. Another agent has been passaged in rabbits (Baker *et al.*, 1954).

The Indiana strain of bovine diarrhœa also causes fever, cough, diarrhœa and mucosal erosions.

It seems fairly clear that the clinical pictures described for the various diseases at least overlap; and that there is little possibility of deciding how many agents are concerned without further comparisons by virological techniques. Calf pneumonia is discussed on p. 380 but this may be associated with diarrhœa and be identical with so-called pneumo-enteritis.

Ecology. Transmission of these infections seems to be through infected fæces. Human beings going from one farm to another may convey infection.

Other Diseases of Cattle

Several other cattle diseases are described, but there is insufficient evidence to separate them from those discussed elsewhere in this book: rinderpest (p. 142), foot-and-mouth disease (p. 31), vesicular stomatitis (p. 318), bovine rhino-tracheitis and vulvo-vaginitis (p. 224), malignant catarrh (p. 233), bovine enteroviruses (p. 19), papular stomatitis (p. 268).

Ephemeral or three-day fever is considered on p. 324.

Forms of stomatitis described under various names are not clearly separable from papular stomatitis (p. 268). Coital exanthema, epivaginitis and orchitis may all be associated with infectious rhino-tracheitis.

At least one form of shipping fever is due to para-influenza 3 (p. 127). Infectious bovine petechial fever is probably a rickettsial infection. Some forms of pneumonia of calves are probably due to a *Mycoplasma.* Jennings & Glover (1952) succeeded in transmitting a calf pneumonia with filtrates.

SCRAPIE

Synonyms: Tremblant du Mouton. Rida (Iceland).
Review: Stamp (1962).

Morphology. The virus has passed a 320 mμ gradocol membrane but not one of average pore size 210 mμ. It is therefore likely to be a large virus.

Physico-chemical characters. An extraordinarily stable virus which withstands boiling for 3 hours; also exposure to 8 per cent. formaldehyde for a short time and 0·35 per cent. formalin for 3 months. It survives well when dried; and for several years at −40° C (Stamp *et al.*, 1959). There are discrepancies in reports as to ether-resistance. The stability being greater than that of other viruses, the possibility has to be considered that an infectious RNA is liberated from the boiled virus-containing material.

Antigenic properties. In spite of intensive effort, no specific serological reactions have been demonstrated.

Cultivation in eggs and tissue culture has been so far unsuccessful.

Distribution. The disease is prevalent in Europe, particularly so in Scotland and has been introduced in infected sheep to Canada, thence to the United States; also to New Zealand and Australia and possibly India.

Pathogenicity. In one form, affected sheep have intense pruritus, so that they rub off their wool on fences and other objects and bite the affected area. There soon follow tremors, inco-ordination and paralysis but death does not occur for several weeks from the first appearance of symptoms. The pruritus may be absent. The natural incubation period is from 1 to 4 years, but after inoculation it may be 6 months to 2 years. Sheep are the only naturally affected species, apart from a single reported case in a goat kept in contact with sheep (Chelle, 1942). Virus is present in various tissues but probably mainly nervous tissues, and these have been chiefly used for passage. Sheep of different breeds show very different susceptibility to inoculation and their susceptibility seems to depend in part on genetic factors, though few agree with the view (Parry, 1960) that it is a hereditary disease. Goats can be experimentally infected by inoculation by various routes and, unlike sheep, are almost 100 per cent. susceptible. The incubation period is longer at first but decreases after goat-to-goat passage (Pattison, Gordon & Millson, 1959). Virus has been segregated into itching and sleepy strains which breed fairly true (Pattison & Millson, 1961). Chandler (1961, 1962) has transmitted an agent from the sleepy strain to mice, the Swiss strain being most susceptible. Rather indefinite symptoms involving the CNS appeared in 10 months but the agent was serially transmissible and the incubation period fell, after passage, to 3 or 4 months. Its identity with scrapie is highly probable; like scrapie, it withstood boiling.

Pathological lesions are unexpectedly few. Vacuolation of neurones, which is scanty in normal sheep and goat brains, occurs much more abundantly in scrapie brains, especially in brain stem and medulla. Much more prominent are vacuoles of unknown cause in the white matter. ~~There is also demyelination~~ (Holman & Pattison, 1943). Lesions in the mice were similar and could be detected in as little as two months. A view that the disease is essentially a myopathy is not generally accepted.

Ecology. Most contact infections have given negative results; a few, however, are positive. Greig (1940) believed that infection could spread from infected pastures. The long incubation period, the confused and confusing role of heredity and the remarkable stability of the agent have combined to baffle investigators.

Control by slaughter has been practised in countries to which the disease has been introduced.

Rida

Rida, a chronic encephalopathy of sheep in Iceland, is probably scrapie though scratching is little in evidence. Reports suggesting a different pathology (Sigurdsson, 1954b) did not take account of confusion between this and a subsequently recognised nervous disease of sheep, Visna.

VISNA

(May be due to the same virus as Mædi, p. 316.)
Reviews: Sigurdsson *et al.* (1957). Sigurdsson (1954b).

Morphology. The virus has passed a 530 but not a 240 mμ gradocol membrane; but centrifugation and electron-microscopy suggest a smaller size than the results of filtration might indicate (Sigurdsson *et al.*, 1960).

Particles 85 mμ across were seen on the surface of cells in culture. They had a dense core, less than half the diameter of the particle, and a single surrounding membrane. They seemed to be released from the cell surface from two-walled buds; the appearances recalled those of the Bittner (p. 171) and Friend (p. 175) viruses (Thormar, 1961a).

Physico-chemical characters. The virus survives storage for some months at $-50°$ C, also alternate freezing and thawing; it is most stable between pH 7·2 and 9·2. It is inactivated by ether and trypsin; also by 0·04 per cent. formaldehyde, 4 per cent. phenol and 50 per cent. ethanol. 28' at 57° inactivated it (Thormar, 1961b).

Antigenic properties. Neutralization tests carried out in tissue culture showed that not only Visna sheep but also sheep suffering from Mædi, a chronic lung disease, frequently had antibodies to the virus: it is possible that Visna and Mædi represent two forms of one infection (Sigurdsson *et al.*, 1960). "Antibodies" were present also in sera of cattle and some other species.

Cultivation. Visna virus has been grown in cultures of ependyma or chorioid plexus from sheeps' brains. Multinuclear giant cells are formed; later there is cell-destruction; the CPE is seen in 2–3 weeks. On passage this time is shortened to 3–15 days, when large inocula are used. Virus may persist in cultures for as long as 4 months. Third and 11th tissue culture passages infected sheep (Thormar & Sigurdardottír, 1962; Thormar, 1963).

Distribution. The disease is only reported from Iceland.

Pathogenicity. Early symptoms are abnormal head posture and lip-trembling. This is a slow demyelinating disease. Other indefinite nervous symptoms lead gradually to paraplegia or total paralysis: the disease may last for weeks or months but is always fatal. Pleocytosis in the CSF is characteristic. The incubation period extends for months. Pleocytosis may appear in less than a month after inoculation but clinical symptoms may be deferred till 18 months later. The disease is transmissible by intracerebral inoculation to sheep; the usual laboratory rodents are resistant.

Pathological lesions are those of diffuse encephalomyelitis with demyelination: they are fully described by Sigurdsson *et al.* (1962).

In early reports the disease was confused with Rida (Sigurdsson, 1954a), a disease probably identical with scrapie.

MÆDI
(may be the same as Visna)

Review: Sigurdsson (1954a).

Morphology and physico-chemical characters unknown: evidence that this is a virus infection is circumstantial.

Hæmagglutination. A hæmagglutinin for cells of vaccinia-positive fowls has been extracted from Mædi sheep lungs at 70° C and pH 8·5: it is, however, not neutralized by sera from infected sheep.

Antigenic properties. *v.* Visna (p. 314) for mention of a possible antigenic relation between these two diseases.

Distribution. The disease is known from Iceland. A possibly similar disease occurs in Texel, off the Dutch coast. Evidence suggests that Mædi was introduced into Iceland in sheep imported from Germany in 1933.

Pathogenicity. Sheep 2 years or more old are affected with wasting and dyspnœa; the disease is highly, possibly uniformly, fatal. It lasts for 3 to 6 months, sometimes longer. The incubation period is about 2 years but lung lesions may be detectable in animals killed 1 month after injection of infected material into nose, lungs and IV. Infection can apparently occur also after feeding and by contact. Laboratory rodents have not been infected.

Pathological lesions. Lungs are much enlarged, weighing as much as twice the normal. There is diffuse perivascular and peribronchiolar infiltration with mononuclear cells but little fibrosis.

Control. The disease was largely but perhaps not completely eliminated from Iceland by a slaughter policy.

Mædi has been confused with Jaagsiekte, another chronic lung disease of sheep, apparently introduced into Iceland from Germany at the same time.

JAAGSIEKTE

Synonyms: Pulmonary adenomatosis. Chronic progressive pneumonia. Lungers.
Its relation to Laikipia lung disease of East Africa is doubtful.
Review: Marsh (1958).

Physico-chemical characters. The infectious agent survives 4 years when frozen (Sigurdsson, 1958).

Cultivation. Reports of cultivation of an agent in egg-yolk (Shirlaw, 1959) await confirmation; a *Mycoplasma* infection may have been concerned.

Habitat. The disease is known from several parts of Europe including Britain, Iceland, South Africa, Peru, United States, possibly also Israel and India.

Pathogenicity. A chronic lung infection usually involving sheep 4 years old or more. Symptoms as with Mædi are those of emaciation and dyspnœa. Cuba-Caparo *et al.* (1961) report 2 cases in goats in Peru. Transmission to sheep is reported by Sigurdsson (1958) after inoculation intranasally and intratracheally; lung lesions were found when the animals were killed 14 months later.
Pathological lesions are quite different from those of Mædi, being those of widespread adenomatosis which gradually replaces the lung tissue (Robertson, 1904; Dungal *et al.*, 1938).

Ecology. Infection was apparently by the respiratory route but most contact experiments failed (Dungal, 1946).

Control. The disease was apparently eliminated from Iceland by a slaughter policy.

Other Sheep Diseases

Blue-tongue is dealt with on p. 320.
Strawberry foot-rot, once thought to be a virus disease, is now regarded as a fungus infection; some cases may, however, be due to contagious pustular dermatitis (p. 263).

Nairobi sheep disease is considered on p. 93.
Enzoötic abortion, considered on p. 377, is due to a *Miyagawanella* as are some forms of pneumonia in sheep (p. 378).
Balano-posthitis is considered on p. 265.
Sheep-pox v. p. 266.

The five viruses next considered are certainly or probably arthropod-borne, but are not considered with the arboviruses on morphological grounds (vesicular stomatitis), because they are ether-resistant (blue-tongue and African horse-sickness) or because their arthropod-transmission is doubtful (ephemeral fever and deer hæmorrhagic fever).

VESICULAR STOMATITIS

Synonym: Sore mouth (cattle and horses).
Review: Hanson (1952).

Morphology and development. An unusual virus morphologically, consisting of short rods 176 × 69 mμ according to Bradish *et al.* (1956) or 154 × 57 mμ (Reczko, 1958, 1961). The pictures of Bradish and his colleagues suggest to them a coiled beaded filament or stack of platelets capped by a spherical granule. Howatson & Whitmore's (1962) pictures indicate that the core consists of a helix with hollow centre. They also observed on the surface of the virus small projections like those of myxoviruses. This is not inconsistent with Reczko's short rod with one rounded and one truncate end. The volume sensitive to X-rays is between 36 and 47 mμ across. The virus is liberated from infected cells by a continuous-release process. There are very few infective particles in a cell at any one time (Franklin, 1958).

Chemical composition. Apparently an RNA virus containing much phospholipid (Prevec and Whitmore, 1963; Chamsy and Cooper, 1963).

Physico-chemical characters. Inactivated in 30 minutes at 58° C. Stable between pH 4 or 5 and 10. Readily inactivated by visible light as well as by UV. Survives 3 or 4 days in allantoic fluid at 37° C and in soil for many days at 4–6° C. Not readily inactivated by alternate freezing and thawing. Ether-sensitive. Resists 0·5 per cent. phenol.

Antigenic properties. There are two serological types, known as Indiana and New Jersey: they are separable by neutralization and CF tests. In precipitin tests in agar-gel, two lines appear when virus reacts with homotypic serum (Brown & Crick, 1957). There is also one antigen—and possibly a second—common to the two serotypes (Myers & Hanson, 1962). CF reactivity is due partly to components of the size of the virus and partly to much smaller ones having sedimentation constants of 20S and 6S (Bradish *et al.*, 1957).

Interference. Cooper & Bellett (1959) have described a "transmissible interfering component" having properties similar to those of interferon.

Cultivation. *In fertile eggs* the virus grows well on the CAM (Burnet & Galloway, 1934); chicks either die within 1 or 2 days or survive, showing proliferative followed by necrotic changes on the membrane. Embryos 7–8 days old give most regular results especially with the NJ strain (Skinner, 1957a). There is good growth also in the allantoic cavity.

It grows well in cultures of chick embryo and kidney or other epithelial tissues of cattle, pig, rhesus monkey, guinea pig and doubtless other species, producing a rapid destructive effect. On monolayers of kidney cells, plaques are produced.

Distribution. A disease of the New World. The virus has been introduced into Europe and perhaps South Africa but outbreaks have been short-lived. It was formerly known especially as a disease of horses; now it is commoner among cattle.

Pathogenicity. The manifestations of the infection simulate foot-and-mouth disease, though it is much milder. Differential diagnosis is practically very important. There are small papules or vesicles in the mouth of affected cattle, horses or sheep, with drooling saliva; but the lesions only last a few days. In most outbreaks secondary lesions on feet and elsewhere are uncommon. Outbreaks in cattle have been described in which the main lesions have been on the teats (Strozzi & Ramos-Saco, 1953). In pigs, foot lesions are commoner. The disease occurs naturally in raccoons and perhaps deer and these may constitute a reservoir of infection. Accidental infection of man is not uncommon: 54 in one laboratory are recorded. It may be inapparent or resemble influenza.

Experimentally almost all species can be infected. Cattle, horses, pigs, sheep, rabbits and guinea pigs develop lesions when inoculated on the tongue. Cattle are not infected by intramuscular injection. The virus produces encephalitis in mice and guinea pigs after IC inoculation; or in young mice after injection intranasally, intramuscularly or elsewhere (Sabin & Olitsky, 1937). Guinea pigs inoculated into foot pads develop vesicles like those of foot-and-mouth disease: they may also show lesions in kidneys and liver. Cotton-rats can be infected IN or IC (Skinner, 1957a); and rabbits by inoculation into the tongue (Skinner, 1957b). In ferrets the virus causes vesiculation and ulceration in the mouth and on the feet (Kowalczyk *et al.*, 1955). Hamsters and chinchillas have died after IN or IC inoculation. Young chicks have been infected IC but continued serial passage failed (Skinner, 1957a). The tongues and foot-pads of fowls and other poultry, particularly ducks and geese, were successfully infected. Geese showed secondary lesions on feet (Skinner, 1959).

Pathological lesions. The vesicles in various species closely resemble those of foot-and-mouth disease.

The chief brain lesion in fatally infected mice is neuronal destruction.

Ecology. The disease occurs rather sporadically and only between June and October. Mechanical transmission by Tabanids and *Stomoxys* has been suspected (Hanson, 1952). Virus has been recovered from wild caught *Phlebotomus*, and multiplication in *Aëdes ægypti* is reported by Mussgay & Suárez (1962). Spread amongst cattle does not readily occur. Contact infection, not always due to cannibalism, may occur amongst experimental mice.

Related viruses. Viruses apparently related to that of vesicular stomatitis have been isolated from birds in South Africa and Egypt (B. M. McIntosh—personal communication, 1963) and from several genera of arthropods in the Caribbean and Central and South America.

BLUE-TONGUE

Synonyms: Sore mouth. Ovine catarrhal fever.
Review: Cox (1954).

Morphology. Earlier reports indicated a diameter of 100–150 mμ by filtration, 108–133 mμ by centrifugation (Polson, 1948).

Later experiments suggest that 50 mμ may be more accurate. Spheres 70–80 mμ in diameter with 92 rod-like capsomeres have been observed (Polson & Decks, 1963).

Chemical composition. Staining with acridine orange and fluorescent antibody dyes indicates that virus is RNA and located in cytoplasm (Livingston & Moore, 1962).

Physico-chemical characters. A very stable virus. Has survived 25 years at room temperature, drying in air and putrefaction. Inactivated by 3 per cent. NaOH or 70 per cent. ethanol. Resistant to ether and bile salts.

Hæmagglutination: active against RBC's of several species.

Antigenic properties. There are numerous serotypes (19 according to Haig—personal communication, 1962), revealed by neutralization and other tests (Neitz, 1948; Howell, 1960). There is some overlapping amongst these and immunization with a heterologous virus gives partial protection. The virus may be antigenically unstable and liable to change. There is probably some common antigenic component. CF antigens are smaller than the virus itself: particles as small as 8 mμ are present and the smaller ones are apparently the least specific (Kipps, 1958).

Cultivation. The virus grows in 6-day old *fertile eggs* inoculated into the yolk-sac and held at 33·5°, or at least below 35° (Alexander *et al.*, 1947); virus is harvested from the embryos and, after 45–50 egg-passages is found to be attenuated for sheep (McKercher *et al.*, 1957).

In tissue cultures of lamb kidney, there is a CPE (Haig *et al.*, 1956) and growth occurs also in cultures of hamster and calf kidney and in some cell-lines of human origin. At least one egg-passage is necessary before adaptation is successful.

Habitat. Africa, especially in the East and South. Spread in recent years to Cyprus, Palestine, Turkey, Spain, Portugal, Pakistan, Japan. First identified in South and West United States in 1952 but may have been unrecognized earlier.

Pathogenicity. A serious disease affecting sheep, especially lambs, with fever, erosions, crusting and cyanosis around the mouth, œdema of head and neck, sometimes pulmonary œdema and lameness due to involvement of hooves and to muscle damage. Cattle and goats suffer much milder symptoms but may have prolonged viræmia. The virus may produce foot-lesions in pigs. Mortality in sheep varies from 5–30 per cent. in different areas.

Experimentally the disease is readily transmitted to sheep. van den Ende *et al.* (1954) infected young mice IC; virus persisted in brains of older ones without producing symptoms. Suckling hamsters were infected IC by Cabasso *et al.* (1955). CF antigens were obtained from their brains or those of suckling mice.

Pathological lesions have been described by Thomas & Neitz (1947) and Moulton (1961); they include hæmorrhages, œdema, mucosal erosions and focal muscle degeneration. No inclusions are described.

Ecology. Infection is transmitted by a nocturnal vector. Virus has been recovered from *Culicoides spp.* in South Africa and from *Culicoides variipennis* in the United States, but proof that these midges are the essential vectors is incomplete. There is doubtless a reservoir in wild animals in Africa, and Blesbuck (*Damaliscus*) were shown to develop viræmia after inoculation (Neitz, 1933).

Control. A vaccine partly attenuated by passage in sheep has now been superseded by virus attenuated in eggs; the temperature of incubation of the eggs was important (Alexander *et al.*, 1947). Vaccine is freeze-dried with special precautions against inactivation. Such a vaccine is now used on a large scale and is effective if sufficiently polyvalent to deal with all strains encountered locally. It is not safe for pregnant ewes. It may protect in the field even if antibodies against all types are not demonstrable.

AFRICAN HORSE SICKNESS

Reviews: Alexander (1935a, b, c, d). Piercy (1961). Rafyi (1961).

Morphology. Polson (1947) estimated the diameter as 48·8 mμ but later (Polson & Madsen, 1954) considered that there were particles of two sizes: 50·8 mμ and 31·2 mμ. There are perhaps 92 capsomeres on a spherical body.

Physico-chemical characters. Specific gravity 1·33 (Polson & Madsen, 1954). Stable between pH 6 and 10. Survives for years in the cold in an oxalate-phenol-glycerol mixture (Alexander, 1935b). The virus is ether-stable; 1 : 1000 formalin inactivates in 48 hours at 24°.

Hæmagglutination. Horse-cells are agglutinated by extracts of infected mouse brains, preferably at pH 6·4 and 37° for about 2 hours (Pavri, 1961).

Antigenic properties. Strains are alike according to the CF test, the antigen having a diameter of 12 mμ (Polson & Madsen, 1954).

Neutralization tests in mice and experience of immunity in horses suggest that there are many serotypes. Differences between these are quantitative and it appears that the virus strains investigated possess the same antigenic components which are present in vastly different proportions (Alexander, 1935c). Differences are not sharp and the numbers of serotypes are variously estimated as from 8 to 28. Probably the virus is antigenically labile.

Cultivation. Neurotropic virus inoculated on the CAM of *fertile eggs*, multiplies mainly in the embryo brain (Alexander, 1938). Growth, without CPE is also reported in chick embryo fibroblasts.

Distribution. African continent. Spread in 1944 and subsequently to the Middle East, Turkey, Pakistan and India, causing serious losses.

Pathogenicity. Causes disease in horses, mules and (in the Middle East) donkeys. In severe cases death occurs from pulmonary œdema. In more chronic ones there is cardiac involvement with œdema, especially of head and neck. Some infections are quite mild.

Goats and zebras are only slightly susceptible but ferrets and dogs can be infected. Packs of hounds have suffered fatal infections after eating meat containing the virus.

Experimentally infection has been transmitted IC to mice, rats and guinea pigs (Nieschulz, 1933; Alexander, 1935a). The neurotropic virus obtained after repeated passage in mice or guinea pigs has lost its pathogenicity for horses, though viræmia still occurs. Other rodents, including gerbilles, are susceptible to the neurotropic virus injected IC.

Pathological lesions in horses consist of pulmonary œdema, hydro-thorax, hydropericardium.

Ecology. Transmission is by nocturnal biting insects. Virus has been recovered from *Culicoides* (du Toit, 1944) which are mainly suspected but which may be only mechanical vectors. *Tabanids* and *Stomoxys* seem to be incriminated in Turkey.

Control. Formalinized vaccine was formerly used. An attenuated live vaccine from mouse brain is now used and is effective. A polyvalent vaccine including 8 serotypes seems adequate to protect against all strains (McIntosh, 1958). Some attenuated virus, especially Type 7, may have neurotropic qualities.

EPHEMERAL FEVER

Synonyms: Three-day sickness. Bovine epizoötic fever.

The diseases described from Africa, Asia and Australia may not all be the same.

Japan. A virus causing a short fever in cattle (Omori, 1961) was antigenically related to blue-tongue but was non-pathogenic for sheep. This virus proved to be very stable when dried or held at —40°.

Australia. Mackerras *et al.* (1940) in Australia passed a virus in series in cattle IV. After an incubation period of 2–3 days, there occurred fever, running eyes and nose, stuffiness, and, in particular, difficulty in swallowing. There was viræmia, and a CF antigen was prepared from WBC-platelet suspensions. In the infrequent fatal cases, there were enlarged lymph nodes and pulmonary emphysema. Transmission by *Culicoides* or other small biting insects was suspected. French (personal communication, 1963) reported that the agent was inactivated by sodium desoxycholate. Sensitivity to ether and bile-salts usually run in parallel: this suggests that Omori's virus from Japan may be different, since blue-tongue, antigenically related to it, is ether-stable.

DEER HÆMORRHAGIC FEVER

Description: Shope *et al.* (1960).

Morphology. Diameter probably 20–30 mμ (Pirtle & Layton, 1961).

Physico-chemical characters. Sensitive to sodium desoxy-cholate. Survives well at −20° or in glycerol.

Antigenic properties. Neutralizing antibodies are demonstrable by tests in deer or in tissue culture. Sera of recovered deer react in the CF test with an antigen from brains of infected mice. Two strains of the virus, from New Jersey and South Dakota, cross-react in this test but in neutralization tests appear to be related but not identical.

Cultivation. The New Jersey strain produces CPE in HeLa cells; there is neutralization by homologous antisera. It was still pathogenic for deer after 3 passages (Mettler *et al.*, 1962). Pirtle & Layton (1961) cultivated the South Dakota strain in embryonic deer kidney cells.

Habitat. Only known from mid- and eastern United States.

Pathogenicity. Has caused fatal epizoötics in Virginian white-tailed deer (*Odocoleus virginianus*), several hundred animals being killed. Mule deer and other species are insusceptible. After an incubation of 6–8 days, animals show symptoms of shock, have multiple hæmorrhages and die in coma. Virus is present in blood and most tissues.
Experimentally the New Jersey virus has been passed IC in suckling mice (Mettler *et al.*, 1962). After the first pass it was 100 per cent. lethal to the mice. After 4 passages it produced only inapparent infection in the one deer tested.
Pathological lesions. There are hæmorrhages in various tissues and may be retroperitoneal œdema and fluids in serous sacs (Karstad *et al.*, 1961). Prothrombin deficiency rather than endothelial damage may cause the hæmorrhages.

Ecology. Infection does not pass by direct contact: an arthropod vector is suspected.

REFERENCES

Alexander, R. A. (1935a) *Onderstepoort J. vet. Sci.*, **4**, 291.
Alexander, R. A. (1935b) *Onderstepoort J. vet. Sci.*, **4**, 323.
Alexander, R. A. (1935c) *Onderstepoort J. vet. Sci.*, **4**, 349.
Alexander, R. A. (1935d) *Onderstepoort J. vet. Sci.*, **4**, 379.
Alexander, R. A. (1938) *Onderstepoort J. vet. Sci.*, **11**, 9.
Alexander, R. A., Haig, D. A., & Adelaar, T. F. (1947) *Onderstepoort J. vet. Sci.*, **22**, 7.

Baker, J. A. (1943) *J. exp. Med.*, **78**, 435.
Baker, J. A. (1946) *Proc. Soc. exp. Biol.* (*N.Y.*), **63**, 183.
Baker, J. A. (1947) *J. Amer. vet. med. Ass.*, **111**, 503.
Baker, J. A., & Sheffy, B. E. (1960) *Proc. Soc. exp. Biol.* (*N.Y.*), **105**, 675.
Baker, J. A., Yorke, C. J., Gillespie, J. H., & Mitchell, G. B., (1954) *Amer. J. vet. Res.*, **15**, 525.
Bay, W. W., Doyle, L. P., & Hutchings, L. M. (1952) *Amer. J. vet. Res.*, **13**, 318.
Bontcheff, N., Ivanoff, M., & Bojadjieff, S. (1959) *Bull. Off. int. Épiz.*, **51**, 252.
Boynton, W. H. (1933) *J. Amer. vet. med. Ass.*, **83**, 747.
Bradish, C. J., Brooksby, J. B., & Dillon, J. F. (1956) *J. gen. Microbiol.*, **14**, 290.
Brandly, C. A., & McClurkin, A. W. (1956) *Ann. N.Y. Acad. Sci.*, **66**, 181.
Brown, F., & Crick, J. (1957) *Nature* (*Lond.*), **179**, 316.
Burnet, F. M., & Galloway, I. A. (1934) *Brit. J. exp. Path.*, **15**, 105.
Cabasso, V. J., Roberts, G. I., Douglas, J. M., Zorzi, R., Stebbins, M. R., & Cox, H. R. (1955) *Proc. Soc. exp. Biol.* (*N.Y.*), **88**, 678.
Casselberry, N. H., Malmquist, H. A., Houlihan, W. A., & Boynton, W. H. (1953) *Vet. Med.*, **48**, 24.
Chamsy, H. M., & Cooper, P. D. (1963) *Virology*, **20**, 14.
Chandler, R. L. (1961) *Lancet*, **1**, 1378.
Chandler, R. L. (1962) *Lancet*, **1**, 107.
Chapin, R. M., Powick, W. C., McBryde, C. N., & Cole, C. G. (1939) *J. Amer. vet. med. Ass.*, **95**, 494.
Chelle, P. L. (1942) *Bull. Acad. Méd.* (*Paris*), **15**, 294.
Cooper, P. D., & Bellett, A. J. D. (1959) *J. gen. Microbiol.*, **21**, 485.
Coronel, A. B., & Albis, F. S. (1950) *Philipp. J. Anim. Ind.*, **11**, 127.
Cox, H. R. (1954) *Bact. Rev.*, **18**, 239.
Cuba-Caparro, A., de la Vega, E., & Copaira, M. (1961) *Amer. J. vet. Res.*, **22**, 673.
Darbyshire, J. H. (1960) *Vet. Rec.*, **72**, 331.
Darbyshire, J. H. (1962) *Res. vet. Sci.*, **3**, 118.
Darbyshire, J. H. (1963) *J. comp. Path.*, **73**, 309.
Daubney, R., & Mahlau, E. A. (1957) *Nature* (*Lond.*), **179**, 584.
Dinter, Z. (1963) *Zbl. Bakt. I. Abt. Orig.*, **188**, 475.
Doll, E. R. Bryans, J. T., McCollum, W. H., & Crowe, M. E. W. (1957) *Cornell Vet.*, **47**, 3.
Done, J. T. (1957) *Vet. Rec.*, **69**, 1341.
Doyle, L. P. (1958) in Dunne, *Diseases of Swine.* Iowa State College Press.
Dreguss, M. N., & Lombard, L. S. (1954) *Experimental Studies in Equine Infectious Anæmia.* Univ. of Pennsylvania Press.
Dungal, N. (1946) *Amer. J. Path.*, **22**, 737.
Dungal, N., Gíslason, G., & Taylor, E. L. (1938) *J. comp. Path.*, **57**, 46.
Dunne, H. W. (1958) *Diseases in Swine.* Iowa State College Press.
Du Toit, R. M. (1944) *Onderstepoort J. vet. Sci.*, **19**, 7.
Elford, W. J., & Galloway, I. A. (1933) *Brit. J. exp. Path.*, **14**, 196.
Fedotov, A. I. (1950) *Veterinariya* (*Moscow*), **27**, 53.
Fontanelli, E., Menascè, I., & d'Ascani, E. (1959) *Zooprofilassi*, **14**, 467.
Franklin, R. M. (1958) *Virology*, **5**, 408.
Gillespie, J. H., & Baker, J. A. (1959) *Cornell Vet.*, **49**, 439.
Gillespie, J. H., Baker, J. A., & McEntee, K. (1960a) *Cornell Vet.*, **50**, 73.
Gillespie, J. H., Coggins, L., Thompson, J., & Baker, J. A. (1961) *Cornell Vet.*, **51**, 155.
Gillespie, J. H., Sheffy, B. E., & Baker, J. A. (1960b) *Proc. Soc. exp. Biol.* (*N.Y.*), **105**, 679.

Gillespie, J. H., Sheffy, B. E., & Baker, J. A. (1959) *Cornell Vet.*, **49**, 439.
Goodwin, R. F. W., & Jennings, A. R. (1959) *J. comp. Path.*, **69**, 313.
Greig, J. R. (1940) *Vet. J.*, **96**, 203.
Gustavson, D. P., & Pomerat, C. M. (1957) *Amer. J. vet. Res.*, **18**, 473.
Haeltermann, E. O., & Hutchings, L. M. (1956) *Ann. N.Y. Acad. Sci.*, **66**, 186.
Haig, D. A., McKercher, D. G., & Alexander, R. A. (1956) *Onderstepoort J. vet. Res.*, **27**, 171.
Hanson, R. P. (1952) *Bact. Rev.*, **16**, 179.
Hanson, R. P. (1957) *J. Amer. vet. med. Ass.*, **131**, 211.
Hermodsson, S., & Dinter, Z. (1962) *Nature (Lond.)*, **194**, 893.
Holman, H. H., & Pattison, I. H. (1943) *J. comp. Path.*, **53**, 231.
Howatson, A. F., & Whitmore, G. F. (1962) *Virology*, **16**, 466.
Howell, P. G. (1960) *Onderstepoort J. vet. Res.*, **28**, 357.
Huck, R. A. (1957) *J. comp. Path.*, **67**, 267.
Huck, R. A. (1961) *Bull. Off. internat. Épiz.*, **56**, 5.
Jennings, A. R., & Glover, R. E. (1952) *J. comp. Path.*, **62**, 6.
Johnston, K. G. (1959) *Aust. vet. J.*, **35**, 101.
Karstad, L., Winter, A., & Trainer, D. O. (1961) *Amer. J. vet. Res.*, **22**, 227.
Keast, J. C., Littlejohn, I. R., & Helwig, D. M. (1962) *Aust. vet. J.*, **38**, 129.
Kipps, A. (1958) *S. Afr. J. Lab. clin. Med.*, **4**, 158.
Koprowski, H., James, T. R., & Cox, H. R. (1946) *Proc. Soc. exp. Biol. (N.Y.)*, **63**, 178.
Kowalczyk, T., & Brandly, C. A. (1954) *Amer. J. vet. Res.*, **15**, 98.
Kumagai, T., Shimizu, T., & Matumoto, M. (1958) *Science*, **128**, 366.
Lang, R., Leftheriotis, E., & Mackiowak, C. (1960) *C.R. Acad. Sci. (Paris)*, **251**, 1593.
Lee, K. M. (1956) *Ann. N.Y. Acad. Sci.*, **66**, 191.
Livingston, C. W., & Moore, R. W. (1962) *Amer. J. vet. Res.*, **23**, 701.
McBryde, C. N., & Cole, C. G. (1936) *J. Amer. vet. med. Ass.*, **89**, 652.
McCollum, W. H., Doll, E. R., Wilson, J. C., & Johnson, C. B. (1961) *Amer. J. vet. Res.*, **22**, 731.
McIntosh, B. M. (1958) *Onderstepoort J. vet. Res.*, **27**, 465.
Mackerras, I. M., Mackerras, M. J., & Burnet, F. M. (1940) *Bull. Counc. sci. ind. Res. Aust.*, no. 136, p. 116.
McKercher, D. G., McGowan, B., Cabasso, V. J., Roberts, G. I., & Saito, J. K. (1957) *Amer. J. vet. Res.*, **18**, 310.
Mansi, W. (1957) *J. comp. Path.*, **57**, 297.
Marsh, H. (1937) *J. Amer. vet. med. Ass.*, **91**, 88 and 330.
Marsh, H. (1958) *Advanc. vet. Sci.*, **4**, 163.
Mettler, N. E., MacNamara, L. G., & Shope, R. E. (1962) *J. exp. Med.*, **116**, 665.
Möhlman, H., & Gralheer, H. (1954) *Arch. exp. vet. Med.*, **8**, 199.
Molnár, I. (1954) *Magy. Állatorv. Lap.*, **9**, 146.
Moulton, J. E. (1961) *Amer. vet. med. Ass.*, **138**, 493.
Mussgay, M., & Suarez, O. (1962) *Virology*, **17**, 202.
Myers, W. L., & Hanson, R. P. (1962) *Amer. J. vet. Res.*, **23**, 896.
Neitz, W. O. (1948) *Onderstepoort J. vet. Res.*, **23**, 93.
Nicolau, S., & Galloway, I. A. (1928) *Spec. Rep. Ser. med. Res. Coun. (Lond.)* No. 121.
Nicolau, S., & Galloway, I. A. (1930) *Ann. Inst. Pasteur*, **44**, 673 and **45**, 457.
Nieschulz, O. (1933) *Zbl. Bakt. I. Abt. Orig.*, **128**, 465.
Norie, F., & Schipper, I. A. (1959) *Proc. Soc. exp. Biol. (N.Y.)*, **100**, 84.
Omori, T. (1961) *Bull. Off. int. Épiz.*, **55**, 1109.
Otta, J., & Jentzsch, K. D. (1960) *Mschr. Vet.-Med.*, **15**, 127.
Parry, H. B. (1960) *Nature (Lond.)*, **185**, 441.

328 UNCLASSIFIED VIRUSES

Pattison, I. H., Gordon, W. S., & Millison, G. L. (1959) *J. comp. Path.*, **69**, 300.
Pattison, I. H., & Millison, G. C. (1961) *J. comp. Path.*, **70**, 182.
Pavri, K. M. (1961) *Nature (Lond.)*, **189**, 249.
Pehl, K. H., & Gralheer, H. (1957) *Arch. exp. vet. Med.*, **10**, 699.
Peters, J. T. (1924) *Presse méd.*, *32*, 105.
Piercy, S. E. (1961) *New Scientist*, **9**, 76.
Pirtle, E. S., & Layton, J. M. (1961) *Amer. J. vet. Res.*, **22**, 104.
Polson, A. (1947) *Onderstepoort J. vet. Res.*, **23**, 137.
Polson, A., & Madsen, T. (1954) *Biochim. biophys. Acta*, **14**, 366.
Porterfield, J. S., Hill, D. H., & Morris, A. D. (1958) *Brit. vet. J.*, **114**, 425.
Prevec, L., & Whitmore, G. F. (1963) *Virology*, **20**, 464.
Rafyi, A. (1961) *Bull. Off. int. Épiz.*, **56**, 216.
Razza, F., & Carusillo, G. (1949) *Riv. med. vet. zootecn.*, **1**, 329.
Reczko, E. (1958) *Zbl. Bakt. I. Abt. Orig.*, **170**, 545.
Reczko, E. (1961) *Arch. ges. Virusforsch.*, **10**, 588.
Reisinger, L., & Reimann, H. (1928) *Wien. tierärztl. Mschr.*, **15**, 219.
Robertson, W. (1904) *J. comp. Path.*, **17**, 221.
Rodionov, M., & Oleynik, H. K. (1946) *Veterinariya (Moscow)*, **23:10–11**, 11.
Rott, R., & Nitschke, E. (1958) *Zbl. Vet.-Med.*, **5**, 629.
Sabban, M. S., El Dahaby, H., & Hussein, H. (1961) *Bull. Off. int. Épiz.*, **55**, 1701.
Sabin, A. B., & Olitsky, P. K. (1937) *J. exp. Med.*, **66**, 15 and 35.
Sheffy, B. E., Coggins, L., & Baker, J. A. (1962) *Proc. Soc. exp. Biol. (N.Y.)*, **109**, 349.
Shirlaw, J. F. (1959) *Bull. epizoot. Dis. Afr.*, **7**, 287.
Shope, R. E. (1958) *J. exp. Med.*, **107**, 609 and **108**, 159.
Shope, R. E., MacNamara, L. G., & Mangold, R. (1960) *J. exp. Med.*, **111**, 155.
Sigurdsson, B. (1954a) *Brit. vet. J.*, **110**, 255.
Sigurdsson, B. (1954b) *Brit. vet. J.*, **110**, 341.
Sigurdsson, B. (1958) *Arch. ges. Virusforsch.*, **8**, 51.
Sigurdsson, B., Pálsson, P. A., & Grímsson, H. (1957) *J. Neuropath. exp. Neurol.*, **16**, 389.
Sigurdsson, B., Pálsson, P. A., & van Bogaert, L. (1962) *Acta neuropathologica*, **1**, 343.
Sigurdsson, B., Thormar, H., & Pálsson, P. A. (1960) *Arch. ges. Virusforsch.*, **10**, 368.
Skinner, H. H. (1957a) *J. comp. Path.*, **67**, 69.
Skinner, H. H. (1957b) *J. comp. Path.*, **67**, 87.
Skinner, H. H. (1959) *Arch. ges. Virusforsch.*, **9**, 92.
Slavin, G. (1938) *J. comp. Path.*, **51**, 213.
Stamp, J. T. (1962) *Vet. Rec.*, **74**, 357.
Stamp, J. T., Brotherston, J. G., Zlotnik, I., Mackay, J. M. K., & Smith, W. (1959) *J. comp. Path.*, **69**, 268.
Stein, C. D., & Gates, D. W. (1952) *Amer. J. vet. Res.*, **13**, 195.
Stein, C. D., & Mott, L. O. (1944) *Vet. Med.*, **39**, 408.
Strozzi, P., & Ramos-Saco, T. (1953) *J. Amer. vet. med. Ass.*, **123**, 415.
Taylor, D. O. N., Gustafson, D. P., & Claflin, R. M. (1963) *Amer. J. vet. Res.*, **24**, 143.
Thomas, A. D., & Neitz, W. O. (1947) *Onderstepoort J. vet. Res.*, **22**, 27.
Thormar, H. (1961a) *Virology*, **14**, 463.
Thormar, H. (1961b) *Arch. ges. Virusforsch.*, **10**, 501.
Thormar, H., & Sigurdadottír, B. (1962) *Acta. path. microbiol. scand.*, **55**, 186.
van Bekkum, J. G. (1959) *Proc. 16th. int. vet. Congr., Madrid*, **2**, 477.

van den Ende, M., Linder, A., & Kaschula, V. R. (1954) *J. Hyg. (Lond.)*, **52**, 155.
von Sprockhoff, H. (1953) *Berl. Münch. tierärtzl. Wschr.*, **66**, 368.
von Sprockhoff, H. (1958) *Z. Immun.-Forsch.*, **115**, 161.
Waldemann, O., & Köbe, K. (1934) *Zbl. Bakt. I. Abt. Orig.*, **133**, 49.
Watanabe, S. (1960) *Jap. J. vet. Sci.*, **22**, 65 and 87.
Wilsdon, A. J. (1958) *Vet. Rec.*, **70**, 3.
Wilson, J. C., Doll, E. R., McCollum, W. H., & Cheatham, J. (1962) *Cornell Vet.*, **52**, 200.
Young, G. A., Kitchell, R. L., Luedke, A. J., & Sautter, J. H. (1955) *J. Amer. vet. med. Ass.*, **126**, 165.
Zichis, J. J. (1929) *J. Amer. vet. med. Ass.*, **126**, 165.
Zwick, W., & Seifried, O. (1924) *Berl. Münch. tierärztl. Wschr.*, **40**, 465.
Zwick, W., Seifried, O., & Witte, J. (1929) *Arch. Tierheilk.*, **59**, 511.

15

Unclassified Viruses of Rodents

PNEUMONIA VIRUS OF MICE

Synonym: PVM.
Original Account: Horsfall & Hahn (1940).

Morphology and development. Diameter 40 mμ (Franklin & Gomatos, 1962). Earlier estimates suggested something larger. There is an eclipse phase and then perhaps a sixteen-fold increase in virus titre with each cycle of development (Ginsberg & Horsfall, 1951). The virus combines with tissue-particles from various species but can be freed from them by heat, trypsinization or alkali. Virus combined with tissue particles has an apparent size of 140 mμ (Curnen, Pickels & Horsfall, 1947).

Physico-chemical characters. Infectivity is destroyed by heating 30 minutes at 56° and infectivity dropped 100-fold in one hour at room temperature. Virus survives well at −76° and also withstands drying (Horsfall & Hahn, 1940). The virus is ether-sensitive.

Hæmagglutination. Agglutinates at room temperature RBC's of mouse, hamster and, irregularly, rabbit, not those of other species tested. Hæmagglutination is much better after freeing of virus from associated tissue-components, preferably by heating for 5 minutes at 75° C. The hæmagglutinin withstands 80° C for 30 minutes but not 100° C for 5 minutes (Mills & Dochez, 1944, 1945).

Antigenic properties. Infectivity and hæmagglutination are both inhibited by antisera from immunized mice or rabbits. Neutralizing antibodies are present in normal mice from stocks of some breeders but not others. Normal sera of some hamsters, cotton-rats, guinea pigs and other species including human beings also neutralize; in the case of the first two species this may well be due to presence of a related latent virus (v., p. 332): for the other species there is no evidence to support this idea.

Interference. PVM interferes with influenza virus in mice and is itself interfered with by influenza and mumps.

Cultivation. There is no good evidence of multiplication in fertile eggs but it apparently survived after 10 passes through chick-embryo tissue-culture (Horsfall & Hahn, 1940). No CPE produced in mouse embryo or monkey kidney tissue-culture. Tennant & Ward (1962) grew the virus in cultures of suckling hamster kidney, recognizing its presence by using mouse RBC's in the hæmadsorption test.

Distribution. Though only recognized in the United States, it is very probably present in most stocks of laboratory mice as a latent infection.

Pathogenicity. Virus can be activated by serial intranasal passage of lung suspensions in apparently normal mice at 7–9 day (not at shorter) intervals. Lung lesions may appear after 1 or 2 passes and gross consolidation after 9 or 10 (Horsfall & Hahn, 1940). It is necessary, however, to pass in mice of an uninfected stock: otherwise nothing may become apparent. Only intranasal inoculation is successful. Syrian hamsters also develop lung lesions after intranasal inoculation, but in them virus is not readily transmissible in series. Davenport (1949) passed virus in series through 11 rabbits intratracheally, but did not increase the virus' pathogenicity for the rabbit. However, he also found a component in normal rabbit lung, which, after heating, agglutinated RBC's much as PVM does.

Pathological lesions in lungs of infected mice showed "dense and often bulky accumulations of cells . . . largely mononuclear" round the bronchi and blood vessels (Horsfall & Hahn, 1940).

Ecology. Virus was not shown to pass from mouse to mouse by contact.

Control. Live or heated virus given intraperitoneally, or sub-lethal doses intranasally, readily immunizes mice against the virus.

Polysaccharides from a number of sources—streptococci, Friedländer bacilli, Shigella, blood group A specific substance and agar, all have a sparing effect on mice inoculated with PVM (Horsfall & McCarty, 1947).

Related Viruses in Other Species

Pearson & Eaton (1940) recovered a virus from Syrian hamsters which behaved like PVM and was antigenically related to it.

Subsequently Eaton & van Herick (1944) obtained a similar agent from cotton-rats (*Sigmodon*). The virus was lethal both to cotton-rats and mice and also serologically related to PVM.

LYMPHOCYTIC CHORIOMENINGITIS
(L.C.M.)

Synonyms: Pneumopathie des Cobayes. Humphreys' disease of guinea pigs.

Original account: Armstrong & Lillie (1934).

Review: (disease in man) Farmer & Janeway (1942).

Morphology. Size 37–55 mμ (by centrifugation), 40–60 mμ (ultra-filtration)) (Scott & Elford, 1939).

Physico-chemical characters. Inactivated in 1 hour at 56° C. Stable in 50 per cent. glycerol in the cold, at −70° C or when lyophilized. Ether-sensitive. The titre of a suspension was much reduced by 1 : 10,000 merthiolate, in contrast to what is found with several arboviruses (Rogers, 1951). Labile below pH 7.

Hæmagglutinin. None reported but virus said to be adsorbed to RBC's of susceptible species (Shwartzman, 1944).

Antigenic properties. Neutralizing antibodies in recovered man and most other species persist for long periods. They may be absent in mice but to demonstrate them incubation of serum and virus for 24 hours at 37° (Traub, 1960) or addition of fresh serum (Ackermann *et al.*, 1962) may be necessary. Complement-fixation and precipitation, in agar-gel and otherwise, are associated with a soluble antigen which is relatively stable at 56° and between pH 4·5 and 9 (Smadel *et al.*, 1940). Complement-fixing antibodies do not persist long after infection. Immunity of mice in infected stocks may be due to "persistent tolerated infection" in sucklings or to active immunity in adults (Weigand & Hotchin, 1961).

Interference is reported between LCM and the viruses of poliomyelitis, encephalo-myocarditis and eastern and western equine encephalitis. There is no evidence that interferon is concerned.

Cultivation. In fertile eggs the virus grows on the CAM but without production of specific lesions (Tobin, 1954). It grows in tissue culture of chick, mouse, cattle, monkey and other species but CPE may only be seen after adaptation. Strains of high virulence grow in a greater variety of cells. Plaques can be obtained in chick embryo monolayers, but only after 12 days' incubation (Benson & Hotchin, 1960).

Pathogenicity. Probably an inapparent infection in naturally infected wild house mice (*Mus musculus*) but it has also been isolated from man, monkeys, dogs and guinea pigs. When first affecting a colony of laboratory mice, it caused symptoms in young mice infected *in utero* but soon became adapted so as to be wholly latent (Traub, 1939). This state of affairs comes about through the operation of immunological tolerance. Some (docile) strains induce this readily while other (aggressive) strains lead to brisk reaction and death (Hotchin *et al.*, 1962).

Disease in stocks of guinea pigs was described as "Pneumopathie des Cobayes" (Lepine & Sautter, 1945); symptoms were of generalized, often fatal, disease with patchy pneumonia and exudates into serous cavities.

The disease in man, occurring in laboratory workers or in people from houses infested with mice, may be inapparent or show itself as an influenza-like fever, as meningitis or as meningo-encephalo-myelitis, the last being sometimes fatal but fortunately rare. The incubation period after deliberate infection of man (Lepine *et al.*, 1937) lasted 36–72 hours. There were 2 or 3 waves of fever.

Experimentally the virus will infect mice of susceptible stocks when injected by various routes, the intracerebral being the most and intranasal the next most effective. 5–12 days after infection the hair of the mice is ruffled, they tremble and have toxic convulsions in which they may die. Guinea pigs are equally susceptible. Infected hamsters (Smadel & Wall, 1942) show prolonged viræmia but usually no symptoms. Monkeys of various species, chimpanzees, rats and dogs can also be infected. The virus does not readily infect rabbits except (Blanc & Bruneau, 1951) in pregnancy, causing abortion. It may, however, give rise to a specific local skin reaction when injected intradermally into rabbits (Roger, 1962). Different strains of virus vary greatly in virulence for different species. In carrier mice of infected stocks, virus meningitis may be produced by intracerebral injection of sterile broth.

Pathological lesions: there is lymphocytic infiltration around blood vessels and chorioid plexuses in all species; also in various other viscera. Mice may show pleural and peritoneal effusions. Guinea pigs and monkeys may have hepatitis. Traub (1962) finds the lesions in mice similar to those of lymphomatosis and discusses whether the virus may not cause that condition.

Ecology. Virus is excreted in stools and urine of infected mice and has been recovered from the nasopharynx of man. Infected dust is suspected as a vehicle for infection. Several reports suggest that arthropods—mosquitoes, bed-bugs (*Cimex*), monkey lice and other species (Milzer, 1942), also worms (*Trichinella*; Syverton *et al.*, 1947)—may be concerned in transmission. At least *Aëdes* mosquitoes and *Cimex* can transmit experimentally. Virus has been recovered from ticks; also from offspring of infected ticks (Reiss-Gutfreund *et al.*, 1962). The virus has been the subject of important studies on ecology by Traub (1936, 1938, 1939). He followed a change in host-parasite relation extending over 4 years: finally all mice were infected *in utero*, carried virus for long periods without symptoms and without developing antibodies, and became less infectious by contact, all infection being transmitted from mothers to offspring. Immuno-logical tolerance is thought to be concerned (Hotchin & Cinits, 1958).

Control. Risk of disease in man is lessened by eliminating wild mice. Guinea pigs may be immunized by giving virus modified by intracerebral passage in mice (Traub, 1937), while UV-irradiated virus has given slight protection to mice.

The taxonomic position of this virus is doubtful. It is an ether-sensitive virus of the same size as larger arboviruses. Since arthropod-transmission is possible, it may be an arbovirus modified so as to be normally transmitted in other ways. On the other hand, Traub's (1962) studies suggested possible affinities with mouse-leukæmia.

EPIDEMIC DIARRHŒA IN SUCKLING MICE

This disease is endemic in many stocks of laboratory mice and causes great trouble to breeders as it is hard to eradicate.

Review: Pappenheimer, 1958.

Morphology. The diameter of particles by electron-microscopy is 65–75 mμ (Adams & Kraft, 1963).

Physico-chemical characters. The virus is filterable and inactivated by heating for 15 minutes at 70° C, not by 30 minutes at 60° C (Kraft, 1957).

Cultivation. Ten serial passages are reported in tissue culture in a line of human liver cells (Chang cells) (Habermann, 1959).

Pathogenicity. Attacks chiefly mice 11–15 days old; diarrhœa causes the hair to be dirty and yellow. The disease is not necessarily fatal but may be up to 50 per cent. and many litters fail to be successfully weaned (Cheever & Muller, 1947). In some outbreaks cytoplasmic inclusions have been found in intestinal epithelium; in others there were intranuclear inclusions: their relation to the disease is uncertain (Pappenheimer & Cheever, 1948).

Ecology. The disease is commoner in first than in later litters of breeding females. Possibly the mothers gradually become more highly immune and pass on antibody in colostrum. Severity also varies with the strain of mice. Infection may be airborne or caused by human agency. Virus is present in fæces. Recovered mice can act as carriers for a time.

Control. A clean stock has been obtained by Cæsarean section and nursing the babies on disease-free females (Cheever & Muller, 1948).

LETHAL INTESTINAL VIRUS OF INFANT MICE

A fatal diarrhœal disease of infant mice (Kraft, 1962) is apparently distinct from the epidemic diarrhœa just described. It is more rapidly fatal and characterized by the presence of numerous multinucleated balloon cells in epithelium throughout the intestinal tract. Infection was transmitted *per os* to mice up to 16 days old. Virus was present to high titre in intestines and their contents: there was sometimes a little in the liver. Heating for 30 minutes at 50° inactivated it: so did ether. Attempted cultivation in eggs and in various tissue cultures was unsuccessful. No hæmagglutinin was demonstrated.

MOUSE HEPATITIS VIRUS (MHV)

Synonym: JHM (a neurotropic variant described by Cheever *et al.*, 1949 and named after J. H. Mueller).

The hepatitis originally described by Gledhill & Andrewes (1951) was found to be due to synergism between two components, M.H.V. and *Eperythrozoön coccoides* (Niven *et al.*, 1952).

Morphology and development. Size estimated as 80–120 mμ (Gledhill *et al.*, 1955) by filtration. Particles, possibly representing the virus, are described by Miyazaki *et al.* (1957) as 70 mμ across and by Starr *et al.* (1960) as 90 mμ across.

Chemical composition. The only evidence is indirect. Armstrong & Niven (1957) and Starr *et al.* (1960) found abnormal RNA accumulation in the cytoplasm at sites where studies with fluorescent antibody suggested that virus was present.

Physico-chemical characters. Inactivated in 30 minutes at 56°. Ether-sensitive. Survives well at −76° and after lyophilization.

Antigenic properties. Neutralizing antibodies can be prepared by hyperimmunizing mice but they are of low titre. Pollard & Bussell (1957) could demonstrate CF antibodies; the best antigen was in the supernatant fluid after hard centrifugation. No evidence exists that the various strains (MHV 1, 2, 3, etc.) described below are antigenically different.

Cultivation. No growth in fertile eggs.
The MHV 1 strain was cultivated by Gompels & Niven (1953) in tissues of mouse embryos from 10–12-day pregnant mice; no CPE was described. Cultivation in mouse liver was described by Miyazaki *et al.* (1957), by Starr *et al.* (1960), and by Vainio (1961), a CPE being seen by the last worker after 3–5 days; he used the MHV 3 strain. Bang & Warwick (1959), working with the MHV 2 strain, found that macrophages in culture were selectively destroyed.

Pathogenicity. The MHV 1 strain of Gledhill & Andrewes (1951), Gledhill, Dick & Andrewes (1952) occurred as a latent infection of a varying percentage of normal mice (10 per cent. for the VS strain). Injected into susceptible newly weaned mice of this strain it produced negligible hepatic damage, but in the presence of the blood parasite *Eperythrozoön coccoides*, itself harmless, it caused fatal hepatitis. In new-born mice it produced a similar effect even in the absence of the *E. coccoides*. Infection was produced by injection by various routes and by feeding.

The mechanism of enhancement of the virus's pathogenicity by *E. coccoides* was studied by Gledhill *et al.* (1955) and Gledhill (1956). Latent hepatitis viruses have also been activated during serial passage of leukæmias and tumours in mice, and the virus's activity has been enhanced not only by *E. coccoides* but also by cortisone, urethane and an enterotoxin from Gram-negative bacteria.

Several strains of virus have been given numbers by Dick *et al.* (1956). MHV 1 is the originally described strain.

MHV 2 (called MHV (Pr) by Nelson) was activated by him during passage of a leukæmia in Princeton mice. It was pathogenic for these mice in the absence of *E. coccoides* but that parasite enhanced its much lower pathogenicity for Swiss mice (Nelson, 1953).

MHV 3 is a strain obtained by Dick *et al.* (1955), pathogenic for weanling mice in the absence of *E. coccoides*, and, after passage, uniformly fatal for them. In older mice it frequently caused ascites.

MHV 4 is suggested as a name for the neurotropic JHM virus of Cheever *et al.* (1949). This caused disseminated encephalomyelitis with demyelination in mice, with some focal liver necrosis. Similar neurotropic derivatives of MH 1 and MH 3 were obtained by Dick *et al.* (1952). Other hepatotropic strains have been recovered particularly during studies of leukæmia, by workers in several countries. The neurotropic strains have also infected cotton-rats and hamsters when injected IC. Other species are insusceptible. Virus is present in blood and viscera, especially liver and kidneys; also in urine and fæces.

Pathological lesions. In fatal infections of suckling mice with MHV 1 or in older ones infected also with *E. coccoides*, the liver appears either yellow or brown and mottled with hæmorrhages; the kidneys are swollen and pale. There is a widespread endothelial and meso-thelial reaction in almost all tissues. Multinucleated giant cells appear in venous channels (Niven *et al.*, 1952). Ruebner & Miyai (1962) considered that earliest lesions were in Küpffer cells. The focal necroses present in the liver soon become confluent. The lesions caused by the neurotropic MHV 4 (JHM) are described by Bailey *et al.* (1949).

Ecology. Virus is present in excreta of weanlings; and the virus is highly infectious amongst young mice (Rowe *et al.*, 1963).

Control. The therapeutic action of tetracyclines in the first report by Gledhill & Andrewes in 1951 is accounted for by the effect of the drug on the *Eperythrozöa*.

The mouse hepatitis virus of Jordan & Mirick (1955) is thought probably to be an encephalitozöon-like protozoon.

MOUSE THYMIC VIRUS

Description: Rowe & Capps (1961).

Morphology. Diameter 75–100 mμ by electron-microscopy. Body made up of granules 19–36 mμ across with an outer wall 10–27 mμ in diameter. Particles in the cytoplasm were 119–132 mμ across. Some filaments were present in nuclei.

Physico-chemical characters. Ether-sensitive. Inactivated in 30 minutes at 50° C. Survived well at −60° C and after shell freezing.

Antigenic properties. Very poor antibody formation in mice.

Habitat. Probably enzoötic in some stocks of laboratory mice and in wild mice (*Mus musculus*).

Pathogenicity. Produces a non-fatal infection in baby mice with massive necrosis of the thymus after 12–14 days, going on to scarring. The virus may persist in the mice for months. Nuclear inclusions are present in affected tissues.

RILEY VIRUS

(Lactic Dehydrogenase Agent)

This virus, described by Riley *et al.* (1960), Riley (1961), Mundy & Williams (1961), is non-pathogenic, is recognized by an increase in the lactic dehydrogenase in blood of affected mice and has been carried along during propagation of numerous mouse tumours. It seems to be 60 mμ across and has not been grown in tissue culture. It is ether-sensitive (Notkins & Shochat, 1963). An infectious RNA has been extracted (Notkins & Scheele, 1963).

MOUSE PAPULE AGENT

This agent (Kraft & Moore, 1961) was the cause of papules, later scabs, on feet, tails and skin of mice of all ages. It was transmissible intradermally. The lesions were entirely local, appearing in 5 days; scabs separated at 14–16 days. Lesions 4–15 days old showed enormous cytoplasmic inclusions. The agent lost 99 per cent. of activity in 1 hour at 37° but survived well at 4°–30°. It was filtered with difficulty and only through a 450 mμ millipore membrane. Rodents other than mice were insusceptible. There was no relation to ectromelia.

Other viruses affecting mice are listed below:
Infectious ectromelia, p. 260.
Mouse adenovirus, p. 190.
Reoviruses Types 2 and 3, p. 45.
(Bennette's (1960) tumour-destroying virus is a reovirus; so also is Stanley's hepato-encephalitis virus.)
K virus, p. 202.
Mouse salivary virus and liver inclusion virus, p. 238.
Encephalomyelitis (TO, FA and GD VII strains), p. 35.
Mammary tumour virus (Bittner), p. 171.
Polyoma, p. 200.
Pneumonitis (Nigg), p. 375.
Infectious catarrh of mice (Nelson, 1937) is due to a *Mycoplasma* (pleuro-pneumonia-like organism). So is rolling disease (Sabin, 1941).
The "grey lung virus" of Andrewes & Glover (1945) has not been grown on a cell-free medium, but in its general behaviour and in sensitivity to antibiotics it so closely resembles a *Mycoplasma* that it can be allotted to that group with fair confidence.
Leukæmia viruses, p. 173.

LATENT RAT VIRUS

Description: Kilham & Olivier (1959).
In some properties this resembles the K virus (p. 202) but it cannot yet be confidently placed in the Papovavirus group, as it seems likely to be a smaller virus.

Morphology. Chandra & Toolan (1961) describe bodies 30 mμ across in the cytoplasm of hamster tissue and tissue cultures, the virus being particularly associated with mitochondria. Rowe *et al.* (1963) and Dalton *et al.*, (1963) report bodies 15 mμ across in nuclei and cytoplasm of infected cells.

Chemical composition. Reported by Rowe *et al.* (1963) to be a DNA virus.

Physico-chemical characters. Passes a Seitz (ST–1) filter. Ether-resistant. Survived heating 2 hours at 80° C, and storage for 6 months at −40° C.

Hæmagglutination. Agglutinates guinea pig RBC's at 23° C–40° C: strains differ in ability to agglutinate rat and human cells. Virus does not elute spontaneously from guinea pig cells; receptor-destroying enzyme destroys guinea pig red cell receptors.

Antigenic properties. Anti-hæmagglutinins and neutralizing antibodies (tested for in tissue-culture) are present in sera of some normal laboratory and wild rats (*R. norvegicus*). The virus is serologically distinct from polyoma, EMC and other rat viruses. One of Toolan's (1960a) strains is identical with Kilham's: another is serologically distinct with at most a little one-way crossing (Moore, 1962).

Cultivation. Growth occurs in rat- but not mouse-embryo tissue cultures. Dense masses of cells form in the cultures, with thin radiating extensions. These CPE's are seen after 9–12 days at 36° C, at which time hæmagglutinins appear in the supernatant fluids. Growth occurs also in hamster embryo but without this characteristic CPE (Moore, 1962). Intranuclear inclusions like those of polyoma can be found in epithelial and connective tissue cells of rat embryo (Dawe *et al.*, 1961).

Pathogenicity. None demonstrated by Kilham & Olivier (1959) but Toolan *et al.* (1960) produced a fulminating infection in suckling hamsters with large doses of virus. Smaller doses have caused dwarfism and a so-called "mongoloid" appearance (Toolan, 1960b; Kilham, 1961). As a result of studying the basis of this appearance, Dalldorf (1960) has described this as an osteolytic virus. Rabson *et al.* (1961) observed inclusions in cytoplasm and nuclei of liver and other cells of infected *Mastomys*.

Ecology. Virus has been recovered from rat tumours and from rats in which human tumours have been growing. It is presumably a virus latent in rats. Its direct isolation from human tumours has been considered as possible, but one awaits evidence that this has been achieved in a laboratory where the virus was not already under study.

VIRUS DISEASES OF RATS

Viruses naturally affecting rats are:
Cytomegaloviruses associated with intranuclear inclusions. *v.*, p. 240.

Snuffling disease of rats (Vrolijk *et al.*) and Nelson's pneumotropic virus of wild rats (1949) are similar to the grey lung virus of mice and therefore, like it, probably due to mycoplasmas. "Viruses" causing endemic pneumonia in rats (Nelson, 1946) have probably a similar cause.

VIRUS DISEASES OF HAMSTERS

A virus related to pneumonia virus of mice (PVM) (*v.*, p. 330) was described in Syrian hamsters (*Cricetus aureus*) by Pearson & Eaton (1940).

Another, related to mouse pneumonitis (*v.*, p. 377) is referred to by Nigg & Eaton, 1944.

Kuttner & Wang found salivary gland inclusions in Chinese hamsters (*Cricetulus griseus*) (*v.*, p. 240).

VIRUS DISEASES OF COTTON-RATS
(*Sigmodon hispidus*)

Cotton-rats may also be affected by a virus related to pneumonia virus of mice (*v.*, p. 330) (Eaton *et al.*, 1944); and may also carry an agent (presumably a *Mycoplasma*) related to "grey lung virus" (Andrewes & Niven, 1950).

VIRUS DISEASES OF GUINEA PIGS

Guinea Pig Paralysis

A sporadic paralytic disease of guinea pigs was described by Römer (1911). It was transmissible to other guinea pigs; attempted transfer to other species was not reported. Römer gives a full account of the symptoms and pathology but almost nothing about the virus's properties. As it has not been recognised during the last 50 years,

23

it is impossible to state whether it is identical with any other known virus or not. Encephalomyocarditis (*v.*, p. 27) is a possibility.

Guinea Pig Epizoötics

Lethal epizoötics amongst guinea pigs have been described by several authors. The viruses described by Humphreys *et al.* (1944) and the Pneumopathie des Cobayes of Lepine & Sautter (1945) were later identified as lymphocytic choriomeningitis (*v.*, p. 332). Some of the other agents may have been the same. At any rate the agents do not seem to have been preserved and cannot now be identified.

Guinea-pig salivary virus is described on p. 238.

REFERENCES

Ackerman, R., Scheid, W., & Jochheim, K. A. (1962) *Zbl. Bakt. I. Abt. Orig.*, **185**, 343.
Adams, W. R., & Kraft, L. M. (1963) *Science*, **141**, 359.
Andrewes, C. H., & Glover, R. E. (1945) *Brit. J. exp. Path.*, **26**, 379.
Andrewes, C. H., & Niven, J. S. F. (1950) *Brit. J. exp. Path.*, **31**, 767.
Armstrong, C., & Lillie, R. D. (1934) *Publ. Hlth. Rep.* (*Wash.*), **49**, 1019.
Armstrong, J. A., & Niven, J. S. F. (1957) *Nature* (*Lond.*), **180**, 1335.
Bailey, O. T., Pappenheimer, A. M., Cheever, F. S., & Daniels, J. B. (1949) *J. exp. Med.*, **90**, 195.
Bang, F. B., & Warwick, A. (1959) *Virology*, **9**, 715.
Bennette, J. G. (1960) *Nature* (*Lond.*), **187**, 72.
Benson, L. M., & Hotchin, J. E. (1960) *Proc. Soc. exp. Biol.* (*N.Y.*), **103**, 623.
Blanc, G., & Bruneau, J. (1951) *C.R. Acad. Sci.* (*Paris*), **233**, 1704.
Chandra, S., and Toolan, H. W. (1961) *J. nat. Cancer Inst.*, **27**, 1405.
Cheever, F. S., Daniels, J. B., Pappenheimer, A. M., & Bailey, O. T. (1949) *J. exp. Med.*, **90**, 181.
Cheever, F. S., & Mueller, J. H. (1947) *J. exp. Med.*, **85**, 405.
Cheever, F. S., & Mueller, J. H. (1948) *J. exp. Med.*, **88**, 309.
Curnen, E. C., Pickels, E. H., & Horsfall, F. L. (1947) *J. exp. Med.*, **85**, 23.
Dalldorf, G. (1960) *Bull. N.Y. Acad. Med.*, **36**, 795.
Dalton, A. J., Kilham, L., & Zeigel, R. F. (1963) *Virology*, **20**, 391.
Davenport, F. M. (1949) *J. Immunol.*, **63**, 81.
Dawe, C. J., Kilham, L., & Morgan, C. D. (1961) *J. nat. Cancer Inst.*, **27**, 221.
Dick, G. W. A., Niven, J. S. F., & Gledhill, A. W. (1956) *Brit. J. exp. Path.*, **37**, 90.
Eaton, M. D., Meiklejohn, G., & van Herick, W. (1944) *J. exp. Med.*, **79**, 649.
Eaton, M. D., & van Herick, W. (1944) *Proc. Soc. exp. Biol.* (*N.Y.*), **57**, 89.
Farmer, T. W., & Janeway, C. A. (1942) *Medicine*, **21**, 1.
Findlay, G. M., & MacCallum, F. O. (1938) *Proc. roy. Soc. Med.*, **31**, 799.
Franklin, R. M., & Gomatos, P. J. (1962) *Proc. Soc. exp. Biol.* (*N.Y.*), **108**, 651.
Ginsberg, H., & Horsfall, F. L. (1951) *J. exp. Med.*, **93**, 151.
Gledhill, A. W. (1956) *J. gen. Microbiol.*, **15**, 292.

Gledhill, A. W., & Andrewes, C. H. (1951) *Brit. J. exp. Path.*, **32,** 559.
Gledhill, A. W., & Dick, G. W. A. (1955) *J. Path. Bact.*, **69,** 311.
Gledhill, A. W., Dick, G. W. A., & Andrewes, C. H. (1952) *Lancet*, **2,** 509.
Gledhill, A. W., Dick, G. W. A., & Niven, J. S. F. (1955) *J. Path., Bact.*, **69,** 299.
Gompels, A. E. H., & Niven, J. S. F. (1953) *J. Path. Bact.*, **66,** 567.
Habermann, R. T. (1959) *Publ. Hlth. Rep. (Wash.)*, **74,** 165.
Horsfall, F. L., & Hahn, R. G. (1940) *J. exp. Med.*, **71,** 391.
Horsfall, F. L., & McCarty, M. (1947) *J. exp. Med.*, **85,** 623.
Hotchin, J., Benson, L. M., & Seamer, J. (1962) *Virology*, **18,** 71.
Hotchin, J., & Cinits, M. (1958) *Canad. J. Microbiol.*, **4,** 149.
Humphreys, F. A., Helmer, D. E., & Gibbons, R. J. (1944) *J. infect. Dis.*, **74,** 109.
Jordan, J., & Mirick, G. S. (1951) *J. exp. Med.*, **102,** 601 and 617.
Kilham, L. (1961) *Proc. Soc. exp. Biol. (N.Y.)*, **106,** 825.
Kilham, L., & Olivier, L. J. (1959) *Virology*, **7,** 428.
Kraft, L. M. (1957) *J. exp. Med.*, **106,** 743.
Kraft, L. M. (1962) *Science*, **137,** 282.
Kraft, L. M., & Moore, A. E. (1961) *Z. Versuchstierk.*, **1,** 66.
Lepine, P., & Sautter, V. (1945) *Ann. Inst. Pasteur*, **71,** 102.
Lepine, P., Mollaret, P., & Kreis, B. (1937) *C.R. Acad. Sci. (Paris)*, **204,** 1846.
Mills, K. C., & Dochez, A. R. (1944) *Proc. Soc. exp. Biol. (N.Y.)*, **57,** 140.
Mills, K. C., & Dochez, A. R. (1945) *Proc. Soc. exp. Biol. (N.Y.)*, **60,** 141.
Milzer, A. (1942) *J. infect. Dis.*, **70,** 152.
Miyazaki, Y., Katsuta, H., Aoyama, K., Kawai, J., & Takaoka, T. (1957) *Jap. J. exp. Med.*, **27,** 381.
Moore, A. E. (1962) *Virology*, **18,** 182.
Mundy, J., & Williams, P. C. (1961) *Science*, **134,** 834.
Nelson, J. B. (1937) *J. exp. Med.*, **65,** 833, 843 and 851.
Nelson, J. B. (1946) *J. exp. Med.*, **84,** 7.
Nelson, J. B. (1949) *J. infect. Dis.*, **84,** 21.
Nelson, J. B. (1953) *J. exp. Med.*, **98,** 433 and 441.
Nigg, C., & Eaton, M. D. (1944) *J. exp. Med.*, **79,** 497.
Niven, J. S. F., Gledhill, A. W., Dick, G. W. A., & Andrewes, C. H. (1952) *Lancet*, **2,** 1061.
Notkins, A. L., & Scheele, C. (1963) *Virology*, **20,** 640.
Notkins, A. L., & Shochat, S. J. (1963) *J. exp. Med.*, **117,** 735.
Pappenheimer, A. M. (1958) *J. nat. Cancer Inst.*, **20,** 861.
Pappenheimer, A. M., & Cheever, F. S. (1948) *J. exp. Med.*, **88,** 317.
Pearson, H. E., & Eaton, M. D. (1940) *Proc. Soc. exp. Biol. (N.Y.)*, **45,** 677.
Pollard, M., & Bussell, R. H. (1957) *Science*, **126,** 1245.
Reiss-Gutfreund, R. L., Andral, J., & Sérié, C. (1962) *Ann. Inst. Pasteur*, **102,** 36.
Rabson, A. S., Kilham, L., & Kirschstein, R. L. (1961) *J. nat. Cancer Inst.*, **27,** 1217.
Riley, V. (1961) *Science*, **134,** 666.
Riley, V., Lilly, F., Huerto, E., & Bardell, D. (1960) *Science*, **132,** 545.
Roger, F. (1962) *Ann. Inst. Pasteur*, **103,** 639.
Rogers, N. C. (1951) *J. Lab. clin. Med.*, **38,** 483.
Römer, P. H. (1911) *Zbl. Bakt. I. Abt. Orig.*, **50,** 30.
Rowe, W. P., & Capps, W. I. (1961) *J. exp. Med.*, **113,** 831.
Rowe, W. P., Hartley, J. W., & Capps, W. I. (1963) *Proc. Soc. exp. Biol. (N.Y.)*, **112,** 161.
Ruebner, B., & Miyai, K. (1962) *Amer. J. Path.*, **40,** 425.
Sabin, A. B. (1941) *Bact. Rev.*, **5,** 1.

Scott, W. McN., & Elford, W. J. (1939) *Brit. J. exp. Path.*, **20**, 182.
Shwartzman, G. (1944) *J. Immunol.*, **48**, 111.
Smadel, J. E., & Wall, M. J. (1942) *J. exp. Med.*, **75**, 581.
Smadel, J. E., Wall, M. J., & Baird, R. D. (1940) *J. exp. Med.*, **71**, 43.
Starr, T. J., Pollard, M., Duncan, D., & Dunaway, M. R. (1960) *Proc. Soc. exp. Biol. (N.Y.)*, **104**, 767.
Syverton, J. T., McCoy, O. R., & Koomen, J. (1947) *J. exp. Med.*, **85**, 759.
Tennant, R. W., & Ward, T. G. (1961) *Proc. Soc. exp. Biol. (N.Y.)*, **111**, 395.
Tobin, J. O'H. (1954) *Brit. J. exp. Path.*, **35**, 358.
Toolan, H. W. (1960a) *Science*, **131**, 1446.
Toolan, H. W. (1960b) *Proc. nat. Acad. Sci. (Wash.)*, **46**, 1256.
Toolan, H. W., Dalldorf, G., Barclay, M., Chandra, S., & Moore, A. E. (1960) *Proc. nat. Acad. Sci. (Wash.)*, **46**, 1256.
Traub, E. (1936) *J. exp. Med.*, **64**, 183.
Traub, E. (1937) *J. exp. Med.*, **66**, 317.
Traub, E. (1938) *J. exp. Med.*, **68**, 229.
Traub, E. (1939) *J. exp. Med.*, **69**, 801.
Traub, E. (1960) *Arch. ges. Virusforsch.*, **10**, 289.
Traub, E. (1962) *Arch. ges. Virusforsch.*, **11**, 667.
Vainio, T. (1961) *Proc. Soc. exp. Biol. (N.Y.)*, **107**, 326.
Vrolijk, H., Verlinde, J. D., & Braams, W. G. (1957) *Antonie v. Leeuwenhoek*, **23**, 173.
Weigand, H., & Hotchin, J. E. (1961) *J. Immunol.*, **86**, 401.

16

Unclassified Viruses of Other Mammals

PANLEUCOPENIA OF CATS

Synonyms: Feline infectious enteritis. Feline agranulocytosis. Cat fever. Cat distemper. Cat plague. Show fever. (Though the matter has been much debated, it is now accepted that these are names for one infection. See also, however, feline pneumonitis, p. 374.)

Review: Gledhill (1952).

Morphology. Diameter estimated at 80–100 mμ (Lepine & Pavilanis, 1948).

Physico-chemical characters. Survives well in 50 per cent. glycerol buffered to pH 7·2. Evidence as to resistance to desiccation is conflicting: it is said to withstand lyophilisation but to be readily inactivated when dried at room temperature. On the other hand, fomites seem to retain infectivity for months under natural conditions. Inactivated by 0·2 per cent. formalin. No information about ether-resistance.

Antigenic properties. Neutralizing antibodies are demonstrable. Hyperimmune sera produced in cats will passively protect kittens.

Cultivation. No multiplication occurs in fertile eggs; nor has the virus been propagated in tissue culture. An apparent success (Bolin, 1957) now seems to have been concerned with another feline virus (*v.*, p. 347).

Distribution: world-wide.

Pathogenicity. Chiefly affects young cats in endemic areas, but cats of any age where virus is newly introduced. There is a fever, the animals becoming very ill at the second peak. The cat is depressed

345

and dehydrated often with vomiting and profuse, sometimes blood-stained, diarrhœa. Discharge from eyes and nose occurs. Mortality when the disease has declared itself is from 65–90 per cent.; but there are probably many unrecognized subclinical infections which result in immunity. The incubation period after contact is rarely over 6 days.

All the *Felidæ* are susceptible, even lions and tigers, though in zoological gardens the virus rather affects the smaller species. Raccoons, of the *Procyonidæ*, are also attacked (Goss, 1948); and, strangely enough, the mink alone of *Mustelidæ*. A fatal virus enteritis in mink was shown by Wills (1952) to be due to this virus: symptoms are similar to those in cats.

Experimentally the disease is transmissible to cats and mink, by injection by various routes; the incubation period may be 48 hours. Animals of other families are resistant.

After an initial leucocytosis, white blood cells, both lymphocytes and polymorphonuclears, progressively disappear from the circulation and may, finally, be almost absent (Lawrence & Syverton, 1938; Hammon & Enders, 1939).

Pathological lesions. Post mortem are found acute enteritis, particularly of the lower ileum, spleen enlargement, swollen mesenteric lymph nodes and a "semi-liquid" aplastic bone-marrow (Jennings, 1947). In intestinal epithelium, also in lymph nodes, intranuclear inclusions are found (Hammon & Enders, 1939). Though they are at times eosinophilic, study of their whole course of development suggests that they differ from Cowdry's Type A inclusions (Lucas & Riser, 1945), occurring in clustered granular and diffuse granular forms and becoming basophilic with ageing.

Ecology. All secretions and excretions contain virus; recovered mink, perhaps also cats, may excrete virus for some time. Rugs and other fomites in houses where cats have died may carry infection to other cats introduced later. Recovered animals are highly immune and maternal antibody may protect kittens for a while. If they encounter the virus during this period, they may undergo a subclinical immunizing infection. Natural transmission through infected arthropods, especially fleas, or through worms, has been suspected but never proved.

Control. A vaccine made by treating infected tissue suspensions with 0·2 per cent. formalin has been successfully used for immunizing kittens (Pridham & Wills, 1959).

OTHER VIRUSES INFECTING CATS

Besides the viruses of panleucopenia (p. 345), and the agent causing feline pneumonitis (p. 374), a number of other viruses have been recovered from cats in tissue culture, mostly coming from the nasopharynx, some of them from kittens with rhinitis. Their relation to disease is mostly uncertain.

The virus of *feline virus rhinotracheitis* (FVR) is probably related to the Herpesviruses and is described on p. 332.

The *kitten-cell-degenerating* (KCD) virus of Fastier (1957) was isolated from cat kidney, is ether-stable and doubtfully pathogenic.

The *Californian feline isolate* (CFI) of Crandell & Madin (1960).

A *rhino-conjunctivitis virus* (Torlone, 1960) still produced symptoms in cats after 8 tissue-culture passages; cells infected in cat tissue-cultures showed paranuclear masses like those due to poliovirus.

Bolin's (1957) virus, at one time thought to be related to panleucopenia, is referred to by Cohen *et al.* (1961) as FVI (feline virus isolate) and by Bittle *et al.* (1961) as FPL. It caused a little fever and anorexia when administered to kittens.

A number of other viruses have been recovered from the nasopharynx of cats—their fæces do not seem to have been much studied. All have produced CPE in tissue-cultures of cat kidney; they seem to be ether-stable and not to agglutinate RBC's of cats or of other species tested. They may well prove to belong to the family of Picornaviruses and some have been referred to as ECCO (enteric cytopathogenic cat orphan) viruses. Five strains, described by Crandell *et al.* (1960) as FRI-6, FRI-12, FRI-14, FRI-29, FRI-278, were separable by neutralization tests from each other and from the FVR, KCE and CFI strains. Bittle *et al.* (1960) isolated 17 strains from cats with rhinitis; some of them corresponded to those of Crandell *et al.* (1960). Hersey & Maurer (1961) compared Bolin's virus, the CF-1, FR-12, FR-29, FR-278, KCD and FVR viruses, using complement-fixation. All but the last two appeared to be closely related by this test, though distinct by neutralization tests.

There seems thus to be a family of feline viruses, probably widely distributed and of doubtful pathogenicity: it does not seem wise to include them amongst Picornaviruses, until some more information is available, particularly as to size and nucleic acid composition. According to a personal communication from J. Prydie (1963) some of them at least may fall into the group of Rhinoviruses.

MISCELLANEOUS VIRUSES INFECTING DOGS

Dog distemper (p. 136) and canine hepatitis (p. 191) have already been considered. So little information is available about other virus diseases of dogs that it will suffice, at present, merely to give references.

Gustavson's (1947) canine *pharyngo-laryngo-tracheitis* was not conclusively proved to be due to a filterable agent.

Contagious rhino-tonsillitis (Fontaine *et al.*, 1957; Goret *et al.*, 1959) was due to a filterable agent, transmissible also to foxes but not other species. Attempts at cultivation in eggs were unsuccessful, but Bromont (1962) reported multiplication with CPE in monkey kidney cultures.

A *virus pneumonia of dogs* (Reculard *et al.*, 1959) was transmissible to dogs, not to other species. Virus was regularly present in the spleen.

A *malignant canine lymphocytopenia* with intracytoplasmic inclusion bodies was described by Reihart *et al.* (1952).

The *contagious venereal lymphosarcoma* of dogs may yet prove to have a causative virus, though demonstration of a cell-free agent has not been achieved (DeMonbreun & Goodpasture, 1934).

The status of all these supposed viruses requires to be investigated.

SIMIAN VIRUSES (SV)

Review: Kalter, 1960.

Many viruses have been isolated from monkeys in the last few years, mainly in cultivating kidney cells, especially of rhesus and cynomolgus monkeys. They have been mainly studied by Hull and his colleagues (1956, 1957, 1958) and have been given serial (SV) numbers irrespective of their taxonomic affinities.

Malherbe & Harwin (1957) have described 15 viruses (SA 1–15) isolated from *Cercopithecus*. Viruses coming from monkey stools (enteroviruses or ECMO—enteric cytopathogenic monkey orphans) have been described by Hoffert *et al.* (1958) and Melnick (1957).

Hull has separated groups on the basis of the type of CPE. Group I viruses (SV 1, 11, 17, 20, 23, 25, 27, 30, 31, 32, 33, 34, 36, 37, 38, 39 and Malherbe's SA 7) are adenoviruses (but see p. 188).

Group II contains enteroviruses of which all but SV 6 are like Coxsackie viruses in the type of CPE they produce. SV 19 is pathogenic for suckling mice: SV 2, 6, 16, 18, 19 and perhaps SA 5 (*v.*, p. 130).

Group III (SV 12, 59 and SA 3) are reoviruses (v., p. 45). SV 4 and 28 and SA 4 cause rather similar CPE but seem not to be reoviruses.

Group IV (SV 26 and 29) viruses have been isolated on single occasions from monkey CNS. Cells infected in culture become small, rounded and clumped. They cannot at present be classified.

Group V (SV 5, 5A and 41) are myxoviruses (v., p. 130) identified by hæmadsorption.

Group VI contains Herpesvirus B (v., p. 216) and SA 8—a similar South African agent.

Group VII contains the vacuolating agent SV 40 and the SA 12, the similar South African virus (v. p. 203).

Group VIII consists of SV 35, SA 1 and SA 6, which again cannot be placed. SV 35 is possibly an enterovirus.

Pathogenicity of B virus (p. 216) and of M 6 (p. 189) for monkeys has been described. SV 12 (Reovirus) and SV 16 (Coxsackie-like) have produced paralysis and death on intracerebral inoculation into monkeys. On the whole, however, there is little evidence that these viruses are natural monkey pathogens. Their presence in monkey kidneys is a likely consequence of herding recently caught monkeys closely together. It is improbable that so many agents would be recovered from monkeys in the wild. One unclassified simian virus requires special mention:

FOAMY AGENT (OR VIRUS)

Review: Plummer (1962).

Several groups of workers (Enders & Peebles, 1954; Rustigian et al., 1955; Ruckle, 1958) have described changes produced by this agent, which is the commonest contaminant of monkey kidney cultures.

Morphology. Diameter estimated to be over 70 mμ by centrifugation.

Physico-chemical characters. Inactivated in 15 minutes at 50° but survived well at −20°. Ether-sensitive.

Hæmagglutination—none detected.

Antigenic properties. Immune rabbit sera neutralize the virus in tissue culture. Johnston (1961) isolated a strain serologically

350   UNCLASSIFIED VIRUSES

distinct from others. In general foamy viruses from various monkey species are antigenically alike.

Interference. Simian myxovirus SV 5 (*v.*, p. 130) interferes with it in culture, a fact making serial propagation in monkey tissues difficult.

Cultivation. It produces syncytia and lace-like degeneration of monkey kidney cells, complete degeneration taking 1 or 2 weeks. Rather less characteristic changes are produced in HeLa and other primate cells (Paccaud, 1957). Brown (1957) was able to propagate it in rabbit kidney and this is the most useful medium. It can persist in cultures even in the presence of homologous antibody.

Distribution. Isolated from 40–65 per cent. of kidneys of rhesus and cynomolgus monkeys and *Cercopithecus pygerythrus*; also isolated from a colony of baboons (*Cynocephalus*). None was isolated from 296 cultures of *Erythrocebus patas* (Plummer, 1962).

Pathogenicity. Not known to be pathogenic.

REFERENCES

Bittle, J. L., Emery, J. B., York, C. J., & McMillen, J. K. (1961) *Amer. J. vet. Res.*, **22**, 374.
Bittle, J. L., York, C. J., Newberne, J. W., & Martin, M. (1960) *Amer. J. vet. Res.*, **21**, 547.
Bolin, V. S. (1957) *Virology*, **4**, 389.
Bromont, P. (1962) Paris (Alfort) thesis.
Brown, L. V. (1957) *Amer. J. Hyg.*, **65**, 189.
Cohen, D., Yohn, D. S., Pavia, R. A., & Hammon, W. McD. (1961) *Amer. J. vet. Res.*, **22**, 637.
Crandell, R. A., & Madin, S. H. (1960) *Amer. J. vet. Res.*, **21**, 551.
Crandell, R. A., Niemann, W. H., Ganaway, J. R., & Maurer, F. D. (1960) *Virology*, **10**, 283.
De Monbreun, W. A., & Goodpasture, E. W. (1934) *Amer. J. Cancer*, **21**, 295.
Enders, J. F., & Peebles, T. C. (1954) *Proc. Soc. exp. Biol.* (*N.Y.*), **86**, 277.
Fastier, L. B. (1957) *Amer. J. vet. Res.*, **18**, 382.
Fontaine, M., Ricq, A., Brion, A., & Goret, P. (1957) *C.R. Acad. Sci.* (*Paris*), **245**, 122.
Gledhill, A. W. (1952) *Vet. Res.*, **64**, 723.
Goret, P., Brion, A., Fontaine, M., Pilet, C., Girard, M., & Girard, M. (1959) *Bull. Acad. vét. Fr.*, **32**, 623, 635.
Goss, L. J. (1948) *Amer. J. vet. Res.*, **9**, 65.
Gustavson, W. L. (1947) *Yale J. Biol. Med.*, **20**, 185.
Hammon, W. McD., & Enders, J. F. (1939) *J. exp. Med.*, **69**, 327.
Hersey, D. F., & Maurer, F. D. (1961) *Proc. Soc. exp. Biol.* (*N.Y.*), **107**, 645.

Hoffert, W. R., Bates, M. E., & Cheever, F. S. (1958) *Amer. J. Hyg.*, **68,** 15.
Hull, R. N., & Minner, J. R. (1957) *Ann. N.Y. Acad Sci.*, **64,** 413.
Hull, R. N., & Minner, J. R., & Mascoli, C. C. (1958) *Amer. J. Hyg.*, **68,** 31.
Hull, R. N., Minner, J. R., & Smith, J. W. (1956) *Amer. J. Hyg.*, **63,** 204.
Jennings, A. R. (1947) *Brit. vet. J.*, **105,** 89.
Johnston, P. B. (1961) *J. infect. Dis.*, **109,** 1.
Kalter, S. S. (1960) *Bull. Wld. Hlth. Org.*, **22,** 319.
Lawrence, J. S., & Syverton, J. T. (1938) *Proc. Soc. exp. Biol. (N.Y.)*, **38,** 914.
Lepine, P., & Pavilanis, V. (1948) *Amer. Inst. Pasteur*, **74,** 155.
Lucas, A. M., & Riser, W. H. (1945) *Amer. J. Path.*, **21,** 435.
Malherbe, H., & Harwin, R. (1957) *Brit. J. exp. Path.*, **38,** 539.
Melnick, J. L. (1957) *Spec. Publ. N.Y. Acad. Sci.*, **5,** 365.
Paccaud, M. (1957) *Ann. Inst. Pasteur*, **92,** 481.
Plummer, G. (1962) *J. gen. Microbiol.*, **29,** 703.
Pridham, J., & Wills, C. G. (1959) *J. Amer. vet. med. Ass.*, **135,** 279.
Reculard, P., Vallée, A., Le Cain, A., Virat, B., & Levaditi, J., (1959) *Bull. Acad. vét. Fr.*, **32,** 603.
Reihart, O. F., Reihart, H. W., & Schenken, J. R. (1952) *N. Amer. Vet.*, **33,** 174.
Ruckle, G. (1958) *Arch. ges. Virusforsch.*, **8,** 139 and 167.
Rustigian, R., Johnston, P., & Reihart, H. (1955) *Proc. Soc. exp. Biol. (N.Y.)*, **88,** 8.
Torlone, V. (1960) *Vet. ital.*, **11,** 915.
Wills, C. G. (1952) *Canad. J. comp. Med.*, **16,** 419.

17

Unclassified Viruses of Birds

DUCK HEPATITIS

Review: Asplin (1961).

Morphology. Said to be spherical with a diameter, by electron-microscopy, of 20–40 mμ (Reuss, 1959).

Chemical composition. An infectious RNA is reported by Vindel (1963).

Physico-chemical characters. Ether-stable. Survived 4 days at room temperature (Reuss, 1959) or 21 days at 37° (Pollard & Starr, 1959). Inactivated in 30′ at 62°, not at 56°. Resisted 0·1 per cent. formaldehyde for 8 hours at 37° (Asplin, 1961).

Hæmagglutination has been looked for without success.

Antigenic properties. Neutralizing antibodies are present in sera of survivors. Hyperimmune serum confers passive immunity. In gel-diffusion tests antigen from liver suspensions or tissue cultures gave two lines of precipitate with immune duck sera.

Cultivation. The virus can be cultivated in fertile hens' eggs, killing most of the embryos in 4 days. Virus is present in allantoic fluid. It becomes attenuated for ducklings by egg-passage and can be used for immunization. Virulence returns after passage through ducks (Asplin, 1958). In cultures of chick embryo tissues the virus multiplies, but without CPE (Pollard & Starr, 1959).

Distribution. Recorded from many European countries including the U.S.S.R.; also from Egypt, United States and Canada.

Pathogenicity. The virus attacks ducklings 3 days to 3 weeks old, mortality being very high. Ducklings may die within an hour of the onset of symptoms. Older ducks are immune but may harbour virus. Other birds and mammals are resistant.

Pathological lesions are mainly those of hæmorrhage, necrosis in the liver, and œdema. Histologically hepatic cell necrosis and proliferation of bile ducts with cellular infiltration are seen: perivascular cuffing may be seen in the CNS (Hanson, 1958).

Ecology. Virus is excreted in the fæces of recovered or latently infected birds and infection may well be by this route, but spread of infection is erratic.

Control. Ducklings hatched from eggs laid by immunized birds resist infection (Asplin, 1956) or they may be immunized with virus attenuated in chick embryos, a virus-infected needle being thrust through the foot-web. Hyperimmune sera may be used for passive protection.

INFECTIOUS BRONCHITIS

Synonym: Gasping disease. The disease is distinct from infectious
   laryngo-tracheitis (*cf.* p. 228).
Review: Hofstad (1959).

Morphology. Domermuth & Edward (1957) have described particles in pairs, chains or clumps, seen in their sections of infected tissues. They were about 178 mμ in diameter and showed some evidence of internal structure. Cunningham (1957) describes particles in cytoplasm about 200 mμ across and others in infected allantoic fluid 60–100 mμ across.

Chemical composition. No evidence as to nucleic acid composition. Cunningham (1960) tried without success to obtain infectious RNA.

Physico-chemical characters. Density 1·15–1·16 in sucrose gradients. Stability at 56° varies from one strain to another; most are inactivated in 30′. The virus does not survive 9–30 hours at 37°. Survived 1 hour at room temperature at pH 2 and (in 1 per cent. NaOH) pH 12 (Dubose *et al.*, 1960). One per cent. formalin and 1 : 10,000 KMnO4 inactivated (Cunningham & Stuart, 1946). Page & Cunningham (1962) followed the rate of inactivation at 56°, 37° and 26°. Said to be ether-stable in one report, but Mohanty and Chang (1963), using standard methods, found it to be sensitive.

Hæmagglutination. Virus modified by trypsin—later treated with a trypsin-inhibitor—will agglutinate fowl RBC's at pH 7·2, contact being at room temperature for 45–60'. Various mammalian cells were not affected. There was no elution. Egg-adapted strains were less active (Corbo & Cunningham, 1959).

Antigenic properties. Neutralization tests using death of inoculated embryos as an end-point reveal two antigenic types (Connecticut and Massachusetts), showing some cross-reactivity (Hofstad, 1958).

Other serotypes probably exist.

Convalescent fowl sera can be used for diagnosis in gel-diffusion tests (Woernle, 1959).

Cultivation. *In fertile eggs*, the virus grows on the CAM without producing definite pocks (Beaudette & Hudson, 1937); also after inoculation into the allantoic cavity; infected embryos are dwarfed or curled into balls and there may be necrotic foci in liver, pneumonia and nephritis (Loomis *et al.*, 1950). The virus grows in cultures of chick embryonic tissues but no definite CPE is described (Fahey & Crawley, 1956).

Distribution. The disease is reported from all continents except South America.

Pathogenicity. Chicks 2–3 days up to 4 weeks old are affected worst. There are depression and gasping and rales are heard; the course is from 6–18 days; mortality is up to 90 per cent. Two serologically distinct strains seem to be the cause of Avian nephrosis (Winterfield & Hitchner, 1962). In laying birds infection causes big drops in egg-production and eggs are defective. Pheasants may be affected.

Experimentally the incubation period after intratracheal inoculation of chicks is 1–2 days. The disease has been transmitted in series in suckling mice inoculated IC (Simpson & Groupé, 1958, 1959).

Pathological lesions. Mucous or caseous exudate in respiratory passage is profuse and may cause blocking. Histological study reveals œdema and epithelial hypertrophy of affected mucous membranes, going on to hyperplasia, cellular exudate and repair (Cunningham, 1960). There are lesions in the oviduct of laying birds (Sevoian & Levine, 1957).

Ecology. The agent is highly infectious and spreads by the respiratory route, but excretion via the cloaca may also be important (Pette, 1959). Birds may be infectious as long as 35 days after recovery (Hofstad, 1945).

Control. Virus attenuated by cultivation in eggs has been administered in drinking-water or as an aerosol: some success is claimed (Hoekstra & Rispens, 1960). The vaccine may be combined with one against Newcastle disease (Markham *et al.*, 1956).

PUFFINOSIS

A disease affecting young Manx shearwaters.
Description: Stoker & Miles (1953).

Morphology. A small virus, passing a 48 mμ but not a 31 mμ gradocol membrane.

Hæmagglutination was not demonstrable.

Antigenic properties. Neutralized by convalescent shearwater serum: complement-fixation could also be shown.

Cultivation was possible on the CAM of fertile eggs. Small pocks were produced after 12 passages. Three passages were also achieved in the allantoic cavity.

Pathogenicity. A disease affecting young Manx shearwaters (*Puffinus puffinus*) after desertion by their parents 2 months after hatching. There were blisters on the feet and patchy lung consolidation. On transmission the disease was fatal to young shearwaters; and lesions were also produced on the webbed feet of ducklings, which often died. Vesicles were also produced on the breast of a pigeon, but chickens and mammals were unsusceptible. Virus was also obtained from a young Herring gull (*Larus argentatus*).
Dane *et al.* (1953) suggest that the shearwaters may have been infected from gulls.

OTHER POULTRY DISEASES

Very little information is available concerning a number of other diseases of poultry, and what there is is largely contradictory. What follows must be accepted with reserve and as provisional only. Not all the agents may prove to be distinct from other viruses.

Blue Comb

Synonyms (probably): Pullet disease, avian monocytosis, avian diarrhœa.

This affects young turkeys and pullets with diarrhœa, hepatic necrosis and monocytosis. The agent is filterable, unaffected by antibiotics and is cultivable in 8-day chick embryos, killing them in 36–72 hours (Watanabe, 1952; Jungherr & Levine, 1941; Tumlin & Pomeroy, 1958).

Hepatitis of Turkeys

A very contagious, lethal virus causing focal hepatitis in turkeys. The agent passed a 0·3 μ millipore membrane, resisted antibiotics, multiplied in the yolk-sac of fertile eggs and thereafter produced hepatitis in 1-day-old turkey poults but not in chicks (Snoeyenbos *et al.*, 1959; Mongeau *et al.*, 1959).

Disease of Muscovy Ducks

Kaschula (1950) described a very fatal disease affecting only Muscovy ducks (*Corina moschata*) in Natal. The agent passed a Seitz filter. It caused diarrhœa after an incubation of 2–4 days: necrotic spots were found on liver and spleen and there was pulmonary œdema. Attempted transmission to other species was unsuccessful.

Spleen Necrosis in Ducks

Trager (1959) while passing malaria strains in ducks encountered a disease fatal in 3–5 days in young ducklings. The agent passed a Selas 03 filter and survived well at −76°. It was neutralized by homologous antiserum but not by duck hepatitis antisera. There were severe anæmia, necrotic lesions in the spleen and hepatitis. A virus encountered in similar circumstances by Dearborn (1946) may be identical.

Other "viruses" affecting poultry are:

Enteroviruses including the chick embryo lethal orphan (CELO) virus (p. 22) and the virus of Avian Encephalomyelitis (p. 21).

Infectious laryngo-tracheitis (p. 228).

GAL virus (p. 190).

Fowl-pox (p. 274).

Ornithosis (p. 370).

Leucosis and related diseases (Chapter VII, p. 161).

Infectious synovitis and tendovaginitis, also a hepatitis of pullets, are thought to be due to *Mycoplasma* infection and are not considered. The "chronic respiratory disease" of chicks and infectious sinusitis of turkeys are in the same category.

REFERENCES

Asplin, F. D. (1956) *Vet. Rec.*, **68**, 412.

Asplin, F. D. (1958) *Vet. Rec.*, **70**, 1226.

Asplin, F. D. (1961) *Bull. Off. int. Épiz.*, **56**, 793.

Beaudette, F. R., & Hudson, C. B. (1937) *J. Amer. vet. med. Ass.*, **90**, 51.

Corbo, L. T., & Cunningham, C. H. (1959) *Amer. J. vet. Res.*, **20**, 876.

Cunningham, C. H. (1957) *Amer. J. vet. Res.*, **18**, 648.

Cunningham, C. H. (1960) *Amer. J. vet. Res.*, **21**, 498.

Cunningham, C. H., & Stuart, H. O. (1946) *Amer. J. vet. Res.*, **7**, 466.

Dane, D. S., Miles, J. A. R., & Stoker, M. G. P. (1953) *J. Anim. Ecol.*, **22**, 123.

Dearborn, E. H. (1946) *Proc. Soc. exp. Biol. (N.Y.)*, **63**, 48.

Domermuth, C. H., & Edward, O. F. (1957) *J. infect. Dis.*, **100**, 74.

Dubosc, R. T., Grumbles, L. C., & Flowers, A. I. (1960) *Amer. J. vet. Res.*, **21**, 740.

Fahey, J. E., & Crawley, J. F. (1956) *Canad. J. Microbiol.*, **2**, 503.

Hanson, L. E. (1958) *Amer. J. vet. Res.*, **19**, 712.

Hoekstra, J., & Rispens, B. (1960) *T. Diergeneesk.*, **85**, 398.

Hofstad, M. S. (1945) *Cornell Vet.*, **35**, 32.

Hofstad, M. S. (1958) *Amer. J. vet. Res.*, **19**, 740.

Hofstad, M. S. (1959) in *Diseases of Poultry*. Ed. Biester and Schwarte. Iowa State Univ. Press. p. 443.

Jungherr, E., & Levine, J. M. (1941) *Amer. J. vet. Res.*, **2**, 261.

Kaschula, V. R. (1950) *J. S. Afr. vet. med. Ass.*, **21**, 18.

Loomis, L. N., Cunningham, C. H., Gray, M. L., & Thorp, F. (1950) *Amer. J. vet. Res.*, **11**, 245.

Markham, F. S., Hammar, A. H., Gingher, P., Cox, H. R., & Storie, J. (1955) *Poult. Sci.*, **34**, 442.

Mohanty, S. B., & Chang, S. C. (1963) *Amer. J. vet. Res.*, **101**, 822.

Mongeau, J. D., Truscott, R. B., Ferguson, A. E., & Connell, M. C. (1959) *Avian Dis.*, **3**, 388.

Page, C. A., & Cunningham, C. H. (1962) *Amer. J. vet. Res.*, **23**, 1065.

Pette, J. (1959) *Mh. Tierheilk.*, **11**, 296.

Pollard, M., & Starr, T. J. (1959) *Proc. Soc. exp. Biol. (N.Y.)*, **101**, 521.

Reuss, U. (1959) *Zbl. Vet.-Med.*, **6**, 209.

Sevoian, M., & Levine, P. P. (1957) *Avian Dis.*, **1**, 136.

Simpson, A. W., & Groupé, V. (1959) *Virology*, **8**, 456.

Simpson, A. W., & Groupé, V. (1958) *Fed. Proc.*, **17**, 535.

Snoeyenbos, G. H., Basch, H. I., & Sevoian, M. (1959) *Avian Dis.*, **3,** 377.
Stoker, M. G. P., & Miles, J. A. R. (1953) *J. Hyg. (Lond.)*, **51,** 195.
Trager, W. (1959) *Proc. Soc. exp. Biol. (N.Y.)*, **101,** 578.
Tumlin, J. T., & Pomeroy, B. S. (1958) *Amer. J. vet. Res.*, **19,** 725.
Vindel, J. A. (1963) *C.R. acad. Sci. (Paris)* **257,** 2565.
Watanabe, M. (1952) *J. Jap. vet. med. Ass.*, **5,** 109.
Winterfield, R. W., & Hitchner, S. B. (1962) *Amer. J. vet. Res.*, **23,** 1273.
Woernle, H. (1959) *Mh. Tierheilk.*, **11,** 154.

18

Virus Diseases of Fish

Reviews: Lucké and Schlumberger (1949)—fish tumours.
Nigrelli (1952).
Much of the literature concerning these viruses dates back forty
years or more to a time before virological techniques were far
developed.

LYMPHOCYSTIS

Morphology. In the large "tumour" cells there are cytoplasmic
inclusions; these contain osmiophilic granules joined in a filamentous
lattice (Weissenberg, 1956). Similar structures have been seen in
flounders, perch and other fish. Grützner (1956) describes bodies
270–460 mμ across, possibly representing virus. The virus has been
filtered but there are no estimates of size based on filtration. Walker
(1962) describes in lymphocystis disease of the pike-perch (*Stizo-
stedion*) bodies about 200 mμ across, with a capsid 12 mμ in diameter
and a nucleoid 150 mμ across consisting of a ball of 10 mμ-wide
threads.

Physico-chemical characters. Virus survives 20 months at
−20° but is apparently easily destroyed by alternate freezing and
thawing. It is probably ether-sensitive and, unlike most animal
viruses, is not readily preserved in 50 per cent. glycerol in the cold.
It survives desiccation but long storage of dried material is not
reported (Wolf, 1962).

Antigenic properties. Recovered bluegills were partly but not
wholly refractory to reinoculation (Wolf, 1962).

Cultivation. Grützner (1956) reported specific changes in cell
cultures of *Lebistes* inoculated with virus. Others have been unsuccessful.

359

Pathogenicity. Lymphocystis is a common chronic but rarely fatal disease affecting fish of several orders. Tumour-like masses of the skin and fins persist for long periods but ultimately regress: secondary "tumours" may appear elsewhere on the skin. Wessing & von Bargen (1959) describe mesenchymal tumours in kidneys of tropical *Pristella* "wandering" to other sites and transmissible to *Lebistes* and other species.

Experimentally, transmission has been accomplished by implantation, injection and other methods. Some workers have had difficulty in transmission between different species, but Wolf (1962) was more successful using several centrarchid fishes. The blue gill (*Lepomis macrochirus*) proved to be a convenient experimental animal which could be bred in hatcheries. Fish of unrelated families were refractory to Wolf's virus.

Large cytoplasmic inclusions occur in "tumour" cells, which may be up to 2000 mμ across. The growths themselves are of soft jelly-like consistency.

Ecology. Outbreaks in nature occur mainly in summer months. Weissenberg (1945) reported spread to healthy fish, but Wolf (1962), who freed his fish from ectoparasites found no spread. Nigrelli (1952) suspected that parasites played a role.

CARP-POX

Synonym: Epithelioma of carp.

Morphology. Goncharov (1960) found virus-like bodies 70–220 mμ across, round or elongated and then constricting on division.

Cultivation. Grützner (1956) inoculated tissue cultures from *Lebistes* and observed specific changes.

Pathogenicity. The pock-like lesions were described by Keysselitz (1908) and Loewenthal (1907).

Infectious Pancreatic Necrosis in Trout

Wolf *et al.* (1960) described this fatal virus disease of young Eastern brook-trout (*Salvelinus fontinatus*). The agent passed a Seitz filter, was inactivated in 1 hour at 60°, survived 4$\frac{1}{2}$ years at −20° and 2$\frac{1}{2}$ years in 50 per cent. glycerol at 4°. It produced CPE in cultures of some salmonid fishes but not those of other species. The virus passed a 50 mμ membrane, was ether-resistant and belongs possibly in the Picornavirus groups (K. Wolf—personal communication, 1963).

Sock-eye Virus

Watson, Guenther & Rucker (1954) describe a fatal epizoötic affecting young sock-eye salmon (*Oncorhynchus nerka*) in hatcheries in the United States. After an incubation period of 1 day or more, affected fish were sluggish with occasional spasms. Hæmorrhagic and eroded areas were seen at bases of fins. Spinal deformities were common amongst survivors. Virus, present chiefly in liver and kidney, was inactivated in 15' at 60°, survived at pH 4 and 10 for an hour; after a large initial fall on freezing, remaining virus survived for 1 year at 0°.

Egtved virus

This caused hæmorrhagic septicæmia amongst European salmonids (Jensen, 1963). The virus is ether-sensitive and has passed a 100 mμ membrane. It has been propagated in cultures of rainbow trout ovarian cells.

Other fish viruses about which very little is known are Chinook salmon virus (Ross, Pelnar and Rucker, 1960); and a virus causing contagious stomatitis of fish in South America (Pacheco, 1935). A virus causation has been suspected also for a number of tumours in fish.

REFERENCES

Goncharov, O. D. (1960) *Probl. Virol.*, **5**, 261.
Grützner, L. (1956) *Zbl. Bakt. I. Abt. Orig.*, **165**, 81.
Jensen, M. H. (1963) *Bull. Off. int. Épiz.*, **59**, 131.
Keysselitz, G. (1908) *Arch. Protistenk.*, **11**, 326.
Loewenthal, W. (1907) *Z. Krebsforsch.*, **5**, 197.
Lucké, B., & Schlumberger, H. G. (1949) *Physiol. Rev.*, **29**, 91.
Nigrelli, R. F. (1952) *Ann. N.Y. Acad. Sci.*, **54**, 1076.
Pacheco, G. (1935) *Mem. Inst. Oswaldo Cruz*, **30**, 349.
Ross, A. J., Pelnar, J., & Rucker, R. R. (1960) *Trans. Amer. Fish. Soc.*, **89**, 160.
Walker, R. (1962) *Virology*, **18**, 503.
Watson, S. W., Guenther, R. W., & Rucher, R. R. (1954) *Sp. sci. Report Series. Fisheries No. 138*, U.S. Dept. of Interior, Fish and Wild Life section.
Weissenberg, R. (1945) *Zoologica*, **30** (part 4), 169.

Weissenberg, R. (1956) *Arch. ges. Virusforsch.*, **7**, 1.
Wessing, A., & von Bargen, G. (1959) *Arch. ges. Virusforsch.*, **9**, 521.
Wolf, K. (1962) *Virology*, **18**, 249.
Wolf, K., Sniesko, S. F., Dunbar, C. E., & Pyle, E. (1960) *Proc. Soc. exp. Biol. (N.Y.)*, **104**, 105.

PART IV

Chlamydozoaceæ

19

Psittacosis-Lymphogranuloma-Trachoma Group

Synonyms: *Chlamydiaceæ. Chlamydozoaceæ.* P-L or P-LV group. *Miyagawanella. Bedsonia.*

Reviews: Weiss (1955). Meyer & Eddie (1951) Wenner, (1958). Cox (1947). Hurst & Hull (1956) (chemotherapy).

This group of organisms lies between the true viruses on the one hand and the rickettsiæ and Gram-negative bacteria on the other. Recent opinion tends towards excluding them from the viruses and placing them alongside the rickettsiæ, to which they are clearly related. The reasons are:

(i) They contain both DNA and RNA.

(ii) There is evidence of presence of a cell wall and this in some, perhaps all, contains muramic acid (Allison & Perkins, 1960), a substance present generally in bacteria and rickettsiæ but not in viruses.

(iii) There is a life cycle in which larger bodies give place to smaller ones and finally to elementary bodies. Much evidence suggests that multiplication by binary fission occurs at least at some stage.

(iv) The agents are susceptible, many of them to sulphonamides or penicillin; all to tetracyclines: this fact may be related to the presence in them of folic acid.

(v) They stain well by Castañedas and Machiavello's methods.

It is, however, suggested that there is a true eclipse phase in the developmental cycle; if so, this cycle has features characteristic of both bacterial and viral multiplication. It is also possible that DNA and RNA are not both of them present at all stages of the cycle.

Psittacosis, ornithosis and agents causing pneumonitis in man, cats, mice and other species, are very closely related, differing hardly at all except antigenically and in pathogenicity for various species: and even so reports from different workers are often in conflict. It is a matter of opinion how many should be given status as separate agents: some are best regarded as serotypes.

If these organisms are regarded as subject to the Code of Nomenclature of Bacteria, the cumbersome generic name *Miyagawanella* has technical priority.

The agents of trachoma and inclusion blenorrhœa stand a little apart from the others and are included in the genus *Chlamydozoön* (= *Chlamydia*). The use of the term virus for the agents will be avoided in this chapter.

Morphology. Spheres, showing wrinkled cell walls on drying for electron-microscopy. Within is a rounded body with a more electron-dense central mass. Since, as described under psittacosis (p. 367) there are bodies of different dimensions during development, estimates of size vary widely: figures of 0·25 to 0·5 μ are given for elementary bodies. Perhaps the best estimate is by electron-microscopy of freeze-dried specimens (*cf.* Crocker & Williams, p. 372).

Chemical composition. RNA and DNA are present (true viruses contain only one or the other). Muramic acid and folic acid are present. Pteroylglutamic acid may be a necessary metabolite.

Physico-chemical characters. Can be preserved at −76° or by freeze-drying, but survive less readily than most viruses. Ether-sensitive; reports as to sensitivity to bile salts are conflicting. The agents probably react very similarly to chemical reagents. Details as to particular tests are listed separately under the various members of the group.

Hæmagglutinins are described for some members.

Antigenic properties. A heat-stable complement-fixing antigen is common to the group but the cross-reaction is less readily demonstrated with the trachoma-like organisms. Specific complement-fixation tests (direct or indirect), agglutination and neutralization of infectivity or "toxin" are used. A lethal endotoxin has been described for most members: this kills mice when injected IV independently of any multiplication of the organisms; it is not separable from the elementary bodies. Neutralization of this toxin apparently gives more specific results in separating the various agents than do other tests. An allergen reacting in skin tests on recovered subjects is common to the group (*v.* under L.G.V., p. 381).

Interference between different members of the group is reported in eggs and in mice.

Cultivation. All the agents grow in fertile eggs, yolk-sac inoculation being chiefly used. Growth also occurs in tissue-culture but this method has been less widely studied.

Pathogenicity. The upper and lower respiratory tracts of birds and mammals are chiefly attacked, with inflammatory lesions resulting, but liver, spleen and other viscera are often involved. Some agents affect the eyes almost exclusively.

Ecology. Latent infection is the normal state of affairs.

Control. Tetracyclines have value against all the agents: penicillin and sulphonamides against some.

PSITTACOSIS

Synonyms: Parrot fever.
Microbacterium multiforme. Miyagawanella psittaci.

The agents of avian origin are commonly separated into those of parrot origin—psittacosis; and those from other birds—ornithosis. The former are in general more pathogenic for mammals including man; but the separation is a rather artificial one, though convenient for the epidemiologist.

Reviews: as listed for the whole group (p. 365). Also Meyer (1959) and Beaudette (1958).

Morphology. The virus bodies were described independently in 1930 by Levinthal, Coles and Lillie; they are often referred to as L.C.L. bodies. The classical account of the developmental cycle is by Bedson & Bland (1932). After infection of cells by elementary bodies, these cease to be demonstrable. Eight to 30 hours later initial bodies, $0 \cdot 8 \, \mu$–$1 \cdot 2 \, \mu$ across, appear. These divide, apparently by binary fission, the bodies seen becoming successively smaller (Swain, 1955). The elementary bodies, representing the final, and most infective stage, are about 450 mμ across (by electron-microscopy) (Kurotchkin *et al.*, 1947). Earlier estimates gave figures of 200–300 mμ.

There is an electron-dense mass centrally; the outer membrane wrinkles and partly collapses on drying for electron-miscroscopy.

Chemical composition—as for the group.

Physico-chemical characters. As for the group. Ether-sensitive but said to resist bile salts (Burnet & Lush, 1940). Inactivated by 25 per cent. ethanol and 40 per cent. methanol in the cold (Wagner et al., 1948). Preserved with some difficulty by freeze-drying, but survives better if suspended in skim-milk with 7·5 per cent. glucose (Schmittdiel, 1961).

Hæmagglutination. Agglutinates mouse RBC's, the reaction being group- rather than strain-specific. The hæmagglutinin is heat-stable and contains lecithin and nucleoprotein. It is probably of the same nature as vaccinia hæmagglutinin but is closely associated with elementary bodies. There is no spontaneous elution from RBC's.

Antigenic properties. The agent contains two antigens: one is group-specific and heat-stable, withstanding boiling or even autoclaving at 135° C; the other is specific and readily inactivated at 60° C (Bedson, 1936). According to Fulton (1953), however, the group reactions are due to degraded specific antigen rather than to a group-antigen. Antigen is released into solution. Heat-stable antigen is reactive in the complement-fixation and presumably in the hæmagglutination test; it is destroyed by potassium periodate and suspensions so treated yield the heat-labile, specific, antigen. The effects of extraction with acid, alkali and ether on the antigens have been studied by Barwell (1952) and Ross & Gogolak (1957). Neutralization of infectivity and of endotoxin and agglutination of elementary bodies have also been studied. Neutralization of infectivity by fowl sera and of endotoxin give more specific results than other tests. It is commonly necessary to use the indirect C-F test in work involving use of fowl sera. An antigenic relation to Bact. anitratum is reported by Volkert & Matthiesen (1958).

Cultivation. In fertile eggs, grows equally well in yolk sac and allantoic sac, though the former has been more used. Amniotic inoculation gives higher titres (Burnet & Foley, 1941). Inoculation on the chorioallantoic membrane may also be useful. Egg-cultivation is convenient for production of active material in quantity, including endotoxin. Various methods of purification—digestion with enzymes, differential centrifugation and absorption—have been used.

In tissue culture of monkey kidney, HeLa cells, L-cells, mouse and chick-embryo tissues, the agent grows readily but the yield is low. The role of nutrients particularly amino acids in permitting active growth has been studied by Morgan (1954).

Distribution. The natural habitat of the psittacosis agent is, by definition, in birds of the parrot family, at least 57 species being spontaneous hosts. These mainly inhabit Australia and South America.

Pathogenicity. In the natural psittacine host, the disease is commonly latent, except when birds are shipped abroad and particularly when they are kept under conditions of bad husbandry. Spontaneous outbreaks in wild Australian and South American parrots are, however, reported. Affected birds, particularly young ones, show ruffled plumage, nasal discharge, watery green diarrhœa and emaciation, often followed by death.

Captive psittacines may spread infection to man; also to Java ricebirds (Oryza) and other captive finches.

Human infections may be subclinical, mild or less frequently severe and fatal. After 1–2 weeks' incubation, sometimes more, there may come a rather prolonged febrile illness with patchy bronchopneumonia and quite a number of complications. Numerous infections of laboratory workers have been reported.

Experimentally the organism infects mice readily by all the usual routes of inoculation. Death occurs in 2–15 days according to virulence. Inoculation intraperitoneally leads to death with peritoneal exudate and some liver necrosis; given intranasally the agent causes pneumonia, either confluent or, with smaller doses, small discrete grey lesions; and intracerebral injection leads in 3–6 days to irritability, ataxia, fits and death. The virus may persist a long time in survivors, particularly after chemotherapy.

Hamsters are also susceptible, other rodents less so, but the virus can be passed in series intracerebrally in rabbits and guinea pigs: there is a febrile response. Pneumonia and meningoencephalitis can be induced in rhesus monkeys (Rivers & Berry, 1931). Parakeets and budgerigars from clean aviaries are readily infected, as are various finches.

Pathological lesions. Lesions in psittacines consist chiefly of focal liver necroses and swollen spleens. In man, the solid-looking pneumonic areas show less uniform consolidation microscopically. Fibrin and desquamated alveolar cells are seen and cells of the exudate, mainly mononuclear, contain small colonies of the agent, readily stained by Machiavello's method. Similar colonies may be seen in Kupffer cells in the small necrotic liver lesions. Lesions are also found in the myocardium and elsewhere. Infected mice show most damage in lung, brain or peritoneum according to the route of inoculation.

Ecology. The disease is endemic in wild birds of the parrot family, infection being transmitted to nestlings. Carriers may excrete the agent in fæces for long periods. Under conditions of crowding and bad husbandry of birds in captivity, the infection is activated, birds begin to die and to disseminate virus widely to other birds in an aviary and to man. The main route of infection is probably inhalation of organisms from dried excreta. One human patient reported by Meyer excreted virus for 8 years.

Control. (*a*) *By quarantine.* Prohibition of importation of parrots and their relatives has controlled outbreaks in man. Slaughter has been necessary in badly affected aviaries. Proper husbandry can also keep the infection in check.

(*b*) *By chemotherapy.* Tetracyclines are very effective and penicillin rather less so against most strains, sulphonamides still less. A number of other compounds have shown some activity. Meyer and his colleagues (1958) have shown that it is possible to eliminate infection from commercial aviaries by adequate treatment with Aureomycin in the food.

(*c*) *By immunization.* Vaccination of volunteers with living virus given subcutaneously has been carried out, but never on a large scale. Formalinized virus is not very effective.

ORNITHOSIS

Synonyms: often included under psittacosis.

The agents coming from birds other than parrots are here included. Their properties are mainly those of psittacosis; only points of difference or facts elicited only for non-psittacine strains will be mentioned. The most important sources of virus are in pigeons, turkeys, fowls, ducks, egrets, fulmar petrels and other sea-birds.

Morphology: chemical composition: physico-chemical characters and hæmagglutinins—as for psittacosis.

Antigenic properties. Differences between various avian strains shown by the more sensitive techniques (use of fowl sera, neutralisation of endotoxins) show differences, but these are less than between avian and most mammalian strains. The endotoxins of turkey and egret strains are very similar to that of the Louisiana strain (*v.* p. 373). Pigeon strains stand rather apart from the others. The agent of meningopneumonitis (*v.* p. 372) is not separable antigenically from ornithosis.

Cultivation—as for psittacosis.

In fertile eggs. The agent from turkeys is very lethal on inoculation into yolk sacs and gives very high titres, up to 10^{-9}.

Distribution, Pathogenicity. Ornithosis is widespread in wild and domestic pigeons; also in the free pigeons in large cities; but pigeon strains seem relatively avirulent for mammals, and are not very apt to infect human beings. Strains isolated from pheasants are similar.

Women dressing young fulmar petrels in the Faeroe Islands have contracted infection, as have people handling ducks in the United States and Czechoslovakia. The disease in ducks may be endemic and unrecognized or may cause serious outbreaks in the flocks. Strains from egrets in the southern United States make potent toxins and are virulent for man. During recent years there have been numerous cases in people handling live or dead turkeys in the United States, particularly in the Far West and in British Columbia. Turkey strains may be very virulent or, in other flocks, fairly mild. The birds in a badly affected flock suffer from respiratory distress, anorexia and yellow diarrhœa preceding death.

Experimentally, all ornithosis strains infect mice much as psittacosis does. Some virulent turkey and egret strains, unlike psittacosis, are virulent for guinea pigs when given intraperitoneally, killing in 6 to 10 days. Strains from poultry, unlike those from parrots, kill pigeons when inoculated intracerebrally. The good toxin-producers from turkeys and egrets will infect rhesus monkeys after intracerebral or intratracheal inoculation. Calves have also been infected with turkey strains.

Pathological lesions. Characteristic lesions in turkey poults in affected flocks are caseo-fibrinous pericarditis and similar lesions in the air sacs and peritoneum, pneumonia and splenomegaly.

Similar lesions may occur in ducks involved in outbreaks but in other birds ornithosis is usually an inapparent infection, serving at times as a source of human infection.

Ecology. Latent infections occur in other bird families as in psittacosis. It may be noted that the agents particularly attack birds with social nesting habits or those which are crowded together in captivity.

Control. As for psittacosis. Chlortetracycline, given in food, has been successfully used to prevent mortality in affected turkey farms. It is not known whether infection can be eliminated by its use (Davis & Delaplane, 1958).

MENINGOPNEUMONITIS AND OTHER MIYAGAWANELLAS CAUSING PNEUMONITIS IN MAN

Others included bear the designations S.F., Louisiana, Chicago, Ann Arbor, Illinois and Bayou.

Review: Meyer & Eddie, 1952.

A number of viruses differing only in minor antigenic and biological characters have been recovered from pneumonitis in man. Since they have shown more tendency than psittacosis ordinarily does to spread from man to man, they have been regarded as being possibly man-adapted members of the group, particularly as infections have occurred in the absence of known contact with birds. Possibly they are of fairly recent avian origin, an origin lost in the course of a short man-to-man chain of infection. The fact that there are so many slightly different ones, each isolated on only a few occasions, speaks against their being established human pathogens.

Morphology. A careful study of meningopneumonitis agent by Gaylord (1954) revealed forms of 5 different sizes; but the findings do not conflict with those described for related organisms. Crocker & Williams (1955) estimated the size by electron-microscopy of freeze-dried preparations. The bodies then appeared 250–270 mμ across—in contrast to 330–435 mμ by the usual technique. Hosaka

& Nishi (1962) observed two forms in their electron-micrographs—one dense-centred, one larger and reticulated. In relation to ruptured nucleoids they saw helical structures 8–11 mμ in diameter.

Chemical composition. Colon (1960) studied the cell wall of meningopneumonitis and thought it resembled that of rickettsia and Gram negative bacteria. Some muramic acid was detected. Smaller (0·25–0·3 μ) particles contained RNA and DNA in equal parts (Tamura & Higashi, 1963).

Physico-chemical characters. As for psittacosis.
Meningopneumonitis survived well in skim-milk at −25° and −70° C, badly at −4° C (Allen *et al.*, 1952).

Hæmagglutination. A hæmagglutinin like that of psittacosis is formed by meningopneumonitis agent.

Antigenic properties. As for psittacosis. Cross-reactions using the toxin neutralization test (Manire & Meyer, 1950; Meyer & Eddie, 1953) show that the Louisiana agent is indistinguishable from egret strains of ornithosis and fairly close to turkey strains, but otherwise not crossing much with other strains of human origin. The Illinois and S.F. strains showed wider reactivity. The meningopneumonitis agent cannot be antigenically separated from ornithosis.

Cultivation. As for psittacosis. Meningopneumonitis has proved convenient for a number of studies on multiplication in eggs or tissue culture (e.g. Sigel *et al.*, 1951). Plaque-counting on sheets of L cells has been used for assay (Higashi & Tamura, 1960).

Pathogenicity. Infections in man are like psittacosis, as are those produced experimentally in mice. The very toxic Louisiana strain is like the egret virus, pathogenic for guinea pigs on injection IP. The varied pathology in different species is described by Fite *et al.* (1946). Meningopneumonitis is the only agent of apparent mammalian origin which is pathogenic for rice-birds, parakeets or pigeons or when given subcutaneously for mice; it can also produce pneumonia in rabbits.

A virus encephalopneumonitis affecting suckling infants has been described from Roumania (Museteanu, 1945) and attributed

25

to an agent of this group. No comparisons with other miyagawanellas are reported.

Laboratory infections with members of this group are described.

Ecology. Isolations have been from the human respiratory tract. The possibility of a fairly recent avian origin has already been mentioned. The origin of meningopneumonitis, whether from man or ferret, was held to be doubtful by Francis & Magill (1938): later work makes a human source seem more likely.

Control. Meningopneumonitis is said to be the least susceptible agent in the group to penicillin (Eaton *et al.*, 1948).

FELINE PNEUMONITIS

Sometimes called cat influenza or distemper, there being much confusion with other infections of cats.

Reviews: Baker (1944) (original description).
Moulder (1954) (biochemical studies).

Morphology. As for psittacosis. Rake *et al.* (1946) described the elementary bodies as behaving like jelly-filled sacs.

Chemical composition. Contains RNA and DNA in the proportion of 2·5 : 1 (Moulder, 1954).

Physico-chemical characters. As for psittacosis.

Said to be inactivated not only by ether but also by sodium dodecyl-sulphate (Brown *et al.*, 1952). Quickly dies out at 37° but is fairly stable at −70°. Inactivated in 30′ at 50° or 10′ at 60°. Survives for 24 hours between pH 6·5 and 7·5 at 0° (Moulder & Weiss, 1951).

Hæmagglutination. Agglutinates mouse RBC's at room temperature, but it is rare to obtain higher titres than 1 : 32. The hæmagglutinin is separable from elementary bodies by centrifugation and is unstable at 50°, (Gogolak, 1954).

Antigenic properties. There is the CF antigen common to all the miyagawanellas. Neutralisation tests with rooster sera showed some crossing with mouse-pneumonitis and meningopneumonitis, less with lymphogranuloma (St. John & Gordon, 1947). Other workers have suggested that the agents affecting cats and mice are fairly closely related.

Cultivation. As for psittacosis. After inoculation into yolk-sacs, deaths occur after 2–3 days. The agent has been titrated (Weiss & Huang, 1954) by counting numbers of infected cells in monolayers of chick entodermal cells in tissue culture.

Pathogenicity. *In cats.* Causes a very chronic, often relapsing, infection of the upper and lower respiratory tract. Nasal passages become blocked with thick purulent secretion. Virus has been recovered from liver and spleen. Death from pneumonia is fairly low. The incubation period is from 6–10 days.

Reports suggesting human infections from cat pneumonia have not been confirmed.

Experimentally, transmission to cats is only by the intranasal route. Mice, hamsters and young guinea pigs inoculated intranasally develop fatal pneumonia, while older guinea pigs and rabbits undergo non-fatal infections. Mice can also be infected IC and IP with large doses (Hamre & Rake, 1944). A potent toxin is formed; given IV to mice it kills in 12–24 hours.

Ecology. Cross-infection in cats is by the respiratory route. Infected mice do not transmit to other mice.

Control. Tetracyclines are the drugs of choice, and are effective in kittens, apparently more so than in infected mice or eggs according to McKercher (1953). Other workers, however, report good activity in mice and in eggs.

Sulphonamides are less effective than against some other miyagawanellas.

Penicillin modifies the agent's development but does not eliminate it.

MOUSE PNEUMONITIS

Synonym: "Nigg virus".
Review: Nigg & Eaton (1944).

Morphology. Possibly the largest of the miyagawanellas—497 mμ by electron-microscopy (Kurotchkin *et al.*, 1947). Multiplication seems to occur in cysts attached to alveolar cells (Weiss, 1949), symptoms occurring when the cysts rupture to liberate elementary bodies.

Physico-chemical characters. Unstable at $-25°$ C. Ether-sensitive.

Hæmagglutination. As for feline pneumonitis.

Antigenic properties. Shares the common CF antigen of the group. To some extent separable from other miyagawanellas by the toxin-neutralization test or by tests for neutralization of infectivity using rooster sera; but lies fairly close to feline pneumonitis.

According to Manire & Meyer (1950) this and L.G.V. are the only miyagawanellas not to form a toxin (con. Rake & Jones, 1944).

Mice from a carrier strain are nevertheless uniformly susceptible to infection.

Cultivation. *In eggs:* Yolk-sac inoculation is to be preferred. De Burgh's (1945) Australian strain could be adapted to the amniotic and allantoic routes.

Pathogenicity. Normally a latent infection in mice.

After activation the agent inoculated IN into mice produces pneumonia. Intracerebral and intraperitoneal inoculation normally do not infect, except with an Australian strain (de Burgh *et al.*, 1945). Symptoms of respiratory distress may appear in 48 hours (with big doses in 24 hours), death following soon after. Titres of 10^6/ml are readily obtained. Hamsters may be infected with big doses; rabbits and guinea pigs usually not.

Ecology. Endemic in many mouse colonies and a frequent source of confusion to workers using mice in attempts to isolate other agents. Carrier mice from such a colony are not immune to inoculation with big doses (Freeman, 1941). Intranasal inoculation of human sera is particularly apt to activate infection.

Infection may be transferred amongst mice by cannibalism.

Control. The most susceptible of the group to penicillin. When mice of an infected stock have to be used in virus work, the agent can be controlled by repeated doses of sulphadiazine IP.

Hamster Virus

An agent with very similar properties was isolated from golden hamsters by Kempf *et al.*, 1945. There is lack of agreement as to the closeness of its antigenic relationship to mouse pneumonitis.

ENZOOTIC ABORTION OF EWES

Morphology. As for psittacosis. Developmental forms are described by Stamp (1951).

Physico-chemical characters. Best preserved by freeze-drying in skim-milk in the presence of glucose (Hörter, 1959).

Hæmagglutination. Not reported.

Antigenic properties. The only mammalian virus to produce a good endotoxin (Meyer, 1959). Shares the common miyagawanella CF antigen. This can be extracted from infected yolk-sacs or from the membranes from aborted sheep. Antibody titres of 1 : 16 are significant for diagnosis in sheep; sera are usually positive 2 weeks after the abortion and for 4 months after. The specific antigen is very labile and less readily demonstrated than with some other miyagawanellas (Monsur & Barwell, 1951).

Cultivation. In yolk sacs: embryos die after 4–13 days (Parker, 1960).

Distribution. First recorded from Scotland. Now known also from Australia, New Zealand, the United States and Bulgaria.

Pathogenicity. Abortions in ewes are caused, usually late in gestation; there is infection of the fœtal membranes. The agent may also cause lambs to be born prematurely or to be weakly. The agent probably lies dormant and is activated by pregnancy. Distribution of virus in the organs of aborted fœtuses is described by McEwen & Holgate, 1956. It may also cause abortions in goats (Staub, 1959).

Experimentally it readily infects mice inoculated IN causing pneumonia; it goes less readily IC or IP. It may also infect and cause abortions in cattle, in gravid rabbits (Giroud & Dumas, 1959) and rats (Payne & Belyavin, 1960). A laboratory infection of man is recorded (Barwell, 1955). An acute disease has been produced experimentally in monkeys (Roger & Roger, 1958).

Cotyledons of the chorion are pink and stained with discharge. Blood-stained transudates are found in serous cavities of aborted fœtuses.

Control. *Vaccines.* A live virus vaccine has proved effective in sheep over 1½ to 2½ years (Foggie, 1959). Vaccines have been made both from fœtal membranes and from chick embryos. They are better given with an adjuvant.

Chemotherapy. Tetracyclines are effective experimentally; penicillin and sulphathiazole also will inhibit growth in eggs (Parker, 1960).

Other Miyagawanellas affecting Sheep

McKercher (1953) has described an agent causing pneumonia in sheep in California; its relation to sheep abortion is not clear. Such a virus did, however, localize in placentæ of ewes (Dungworth, 1963). There is similar doubt about agents of this group causing pneumonia in sheep or lambs in other countries (Dungworth & Cordy, 1962).

A *Miyagawanella* causing polyarthritis in sheep is also recorded (Mendlowski *et al.*, 1960). It reproduced the disease in lambs after 2–11 passages in eggs and also caused a general infection in guinea pigs.

An agent similar to that causing abortion in ewes was associated with abortion in cattle (Storz *et al.*, 1960).

Pneumonitis of Goats

A *Miyagawanella*, with elementary bodies 300–400 mμ in diameter and crossing with other agents in the CF test, has been reported to cause pneumonia in goats in Japan. It was transmissible to cattle, horses, sheep, pigs, dogs, cats, guinea pigs and mice and excreted in the fæces. It was sensitive to tetracyclines, less so to penicillin, hardly at all to sulphonamides (Saito, 1954; Omori *et al.*, 1953). A similar agent is recorded from the Tchad district of Central Africa (Provost, 1958). No detailed comparisons with the other agents are reported.

BOVINE ENCEPHALOMYELITIS

Synonyms: Sporadic bovine encephalomyelitis (S.B.E.). Buss disease.

Reviews: Menges *et al.* (1953).
Wenner (1958).

Morphology. As for psittacosis. Elementary bodies 375 mμ across are described by Menges *et al.*, 1953.

Hæmagglutination. Not reported.

Antigenic properties. There is the usual relation by the CF test to others of the group. A reported relation to the Lansing strain of poliomyelitis is now considered improbable.

Cultivation. Growth is reported to occur in yolk-sacs, not the allantois (Wenner *et al.*, 1953). Destroys bovine kidney cells in culture (Boháč, 1960).

Pathogenicity. In cattle, the only naturally susceptible host, the agent causes fever, cough, weakness, emaciation, arthritis and diarrhœa. Nervous symptoms (staggering, opisthotonos) are secondary to vascular lesions. There may be mild or inapparent infections but 40–60 per cent. of cattle with established symptoms die.

Experimentally, calves can be infected by inoculation IC or SC, the incubation period varying from 4 to 27 days. Visceral manifestations are reproduced more readily than nervous ones.

Unlike other miyagawanellas is ordinarily not pathogenic for mice, but when given IP to guinea pigs, it infects and often causes death in 4 or 5 days with fibrinous peritonitis (Konrad & Boháč, 1959). A laboratory worker has been infected. In contrast to other workers Chang & Wenner (1951) could infect mice, also cotton-rats and monkeys.

Ecology. The mode of transmission is unknown, perhaps because the disease is often inapparent; hence the sporadic nature of clinical disease.

Control. Aureomycin is the most potent drug against this infection, penicillin less so, sulphonamides hardly at all.

Workers in Czechoslovakia suggest that the agent may belong to Giroud's (1956) genus Neorickettsia, a group of agents intermediate between Miyagawanella and Rickettsia.

Other Miyagawanellas affecting Cattle

An agent obtained from the intestinal tract of cattle multiplied in eggs and infected guinea pigs (York & Baker, 1951). They suggest the name *Miyagawanella bovis*; it may cause enteritis in calves deprived of colostrum (York & Baker, 1956). An agent of the group was recovered from lung lesions of cattle and sheep in Czechoslovakia by Gmitter (1960). Bovine pneumo-enteritis due to a miyagawanella was described in Italy by Messieri (1959), and similar agents are reported from Japan (Omori *et al.*, 1960). But Palotay & Christensen (1959) produced respiratory infection after intratracheal inoculation with strains from acute respiratory disease, from encephalitis or from healthy bovine stools. The agent causing abortions in cattle has been mentioned above (p. 378). It is quite impossible on present evidence to say whether there is only one or a number of bovine members of the group.

One laboratory infection with a bovine agent has been reported.

OPOSSUM VIRUSES A AND B

Roca-Garcia (1949) isolated two agents of the group from opossums (*Didelphis* and *Caluromys*) in captivity in Colombia. Opossum virus A had the usual properties of the group. It was pathogenic (IP) for several opossum species; also for mice IN or IC but not IP; but not for guinea pigs. It was cultivated in yolk-sacs, where it produced an endotoxin; also in cultures of mouse and chick embryo tissues. Sulphonamides were not effective against it. The opossum B virus differed antigenically and was not pathogenic for mice IP.

HEARTWATER
Cowdria (Rickettsia) ruminantium

The agent of this disease is often classed with rickettsiæ, which it resembles in being arthropod-transmitted. On the other hand the agent morphologically resembles miyagawanellas more closely and is, like them, susceptible to sulphonamides and tetracyclines. Doubtless it lies between the two groups (Rake, Alexander & Hamre, 1945).

It affects cattle, sheep and goats—also springbok—with fever, œdema and gastro-enteritis. Occurrence of pericardial effusions gives the disease its name. The agent is found in endothelial cells particularly of kidney and brain. It is transmitted by the Bont tick, *Amblyomma hebræum*. It survives up to 90 days in mice injected IP but there is no evidence that it multiplies. Live vaccine given to young calves, which are relatively insusceptible, has been used in the field (Neitz & Alexander, 1945).

LYMPHOGRANULOMA VENEREUM (LGV)

Synonyms: Lymphogranuloma inguinale. Lymphopathia venereum. Climatic or tropical bubo. Poradenitis. Maladie de Nicolas et Favre. *Miyagawanella lymphogranulomatis.*

Reviews: Meyer (1959).
Rake (1956)—especially diagnosis.
Koteen (1945)—largely clinical.

Morphology. The size by gradocol filtration is given as 120–180 mμ; by electron-microscopy 438 ± 47 mμ (Kurotchkin *et al.*, 1947)—an even wider discrepancy than for others of the group. The general appearances and developmental cycle are as described for psittacosis (Findlay *et al.*, 1938; Rake & Jones, 1942). It stains by Macchiavello's and Castañedas methods.

Physico-chemical characters. Rather more stable than other miyagawanellas. Survives for several weeks in pus or egg-yolk at 0–5° and for months at −72° or years after freeze-drying. Less well preserved at −32° or in 50 per cent. glycerol. 0·1 per cent. formalin or 0·5 per cent. phenol inactivate it in 24–48 hours. It is ether-sensitive.

Hæmagglutination. Not reported.

Antigenic properties. Contains the usual group CF antigen; the activity of this is improved by boiling or phenol treatment; but a specific CF antibody can be demonstrated by absorption of sera with steamed antigen (Bedson *et al.*, 1949). The CF test has value for diagnosis of human infections but of course past infection with psittacosis would cloud the issue. Neutralizing antibodies can be detected by the aid of tests in mice: for these the IN rather than the

IC route is preferable. A toxin can be extracted from yolks of chick embryos moribund after infection; this is neutralized specifically by antisera. Those made in fowls are fairly specific also in neutralization tests in mice.

Agglutination of elementary bodies has also been reported.

An antigen is used in intradermal tests for diagnosis in man (Frei test). This was originally made by heating pus from human infections, later from mouse brains, now—much better—from infected yolks; the last preparation is sold as Lygranum (Rake *et al.*, 1941). Its stability is variable and it gives cross-reactions in other miyagawanella infections. Antigen extracted with dilute acid is said to give much more specific reactions (Barwell, 1952) but has not been widely tested.

Cultivation. *Eggs.* It grows well in the yolk-sac, reaching high titres, but much less readily on chorioallantoic membranes.

Tissue-culture. Cultivation is reported in various tissues of mouse, rabbit, chick and other species. It even multiples in deep, almost anaerobic, cultures of Maitland type (Takemori, 1948).

Distribution. LGV is (apart from trachoma and inclusion conjunctivitis) the specifically human parasite of the group and does not naturally occur in other species. It is widespread, but infection is recognized most often in the tropics and around sea-ports. It normally inhabits the genito-urinary tract.

Pathogenicity. A venereal infection in man. After a few days' incubation a small vesicle appears, soon forming a lymphogranulomatous chancre. The infection may then clear up or proceed to lymphadenitis, local or general. There may be general infection with great variety of symptoms including rash, pneumonitis and meningoencephalitis. The buboes are apt to break down and discharge. Proctitis may occur and lead to rectal stricture. Non-venereal infections also occur, sometimes in children, sometimes affecting the eye, leading to an oculo-glandular syndrome. Numerous laboratory infections have occurred; they may be inapparent or occur as generalised infections without local lesions.

Experimentally, monkeys of several genera have been infected by the IC and other routes. Local inflammation and lymphadenitis are produced.

Mice infected IC develop symptoms of meningitis. With virulent strains the incubation period is 2–4 days but not all strains will go progressively in mice. Some take 1–2 weeks to produce symptoms and kill less than half the animals. Inoculation IN gives rise to pneumonia and with small doses countable focal lung lesions are produced—a finding useful for quantitative studies (van den Ende & Lush, 1943).

Guinea pigs, rabbits, and even dogs, cats and sheep, have been infected but not readily; birds are resistant.

Pathological lesions. Ulcers are infiltrated with plasma cells and histiocytes containing colonies of the agent. There appear in lymph nodes and elsewhere tubercle-like nodules due to epithelioid transformation of macrophages. Later, fibrous tissue contracts and leads to strictures. Lesions in infected mice and other animals are much as in others of the group.

Ecology. As already mentioned the disease is mainly but not exclusively venereal. Prostitutes and others may harbour an inapparent infection.

Control. *Chemotherapy.* Tetracyclines are the most valuable drugs, but are not invariably effective. Sulphonamides are preferred by some clinicians. It is easier to obtain clinical cure than eradication of infection. Penicillin is more effective against the experimental disease in mice than in man.

TRACHOMA

Synonyms: Granular conjunctivitis. *Chlamydozoön trachomatis.* *Chlamydia trachomatis.* (The generic name *Chlamydozoön* is chiefly used but Rake in the 1957 edition of Bergey's manual uses *Chlamydia*; there is doubt as to which is correct.)

Reviews: Thygeson (1958).
Collier (1959).
Bernkopf (1962).

Morphology. A developmental cycle occurs as with psittacosis but interpretations by various authors are widely different. The earliest forms are commonly described as initial bodies and are up to several μ in diameter; these first increase in size, then break up into elementary bodies about 250 mμ across. Colonies of organisms form the Halberstaedter-Prowazek bodies and are embedded in a glycogen-containing matrix staining with iodine. These large inclusions may also replace almost all the cytoplasm and finally rupture releasing elementary bodies. Some strains form compact aggregates of elementary bodies around glycogen-containing vacuoles. By electron-microscopy the elementary bodies have the same appearance as miyagawanellas and an apparent size of 300–500 mμ.

Armstrong et al. (1962) suggest that there is a true eclipse, as with viruses in general, the infecting particles losing their identity. The first change seen by electron-microscopy consists of development of a reticular focus with incomplete limiting membranes. No formed bodies are present in this until between 24 and 48 hours after infection when large bodies up to 3 or 4 μ across can be seen. In specimens examined later these developmental forms are progressively smaller. They almost certainly divide by binary fission and perhaps by budding. The final product, the elementary body, is about 0·5 μ across.

Chemical composition. No information is available except that concerning the glycogen matrix. The elementary bodies stain by Castañedas and Macchiavello's methods as do miyagawanellas.

Staining with acridine orange indicates that the initial bodies contain mainly RNA and the elementary bodies mainly DNA (Bernkopf et al., 1962). DNA synthesis precedes by some hours its incorporation into particles (Tanami et al., 1961).

Physico-chemical characters. The agent can be preserved by lyophilization and survives for months at $-60°$ in a medium containing sucrose, glutamate and phosphate (Murray et al., 1960). It soon dies out at $37°$; and 15 minutes at $45°$ suffice to inactivate it. It is sensitive to ether and desoxycholate. 0·04 per cent. formaldehyde inactivates.

No **hæmagglutinin** is reported.

Antigenic properties. There is a cross-reaction with agents related to psittacosis by the complement-fixation test particularly with boiled antigens (Rake et al., 1942). This is weaker than between individual miyagawanellas, possibly because human subjects furnishing immune sera have been suffering from a local, not a generalized disease. However, there seems to be relatively more specific than group reactivity as compared with miyagawanellas. The heat-stable antigen is a lipo-polysaccharide-protein complex as with miyagawanellas and appears when large forms predominate (Reeve & Taverne, 1962). Elementary bodies purified with a fluorocarbon can be agglutinated by antisera; examination is with dark-field illumination (Bernkopf *et al.*, 1960). There appear to be at least two serological types in Saudi-Arabia (Bell *et al.*, 1959).

Cultivation. *In fertile eggs.* Several early reports of cultivation in fertile eggs failed to carry conviction. However, claims by Tang *et al.* (1957) to have grown the agent in yolks of fertile eggs were soon confirmed by others (Collier & Sowa, 1958). Big doses of streptomycin were used to control the bacteria in the original inocula, and 8-day fertile eggs were inoculated and incubated at 35°. Cultivated virus has reproduced trachoma in volunteers as well as in baboons.

In tissue-culture. Trachoma has now been cultivated in HeLa cells, the FL line from human amnion and other cell lines. The virus has been titrated by counting inclusion bodies in infected HeLa monolayers (Furness *et al.*, 1960).

Distribution. The natural habitat is the human eye. The disease is extremely prevalent particularly in the Middle East and in many tropical countries especially where standards of hygiene are low. In the United States it occurs amongst American Indians.

Pathogenicity. The natural disease has an insidious onset and affects many young children. Follicular conjunctivitis leads to keratitis, the upper eyelid being especially affected. In later stages scarring causes various deformities and blindness, especially following secondary bacterial infection.

After *experimental* inoculation of man, the incubation period is 3–7 days. The disease is transmissible to anthropoid apes, baboons and other monkeys, but the disease is much milder than in man. The characteristic inclusions occur regularly in apes, sometimes in baboons, not at all in other monkeys. Recently the agent has been adapted to cause encephalitis after IC inoculation of 5-week-old mice with the Chinese strain (Hurst & Reeve, 1960). Bernkopf (1959), using the same strain, infected suckling mice using several routes of inoculation.

Fatal lung consolidation can also be produced by IN inoculation of older mice (Watkins & Mackenzie, 1962).

A toxin is formed which kills mice when given IV (Murray *et al.*, 1960) and also produces follicular conjunctivitis on inoculation into human eyes.

Pathological lesions. The characteristic inclusions have been described above. Development of conjunctival and corneal lesions is followed by subepithelial infiltration, blood-vessel infiltration (pannus), later cell-necrosis and scarring.

Ecology. In the Middle East, infection is commonly by direct contact to children under one year of age from an affected mother. Probably only acute cases are very infectious. Fomites and flies are also suspected of playing a role. Trachoma is a disease associated with poor hygienic conditions.

Control. *Quarantine* has been used to exclude cases from some countries.

Chemotherapy. Treatment by sulphonamides and tetracyclines is very effective in early cases, provided that treatment is continued long enough. Chemotherapy cannot of course deal with results of scar-formation. Drug-resistance has not caused trouble.

Immunization. There have been several promising reports indicating that an effective vaccine may become available (Grayston *et al.*, 1960, 1963).

INCLUSION CONJUNCTIVITIS

Synonyms: Inclusion blenorrhœa. Paratrachoma. Ophthalmia neonatorum (one form). Swimming-pool conjunctivitis (one form). *Chlamydozoön oculogenitale*

Morphology. Not distinguishable from trachoma. There are initial bodies and elementary bodies; the inclusions have a glycogen matrix.

Physico-chemical characters. As for trachoma. Inactivated by bile. Survives for a few days in 50 per cent. glycerol.

Antigenic properties. Not as yet distinguished from trachoma.

Cultivation. In fertile eggs.

Cultivated in yolk-sac by Jones, Collier & Smith (1959); also by Hurst & Reeve (1960) who found it more toxic than trachoma, killing most of the embryos in 2 or 3 days. Multiplication in HeLa cells has been studied by Furness (1962).

Pathogenicity. The normal habitat is probably the genito-urinary tract in both sexes, the eyes of babies being infected during child-birth. The disease in man is milder than trachoma, but though it may last for months it is self-limited and pannus and scarring do not occur. In babies it presents as an acute purulent conjunctivitis; in adults it is commonly a follicular conjunctivitis with but little exudate and in contrast to trachoma, the lower lid is more affected than the upper.

Man is the only natural host.

Experimental transmission to man has been carried out, the incubation period being 5–12 days. Baboons have been infected by the conjunctival route; inclusion bodies developed (Collier, 1959). Mice have also been infected by IC inoculation (Hurst & Reeve, 1960).

Ecology. Eye-to-eye transmission is rare.

Control. *Chemotherapy.* Topically applied sulphacetamide and sulphadiazine are effective, more so in children than in adults; in the latter sulphonamides given orally are more successful. Tetracyclines are also effective, penicillin less so.

CAT SCRATCH DISEASE

Synonyms: Cat-bite disease. Benign reticulosis.

There is doubt as to whether or not the agent of this disease should be included in the psittacosis family.

Morphology. Mollaret *et al.* (1956) report finding elementary bodies like miyagawanellas in pus from human cases but others fail to confirm this.

Antigenic properties. A number of cases have given positive complement-fixation with psittacosis group antigen. Many cases, however, are negative: so the justification for including the agent with this group of organisms remains doubtful. Heated pus from cat-scratch infections will elicit a skin reaction in a high percentage of cases (Mollaret *et al.*, 1951; Foshay, 1952). Frei antigen, however, usually fails to do so; nor do cat-scratch antigens give reactions in Frei-positive patients.

Cultivation. Attempts at cultivation in eggs and in tissue culture have been unsuccessful.

Pathogenicity. *Symptoms* in man usually come on 1 to 7 weeks after a scratch or bite by a cat; they may occur, however, without any such history. Enlarged, often tender lymph-nodes appear in the area draining the lesion; they may be very chronic and may suppurate and discharge. Generalized lymphadenopathy and rash may occur. There are commonly fever, malaise, nausea and aching of lymphs.

Encephalitis and pneumonia are rare complications.

There is no evidence that cats are themselves affected.

Experimental transmission to a human volunteer and to a *Cercopithecus* monkey are reported (Mollaret *et al.*, 1951, 1956). Other species have proved insusceptible.

Pathological lesions. The granulomatous lymphadenitis characteristically shows areas of structureless necrosis surrounded by epithelioid and some giant cells.

Ecology. Cats may be merely passive carriers of the infecting agent.

Control. Evidence that tetracyclines are beneficial is inconclusive.

SALMON POISONING
(in dogs)

Review: Philip, 1955.

This is a disease caused by another agent lying on the borderline between Rickettsia and Miyagawanella. Philip classifies it as a *Neorickettsia* and it therefore demands only passing mention in this book.

Another agent, classified as a *Neorickettsia* by Giroud & Jadin (1959), caused infections of Africans in the Belgian Congo; outbreaks may have originated from infected cattle, sheep or goats (*cf.*, p. 378).

REFERENCES

Allen, E. G., Kaneda, B., Girardi, A. J., Scott, T. M., & Sigel, M. M. (1952) *J. Bact.*, **63**, 369.
Allison, A. C., & Perkins, H. R. (1960) *Nature (Lond.)*, **788**, 796.
Armstrong, J. A., Valentine, R. C., & Fildes, C. (1962) *J. gen. Microbiol.*, **30**, 59.
Baker, J. A. (1944) *J. exp. Med.*, **79**, 159.
Barwell, C. F. (1952) *Brit. J. exp. Path.*, **33**, 258 and 268.
Barwell, C. F. (1955) *Lancet*, **2**, 1369.
Beaudette, F. R. (1958) (Ed.) *Progress in Psittacosis Research and Control.* Rutgers University Press.
Bedson, S. P. (1936) *Brit. J. exp. Path.*, **17**, 109.
Bedson, S. P., Barwell, C. F., King, E. T., & Bishop, L. W. J. (1949) *J. clin. Path.*, **2**, 241.
Bedson, S. P., & Bland, J. O. W. (1932) *Brit. J. exp. Path.*, **13**, 461.
Bell, S. D., Snyder, J. C., & Murray, E. S. (1959) *Science*, **130**, 626.
Bernkopf, H. (1959) *Bull. Res. Coun. Israel*, **8E**, 25.
Bernkopf, H. (1962) *Progr. med. Virol.*, **4**, 119.
Bernkopf, H., Mashiah, P., & Vanag, K. A. (1962) *Ann. N.Y. Acad. Sci.*, **98**, 62.
Bernkopf, H., Nishmi, M., Maythar, B., & Feitelberg, I. (1960) *J. infect. Dis.*, **106**, 83.
Boháč, J. (1960) *Veteirnárstv.*, **10**, 81.
Brown, A., Itatani, M. K., & Moulder, J. W. (1952) *J. infect. Dis.*, **91**, 184.
Burnet, F. M., & Foley, M. (1941) *Aust. J. exp. Biol. med. Sci.*, **19**, 235.
Burnet, F. M., & Lush, D. (1940) *Aust. J. exp. Biol. med. Sci.*, **18**, 141.
Chang, T. W., & Wenner, H. A. (1951) *Proc. Soc. exp. Biol. (N.Y.)*, **78**, 659.
Collier, L. H. (1959) *Brit. med. Bull.*, **15**, 231.
Collier, L. H., & Sowa, J. (1958) *Lancet*, **1**, 993.
Colón, J. I. (1960) *J. Bact.*, **79**, 741.
Crocker, T. T., & Williams, R. C. (1955) *Proc. Soc. exp. Biol. (N.Y.)*, **88**, 378.
Davis, D. E., & Delaplane, J. P. (1958) *Amer. J. vet. Res.*, **19**, 169.
De Burgh, P., Jackson, A. V., & Williams, S. E. (1945) *Aust. J. exp. Biol. med. Sci.*, **23**, 107.
Dungworth, D. L. (1963) *J. comp. Path.*, **73**, 68.
Dungworth, D. L., & Cordy, D. R. (1962) *J. comp. Path.*, **72**, 49 and 71.
Eaton, M. D., Dozois, T. F., van Allen, A., Parish, V. L., & Schwalm, S. (1948) *J. Immunol.*, **58**, 251.
Findlay, G. M., Mackenzie, R. D., & MacCallum, F. O. (1938) *Nature (Lond.)*, **141**, 877.
Fite, G. L., Lawson, C. L., & Olson, B. (1946) *Publ. Hlth. Rep. (U.S.)*, **61**, 1100.
Foggie, A. (1959) *J. comp. Path.*, **64**, 141.
Foshay, L. (1952) *Lancet*, **1**, 673.
Francis, T., & Magill T. P. (1938) *J. exp. Med.*, **68**, 147.
Freeman, G. (1941) *Proc. Soc. exp. Biol. (N.Y.)*, **48**, 568.
Fulton, F. (1953) *An. Inst. Med. trop. (Lisboa)*, **10**, 491.
Furness, G. (1962) *J. gen. Microbiol.*, **27**, 290.
Furness, G., Graham, D. M., & Reeve, P. (1960) *J. gen. Microbiol.*, **23**, 613.
Gaylord, W. H. (1954) *J. exp. Med.*, **100**, 575.
Giroud, P. (1956) *Laval méd.*, **21**, 535.
Giroud, P., & Dumas, N. (1959) *C.R. Acad. Sci. (Paris)*, **249**, 978.
Giroud, P., ; Jadin, J. (1954) *Bull. Soc. path. Exot.*, **47**, 578.
Gmitter, J. (1960) *Sborn. čes. Akad. zemédélk. věd. Vet. Med.*, **5**, 457.

Gogolak, F. M. (1954) *J. infect. Dis.*, **95**, 220.

Grayston, J. T., Wang, S.-P., Woolridge, R. L., Yang, Y.-F., & Johnston, P. B. (1960) *J. Amer. med. Ass.*, **172**, 1577.

Grayston, J. T., Woolridge, R. L., Wang, S.-P., Yen, C.-H., Yang, C.-Y., Cheng, K.-H., & Chang, I.-H. (1963) *Proc. Soc. exp. Biol. (N.Y.)*, **112**, 589.

Hamre, D., & Rake, G. (1944) *J. infect. Dis.*, **74**, 206.

Higashi, N., & Tamura, A. (1960) *Virology*, **12**, 578.

Hörter, R. (1959) *Zbl. Bakt. I. Abt. Orig.*, **175**, 356.

Hosaka, Y., & Nishi, Y. (1962) *Biken's J.*, **5**, 21.

Hurst, E. W., & Hull, R. (1956) *Pharmacol. Rev.*, **8**, 199.

Hurst, E. W., & Reeve, P. (1960) *Nature (Lond.)*, **186**, 336.

Jones, B. R., Collier, L. H., & Smith, C. H. (1959) *Lancet*, **1**, 902.

Kempf, A. H., Wheeler, A. H., & Nungester, W. J. (1945) *J. infect. Dis.*, **76**, 135.

Konrad, J., & Boháč, J. (1959) *Vet. Čas.*, **8**, 228.

Koteen, H. (1945) *Medicine*, **24**, 1.

Kurotchkin, T. J., Libby, R. L., Gagnon, E., & Cox, H. R. (1947) *J. Immunol.*, **55**, 283.

McEwen, A. D., & Holgate, S. (1956) *Vet. Rec.*, **68**, 690.

McKercher, D. G. (1953) *Science*, **115**, 543.

Manire, G. P., & Meyer, K. F. (1950) *J. infect. Dis.*, **86**, 241.

Mendlowski, B., Kraybill, W. H., & Segre, D. (1960) *Amer. J. vet. Res.*, **21**, 74.

Menges, R. W., Harshfield, G. S., & Wenner, H. A. (1953) *J. Amer. vet. med. Ass.*, **122**, 294.

Messieri, A. (1959) *Atti Soc. ital. Sci. vet.*, **8**, 702.

Meyer, K. F. (1959) in *Viral and Rickettsial Infections of Man*. 3rd ed. p. 701. Ed. Rivers & Horsfall. London: Pitman Medical.

Meyer, K. F., & Eddie, B. (1951) *J. infect. Dis.*, **88**, 109.

Meyer, K. F., & Eddie, B. (1952) *Arch. ges. Virusforsch.*, **4**, 579.

Meyer, K. F., & Eddie, B. (1953) *Proc. Soc. exp. Biol. (N.Y.)*, **83**, 99.

Meyer, K. F., Eddie, M., Richardson, J. H., Shipkowitz, N. L., & Muir, R. J. (1958) *Progress in Psittacosis Research and Control*. p. 163. Rutgers Univ. Press.

Mollaret, P., Reilly, J., Bastin, R., & Tournier, R. (1956) *Presse méd.*, **64**, 1177.

Mollaret, P., Reilly, J., Bastin, R., & Tournier, R. (1951) *Presse méd.*, **59**, 701.

Monsur, K. A., & Barwell, C. F. (1951) *Brit. J. exp. Path.*, **32**, 414.

Morgan, H. R. (1954) *J. exp. Med.*, **99**, 451.

Moulder, J. W. (1954) *Bact. Rev.*, **18**, 170.

Moulder, J. W., & Weiss, E. (1951) *J. infect. Dis.*, **88**, 56.

Murray, E. S., Bell, S. D., Hanna, A. T., Nichols, R. L., & Snyder, J. C. (1960) *Amer. J. trop. Med. Hyg.*, **9**, 116.

Museteanu, C. (1960) *Zbl. Bakt. I. Abt. Orig.*, **178**, 426.

Neitz, W. O., & Alexander, R. A. (1945) *Onderstepoort J. Vet. Res.*, **20**, 137.

Nigg, C., & Eaton, M. D. (1944) *J. exp. Med.*, **79**, 497.

Omori, T., Ishii, S., & Matumoto, M. (1960) *Amer. J. vet. Res.*, **21**, 564.

Omori, T., Ishii, S., Harada, K., Ichikawa, O., Murase, N., Katada, M., & Araumi, W. (1953) *Exp. Rep. Gov. Sta. Anim. Hyg. Jap.*, **27**, 101.

Palotay, J. L., & Christensen, N. R. (1959) *J. Amer. vet. Med.*, **134**, 222.

Parker, H. D. (1960) *Amer. J. vet. Res.*, **21**, 243.

Payne, J. M., & Belyavin, G. (1960) *J. Path. Bact.*, **80**, 215.

Philip, C. B. (1955) *J. Parasit.*, **41**, 125.

Provost, A. (1958) *Rev. Élev.*, **10**, 113.

Rake, G. (1956) in *Diagnostic procedures for Virus and Rickettsial Diseases*, p. 453. Amer. Publ. Hlth. Ass.
Rake, G., Alexander, R. A., & Hamre, D. (1945) *Science*, **102**, 424.
Rake, G., & Jones, H. P. (1942) *J. exp. Med.*, **75**, 323.
Rake, G., & Jones, H. P. (1944) *J. exp. Med.*, **79**, 463.
Rake, G., Rake, H., Hamre, D., & Groupé, V. (1946) *Proc. Soc. exp. Biol. (N.Y.)*, **63**, 489.
Rake, G., Shaffer, M. F., Jones, H. P., & McKee, C. M. (1941) *Proc. Soc. exp. Biol. (N.Y.)*, **46**, 300.
Rake, G., Shaffer, M. F., & Thygeson, P. (1942) *Proc. Soc. exp. Biol. (N.Y.)*, **49**, 545.
Reeve, P., & Taverne, J. (1962) *J. gen. Microbiol.*, **27**, 501.
Rivers, T. M., & Berry, G. P. (1931) *J. exp. Med.*, **54**, 105, 119 and 129.
Roca-Garcia, M. (1949) *J. infect. Dis.*, **40**, 275.
Roger, F., & Roger, A. (1958) *Ann. Inst. Pasteur*, **94**, 379.
Ross, M. R., & Gogolak, F. M. (1957) *Virology*, **3**, 343.
St. John, E., & Gordon, F. B. (1947) *J. infect. Dis.*, **80**, 297.
Saito, Y., Shimada, F., Masu, S., Toda, M., & Imanishi, N. (1954) *Kitasato Arch. exp. Med.*, **27**, 103.
Schmittdiel, E. (1961) *Zbl. Bakt. I. Abt. Orig.*, **181**, 446.
Sigel, M. M., Girardi, A. J., & Allen, E. G. (1951) *J. exp. Med.*, **94**, 401.
Stamp, J. T. (1951) *J. comp. Path.*, **61**, 215.
Staub, H. (1959) *Dtsch. tierärztl. Wschr.*, **66**, 98.
Storz, J., McKercher, D. G., Howarth, J. A., & Straub, O. C. (1960) *J. Amer. vet. med. Ass.*, **137**, 509.
Swain, R. H. A. (1955) *Brit. J. exp. Path.*, **36**, 507.
Takemori, N. (1948) *Kitasato Arch. exp. Med.*, **21**, 267.
Tamura, A., & Higashi, N. (1963) *Virology*, **20**, 396.
Tanami, Y., Pollard, M., & Starr, T. J. (1961) *Virology*, **15**, 22.
Tang, F. F., Chang, H. L., Huang, Y. T., & Wang, K. C. (1957) *China med. J.*, **75**, 429.
Thygeson, P., & Nataf, R. (1958) *Rev. int. Trachome*, **35**, 177.
van den Ende, M., & Lush, D. (1943) *J. Path. Bact.*, **55**, 81.
Volkert, M., & Matthiesen, M. (1958) *Acta path. microbiol. scand.*, **44**, 278.
Wagner, J. C., Golub, O. J., & Andrew, V. W. (1948) *Proc. Soc. exp. Biol. (N.Y.)*, **69**, 202.
Watkins, J. F., & Mackenzie, A. M. R. (1962) *J. gen. Microbiol.*, **30**, 43.
Weiss, E., & Huang, J. S. (1954) *J. infect. Dis.*, **94**, 107.
Weiss, E. (1955) *Ann. Rev. Microbiol.*, **9**, 227.
Wenner, H. A. (1958) *Advanc. Virus Res.*, **5**, 39.
Wenner, H. A., Harshfield, G. S., Chang, T. W., & Merges, R. W. (1953) *Amer. J. Hyg.*, **57**, 15.
York, C. J., & Baker, J. A. (1951) *J. exp. Med.*, **93**, 587.
York, C. J., & Baker, J. A. (1956) *Ann. N.Y. Acad. Sci.*, **66**, 210.

Note on Virus Classification

The data collected together in this book may be of help in constructing a systematic classification of viruses. It is already apparent that a primary division into RNA and DNA viruses is fundamental; also that further basic criteria are concerned with possession of a cubical or helical symmetry in the arrangement of protein subunits and with presence or absence of an outer envelope enclosing a more rigid structure. Sensitivity to inactivation by ether, chloroform or desoxycholic acid is fairly well correlated with presence of this last character. Lwoff, Tournier and Horne have proposed a system of viruses in which the above characters are used as the basis of a virus hierarchy. This system brings together into one category certain plant and animal viruses which are morphologically alike. Such similarity may, however, depend either on a common evolutionary origin or on convergent evolution; there may in fact be a limited number of ways in which very small particles with the biological activity of viruses can be constructed. Table 1, which forms the frontispiece, includes therefore only viruses of vertebrates.

New facts are almost sure to be discovered soon, throwing fresh light on classification. We should soon know whether the viruses included here as arboviruses do in fact form a homogeneous group and what their structure is. Revelation of the internal structure of the RNA viruses causing tumours and leukæmias in fowls and rodents should show whether these are closely related to myxoviruses or not. Finally, many of the unclassified viruses in Part III should soon find a logical place in the virus scheme.

This book has made no use of the binomial names proposed by Holmes, Zhdanov and others, since a large majority of virologists is against the use of such names at the present time. It may become desirable to construct a code of virus nomenclature, largely independent of that in use for Bacteria.

Index